Geochemistry of Beryllium

AND GENETIC TYPES OF BERYLLIUM DEPOSITS

A SERIES OF BOOKS IN GEOLOGY

Editors: James Gilluly
A. O. Woodford

Stratigraphy and Sedimentation (Second Edition)
W. C. Krumbein and L. L. Sloss

Principles of Geology (Second Edition)
James Gilluly, A. C. Waters, and A. O. Woodford

Petrography: An Introduction to the Study of Rocks in Thin Sections
Howel Williams, Francis J. Turner, and Charles M. Gilbert

Rocks and Mineral Deposits
Paul Niggli

Geology of Petroleum
A. I. Levorsen

Stratigraphic Geology
Maurice Gignoux

Elementary Seismology
Charles F. Richter

Mineralogy: Concepts, Descriptions, Determinations
L. G. Berry and Brian Mason

General Crystallography: A Brief Compendium
W. F. de Jong

Paleogeologic Maps
A. I. Levorsen

History of the Earth: An Introduction to Historical Geology
Bernhard Kummel

Laboratory Studies in Geology
James C. Brice, John P. Miller, and Robert Scholten

Tectonics
Jean Goguel

Beryllium: Evaluation of Deposits During Prospecting and Exploratory Work
A. A. Beus

Fluvial Processes in Geomorphology
Luna B. Leopold, M. Gordon Wolman, and John P. Miller

Ore Deposits
Charles F. Park, Jr., and Roy A. MacDiarmid

Historical Geology
A. O. Woodford

Geochemistry of Beryllium and Genetic Types of Beryllium Deposits
A. A. Beus

Geochemistry of Beryllium

AND GENETIC TYPES OF BERYLLIUM DEPOSITS

A. A. Beus INSTITUTE OF MINERALOGY, GEOCHEMISTRY, AND CRYSTAL CHEMISTRY OF RARE ELEMENTS, ACADEMY OF SCIENCE, MOSCOW, THE USSR

Edited by

LINCOLN R. PAGE UNITED STATES GEOLOGICAL SURVEY

Translated by

F. LACHMAN FOR THE GEOCHEMICAL SOCIETY

Preliminary Editing by

R. K. HARRISON assisted by Miss I. J. Muir
ATOMIC ENERGY DIVISION, GEOLOGICAL SURVEY OF GREAT BRITAIN

PUBLICATION ARRANGED BY THE GEOCHEMICAL SOCIETY

W. H. Freeman and Company

SAN FRANCISCO AND LONDON

This book was first published by the Academy of Sciences of the USSR in Moscow, in 1960, under the title ГЕОХИМИЯ БЕРИМИЯ ИТЕ НЕТИЧЕСКИЕ ТИПЫ БЕРИМЕЫХ МЕСТОРОЖАЕНИИ.

Editor-in-chief was K. A. Vlasov, Corresponding Member of the Academy of Sciences of the USSR. Originals of the illustrations were supplied by the author for use in this publication.

Translation and editing costs paid by a grant from the National Science Foundation to the Geochemical Society. Publication arranged by the Translations Committee of the Society, Earl Ingerson, Chairman.

Printed in the United States of America

Library of Congress Catalog Card Number 65-19560

Editor's Note

Geochemistry of Beryllium and Genetic Types of Beryllium Deposits, a comprehensive compilation of mineralogic and geochemical data concerning beryllium in rocks and mineral deposits of the USSR, emphasizes the author's theoretical views about the origin of abnormal concentrations of beryllium. This is a fitting sequel to his earlier book, *Beryllium: Evaluation of Deposits During Exploratory Work,* published in 1956, which is concerned primarily with the practical aspects of the recognition and exploration of economic deposits of beryllium.

Although the author draws many of his examples from outside the Soviet Union, he refers mainly to the older literature. It is regrettable that he has not considered here the many important, more recent publications by geologists in the geological surveys of the United States, United Kingdom, Canada, and other countries, since they present a wealth of data on beryllium from other points of view.

Like the earlier work, this book contains many terms, such as "block microcline," "block quartz," "paragensis," and "replacement complex," which, as translated, tend to have different meanings from those in common use by students of beryllium in the Western World. Many words like "albitization," "greisenization," and "muscovitization" are used by the author to designate rock units as well as processes, and the term "vein" is used synonymously with pegmatite. Also, the terms "crossing line" and "pure line" pegmatites have been used, rather than the more appropriate words "desilicated" and "normal." This procedure has resulted in occasional confusion and inaccuracies in the translation and editing. Although the usage of these words and terms may appear incorrect to many geologists, the editor has retained them in order not to change the author's meaning.

February 1965 LINCOLN R. PAGE

Contents

PART II | GENETIC TYPES OF BERYLLIUM DEPOSITS

PART III | GEOCHEMISTRY OF BERYLLIUM

Introduction

In 1797, while carrying out the chemical analysis of emerald and beryl to prove their analogous composition, the French chemist Vauquelin discovered the oxide of a new element, which he called the beryl earth (la terre du béryl), after the name of the analyzed mineral. In 1798 the new element was given the name glucinium, because of the taste of its salts (Greek: *glukus* = sweet): this name has not been widely accepted, and today it is used only in France. The modern name of the element–beryllium)–was introduced into literature by Klaproth and by Professor F. I. Gize; very soon it was universally recognized.

Beryllium metal was made for the first time in 1828 by the famous German scientist Wöhler and simultaneously by the French scientist Bussy,[1] who produced beryllium metal powder by reducing beryllium chloride with metallic potassium.

After a thorough study of beryllium salts, the Russian chemist I. V. Avdeev (1842) determined its atomic weight (9.26) and demonstrated that beryllium oxide, notwithstanding its chemical similarity to aluminum oxide, is analogous to magnesium oxide, and that beryllium is a bivalent element, not a trivalent one as was thought previously. Avdeev's investigations were later utilized and borne out by D. I. Mendeleev (1898) in his work on the periodic law. Considerable progress in the study of the properties of beryllium was made by the lengthy research of the French chemist and metallurgist Lebeau, who developed in 1899 a new method of produc-

[1] The transliteration of the original, Bloussin or Bluissenon, does not appear in the Dictionnaire de Biographie Française (*v*, 1954, col. 725). This is therefore almost certainly in error for *Bussy,* Antoine-Alexandre-Brums, 1794–1882, *ibid, vi,* 1955, col. 720, Ed.

ing beryllium metal by the electrolysis of sodium tetrafluoroberyllate melt. He also studied the properties of alloys of beryllium with copper, chromium, tungsten, molybdenum, and carbon. He was the first to notice a marked variation in the properties of copper with the addition of a few tenths of one percent of beryllium.

In the 1920's the production of beryllium on an industrial scale began simultaneously in the United States (Beryllium Development Company of America) and Germany (Siemens-Halske). Until the 1940's the production and use of beryllium was rather small. However, because of the growing need in engineering for certain high-grade materials endowed with new properties that can be produced only with the use of beryllium, the consumption of beryllium in the forms of compounds, alloys, and metal articles has greatly increased—especially in recent years. The discovery of beryllium's usefulness in the nuclear industry soon increased the demand for beryllium ore even more and brought about much of the survey and geological exploration work in this field. According to data published in the foreign press, the consumption of beryllium increased during World War II to five times the prewar figure. In the postwar years the production of beryllium concentrates continued to increase (it is now more than 9,000 tons per year), and the annual consumption of beryllium, which was no more than a single ton before the war, already exceeds 200 tons and continues to increase.

Thus the history of the utilization of beryllium and its minerals by mankind can be divided into four separate periods:

1. *From ancient times until the beginning of the nineteenth century*—Utilization of the transparent varieties of beryl, chrysoberyl, phenacite, and euclase as precious ornaments.
2. *From the beginning of the nineteenth century until the 1920's*—Investigation of the chemical and physical properties of beryllium with a view to its utilization in industry and engineering.
3. *From the 1920's until the end of the 1930's*—The period of limited industrial use of beryllium alloys and compounds. Continuation of the detailed investigation of the physical properties of beryllium.
4. *From the beginning of World War II until the present time*—The period of rapid increase in the industrial use of beryllium in various new fields of engineering (including military and nuclear engineering).

Closely related to these developments in the use of beryllium in industry and engineering was a parallel increase in investigations of beryllium mineralogy and geochemistry, and in the study of its deposits.

Deposits of the most abundant beryllium mineral, beryl, were known to mankind even in very ancient times and were prospected and mined as sources of precious stones that have been highly valued throughout history. A typical example is the deposit of emeralds in the Arabian desert, which was known to the Egyptians and mined more than three thousand years ago. The famous emerald deposits in Colombia, which until quite recently supplied a high-grade material for cut emeralds, had apparently been exploited by the natives since prehistoric times.

We do not know exactly when and where the first deposits of beryl, aquamarine, and emerald were discovered in the territories of the USSR. Before the beginning of our era, however, the boundless area of what the Greeks called the Hyperborean country was famous for gems that were carried through the Crimea southwards into Asia Minor, Greece, and Rome. Is it not the Ural emeralds and aquamarines that are mentioned by Pliny (in the 70's of the first century A.D.), where he writes about the "very noble emeralds of the Scythians," or by other Greek and Roman writers who describe the fabulous precious stones from the mysterious Rhipaei Montes?[2] It is difficult to interpret these blurred pages of the remote past, particularly since later, when new states and nations were formed, the deposits of gems in this part of the world were lost and forgotten, to be rediscovered only in the seventeenth century.

The first deposits of precious beryl and topaz in Russia were discovered by the miner Michael Tumashev (Fersman, 1946) in the Murzinki area in the Central Urals in 1668. Almost sixty years later (1724), a certain Gudkov, who lived in Nerchinsk, rediscovered the Sherlovogorsk aquamarine deposit, which had been known in ancient times to Chinese prospectors. Finally it was announced in 1831 that the first emeralds (within the future "emerald-bearing zone" of the Ural mountains) had been found. This was the beginning of the exploitation, still very limited, of the deposits of beryllium minerals in our country.

Until the last decade of the nineteenth century the investigations conducted in all countries were mostly mineralogical and relied upon an extremely schematic description of deposits and of the conditions in which the minerals could be found. This "early period", however, proved to be very fruitful for the advancement of beryllium mineralogy. As a result of painstaking investigations by famous mineralogists and chemists, the number of known beryllium minerals increased until, at the beginning of the twentieth century, seventeen beryllium minerals were known—that is, nearly one-half of the number known at present. Important contributions to the mineralogy of beryllium were made in the period 1825–1910 by such outstanding scientists as G. Rose, Lacroix, Flink,[3] and especially Brögger, who discovered and described six new beryllium minerals in 1890.

In the Russian scientific literature, detailed descriptions of beryllium minerals from the deposits in eastern Russia began to appear at the end of the eighteenth century (Severgin, 1795). The systematic investigation of the mineralogy in Russia, however, started late in the 1820's (Menge, 1826; Rose, 1846; Koksharov, 1852–1862; and others).

[2] According to the Oxford Classical Dictionary, between 57° 30′ and 63° 21′ N, Ed.
[3] Reference not available, Ed.

An outstanding contribution was made by the eminent Russian scientist-mineralogist N. Koksharov; his classical research in the field of mineralogy serves even today as a model of detailed mineralogical investigation. Between 1852 and 1862, he described in detail the properties and conditions of occurrence of many beryllium minerals known at that time in Russia (beryl and its varieties, alexandrite, chrysoberyl, phenacite, euclase, rhodizite, and herderite).

Investigations of the Russian beryllium minerals were intensified towards the end of the nineteenth and at the beginning of the twentieth centuries; the principal workers were K. A. Skal'kovskii (1868), P. V. Eremeev (1893, 1895), V. I. Vernadskii (1908), P. P. Pilipenko (1909), and K. A. Nednadkevich (1911). Perhaps the most important investigations were those of V. I. Vernadskii, who was the first to study the chemical composition of alkali beryls and who suggested an original treatment of their structure.

The success of these studies of the properties of beryllium, which established the foundations for its industrial application, had an unavoidable effect on the development of the investigation of beryllium deposits. Practical demands no longer allowed purely mineralogical investigation. Study of the problem of beryllium's industrial utilization led directly to the study of its natural deposits.

The first published descriptions of Russian deposits of precious beryl were prepared in the middle and second half of the nineteenth century (Titov, 1855; Miklashevskii, 1862; Kalugin, 1880), but detailed investigations of beryl deposits began in Russia only under Soviet rule, in connection with the large-scale experiments on beryllium compounds that began in 1922.

In many publications of that period (Sushchinskii, 1925, 1928, etc.), including A. E. Fersman's *Precious and Colored Gemstones of Russia* (1922), beryl was still considered to be a jewelers' material; yet in all papers there was evident interest in the deposit as the source of this useful mineral.

Detailed investigations were made of the emerald mines of the Urals (Fersman, 1925b, 1925c; Gavrusevich, 1946; Porvatov and Karasik, 1925[4]; Pyatnitskii, 1929, 1932a, 1932b, 1934; Uspenskii, 1932, 1938a, 1938b, 1939; Vlasov, 1936a, 1936b; Brezer, 1937), the Sherlova Mountain deposits (Boldyrev and Lui, 1929; Kholmov, 1929; Levitskii, 1933), the pegmatites of the Altai (Boldyrev, 1932; Dovgal', 1934). Also investigated were the helvite-containing corundum veins of the southern Urals (Kitaev, 1928), of the pegmatitic fields of Central Asia (Gavrusevich, 1932; Strelkin, 1935; Sosedko, 1934, 1935, 1937), of the Northern Caucasus (Naprasnikov, 1933; Kuznetsova, 1931, 1936, 1946), and of eastern Siberia (Yakzhin, 1937). A general description of various genetic types of beryllium deposits was ad-

[4] Reference not available, Ed.

vanced for the first time in an interesting paper by D. I. Shcherbakov (1936).

On the basis of the abundant accumulated experimental material, Soviet mineralogists and geochemists, headed by A. E. Fersman, developed between 1925 and 1940 original theories of the genesis of beryllium deposits. In subsequent years, these theories played a decisive part in determining the trend and scope of scientific research on beryllium. Of considerable scientific and practical importance is A. E. Fersman's theory (1925b, 1925c, 1939, 1933–1939, 1940) of the genesis of the desilicated emerald-bearing veins in the Urals. This theory, whose validity has been largely substantiated by the investigations of P. P. Pyatnitskii (1929, 1932a, 1932b) and K. A. Vlasov (1938a, 1938b), at present provides the most widely accepted explanation of the formational peculiarities the emerald deposits of the Urals.

Fersman's theory of formation of pegmatites, developed from his study of abundant material, was presented in its final form in his classical monograph *Pegmatites* (1940). The type of pegmatite investigation that he began has been developed in the USSR by his pupils and followers, and it plays a leading part in both theory and practice. Interest in the study of beryllium deposits greatly increased after 1940, owing to the recognition of the value of the metal and its alloys in various fields of industry and engineering. The rare-metal pegmatite fields in various areas of the USSR have been subjected to detailed study[5] by M. F. Strelkin, A. I. Ginzburg, V. I. Kuznetsov, A. A. Beus, V. A. Kornetova, S. I. Kogan, and others. The helvite-containing skarns have been investigated in detail[6] by M. M. Konstantinov, A. D. Kalenov, A. V. Zolotova, M. S. Tsybul'skaya, A. M. Zasedatelev, and others, and the beryllium-bearing greisen deposits by M. D. Dorfman, A. A. Beus, and others. A whole series of theoretical generalizations have been published; these are based on the vast amount of data gathered during the extensive geological prospecting and geological exploration for rare metals that took place in the USSR after 1940 and, especially, after 1945. The research of K. A. Vlasov (1943, 1946, 1952) was of great importance in the development of the investigation of pegmatitic rare-metal deposits, including beryl. His textural-paragenetic classification of granitic pegmatites became a valuable aid for geologists. The new theoretical ideas were used in a number of studies relating to practical methods of prospecting and evaluating the pegmatitic rare-metal deposits (e.g., Ginzburg, 1948; Beus, 1955, 1956a). The accumulated data made it possible to introduce many new features into the analysis of the structure and genesis of the beryl-bearing pegmatites, and to establish a number of critical factors bearing on the rare-metal concentration in these pegmatites, including beryllium (Vlasov, 1946, 1951, 1952, 1956a, 1956b; Beus, 1948, 1950, 1951, 1953a, 1953b, 1954, 1955, 1956a, 1956b, 1956c, 1957; Ginzburg, 1952a, 1952b, 1955a, 1955b).

The intensive study of the pegmatitic rare-metal deposits that began in

[5] Specific references not available, Ed.

[6] Specific references not available, Ed.

all countries after World War II, also enriched the mineralogy of beryllium considerably.

During the brief period between 1948 and 1955, four new beryllium phosphates were found in the pegmatites of various countries—hurlbutite, faheyite, morasetite, and väyrynenite (Mrose, 1952; Lindberg and Pecora, 1953; Lindberg and Murata, 1953; Volborth, 1954a, 1954b, 1954c); new beryllium-containing minerals from the margarite group, namely bowleyite (‡bityite, Ed.) (Rowlege and Hayton, 1948; Fleischer, 1950) and beryllium-margarite (Beus and Fedorchuk, 1955) were described, and bavenite was studied in detail (Fleischer and Switzer, 1953).[7]

Much new material was introduced into the mineralogy of beryllium by the detailed and lengthy investigations carried out by Soviet mineralogists in the interesting alkalic province of the Kola Peninsula. After a new beryllium silicate, chkalovite, had been discovered in 1939 in the alkalic pegmatites of the Lovozero massif (Gerasimovskii, 1939a, 1939b), seven beryllium minerals were successively discovered in the pegmatites of that province; four were found to be new species: beryllite (Kuz'menko, 1954), karpinskyite (Shilin, 1956), spherobertrandite and gelbertrandite (Semenov, 1957a). It should be noted that the study of the mineralogy of beryllium in alkalic pegmatites has made possible a new approach to the previously neglected field of the geochemistry of beryllium, namely its history in the hypergene processes. In the next few years we can expect the discovery of new beryllium minerals directly related to both alkalic pegmatites and the supergene zone in pegmatite deposits.

In reviewing the history of investigations in the field of beryllium geochemistry proper, we should stress that, until recently, such investigations were complicated by the difficulty of determining the presence of small amounts of beryllium in rocks and minerals. As a result of the similarity between the chemical properties of beryllium and aluminum, beryllium was not discovered at first even in the beryllium minerals, barylite, milarite, and bavenite. Spectral determination methods for small amounts of beryllium were first developed in the 1930's (Goldschmidt and Peters, 1932), and methods of accurate chemical analysis were not perfected until the late 1940's (Sandell, 1949).

Since the end of the 1880's, however, gifted chemist-mineralogists in various countries have found small amounts of beryllium in some minerals, especially in the tantaloniobates and silicates which do not contain aluminum: chevkinite (Doelter, 1914–1925), hyalotekite (Lindström, 1888–1889), fergusonite, yttrotantalite, and samarskite (Blomstrand, in Brögger, 1906), and clinohumite (Zambonini, 1919).

The interest in the occurrence of beryllium in minerals and rocks increased particularly after Palache (Palache and Bauer, 1930; Palache, 1931)

[7] In the USSR E. I. Kutukova (1946) found bavenite and described it in 1946. Its chemical analyses, carried out by V. S. Saltykova and M. E. Kazakova, provided the correct BeO content of bavenite.

had published interesting data on the presence of considerable proportions of beryllium in vesuvianite and milarite, where it was previously determined as aluminum. When discussing the results of Palache, H. S. Washington (1931) suggested that beryllium occurred much more widely than was previously believed, since its similarity to aluminum may have caused it to be often overlooked in rocks and minerals. Washington's assumptions were found to be exaggerated, but they have undoubtedly played an important part in the development of further investigations of the occurrence of beryllium in the earth's crust.

In 1932 W. M. Goldschmidt and C. Peters published a critical geochemical investigation, in which for the first time the average content of beryllium in various rock types and in the earth's crust was computed from data obtained by research. Notwithstanding the restricted number of analyses, the investigations of Goldschmidt and his co-workers (1932, 1933, 1945) became the classical research in beryllium geochemistry, and the foundation of later scientific work in this field. The numerical data published by these authors in 1932–1933 remained virtually unchanged and without any supplement until the publication of E. B. Sandell's work in 1952. An analysis of all available data pertaining to the geochemistry of beryllium shows that even the later investigations have not so much changed, as supplemented and more accurately refined, the figures and statements adduced in Goldschmidt's publications.

In the period between 1933 and 1952, there were no important investigations relating to the geochemistry of beryllium, although small incidental research projects in the occurrence of beryllium in various rocks and minerals were conducted in various countries.

From a number of deposits in the USSR, V. A. Zil'bermints and E. V. Rozhkova published in 1933 the data on the beryllium content of vesuvianite, which failed to bear out the assumptions of H. S. Washington (1931) relating to the wide occurrence of high beryllium concentrations in vesuvianite. Later papers by Yu. M. Tolmachev and A. N. Filippov (1934, 1935) reported interesting data about the beryllium content of nepheline in the Khibin massif and in some amazonite.

The data on the geochemistry of beryllium that were available at the end of the 1930's were summarized in a number of publications by A. E. Fersman (1933–1939, 1940), who paid special attention to the characteristics of the behavior of beryllium in alkalic magmas and in the formation process of pegmatites. He was the first scientist to calculate the mean content of beryllium in granitic pegmatites and to derive, from the results of previous investigators, the mean content of beryllium in the earth's crust, including the hydrosphere.

At the same time, material relating to the presence of beryllium as an isomorphous impurity in various minerals was obtained in other countries. I. Oftedal (1939) established the constant occurrence of beryllium in thorites. Peculiar beryllium allanites were studied in detail by T. Iimori

(1938) and P. Quensel (1944). E. Preiss and S. Gliszezynski (1950) determined the increased beryllium content of some wavellites.

There appeared also, from time to time, isolated data on the occurrence of beryllium in rocks, ores, and natural waters. F. Rodolico and R. Pierruccini (1942) published their investigations on the occurrence of beryllium in some Italian volcanic and sedimentary rocks. A. Rezek and K. Tomic (1942) found beryllium in the evaporite of water from mineral springs. Finally, E. B. Sandell and S. S. Goldich (1943) studied the occurrence of a number of rare elements, including beryllium, in some volcanic rocks in the United States, and T. G. Sahama (1945) carried out similar research on the rocks of southern Lapland. S. Landergren (1948) adduced interesting data on the occurrence of beryllium and other rare elements in Swedish iron ores.

It should be noted that all of the investigations on the geochemistry of beryllium carried out from 1933 to 1952 are unsystematic. Even in the most detailed geochemical researches of Sandell and Goldich, Sahama, and Landergren, very little attention is given to the geochemistry of beryllium, and the authors virtually give only an account of the numerical data obtained, without making any generalizations or dealing with questions related to the behavior of the element in natural conditions. This is why Rankama and Sahama in the section "Beryllium" of their excellent compilation, *Geochemistry* (1950), were unable to add anything basically new to the conclusions of Goldschmidt, and only repeated his fundamental statements and gave an account of the numerical data (mostly disconnected) that had appeared after 1933.

The first systematic research in the geochemistry of beryllium after Goldschmidt and Peters, was carried out by E. B. Sandell (1952) who somewhat earlier had developed the method of the fluorometric determination of small amounts of beryllium with morin (Sandell, 1940). Sandell's morin method, which enables 0.1×10^{-4} percent Be to be determined in a sample of 0.1 g, is at present the most accurate and sensitive method for determining small amounts of beryllium. This method opened a new period in the geochemistry of beryllium, by making it possible to study rocks and minerals in which the beryllium content is below 3×10^{-4} percent, the limit of sensitivity of modern methods of qualitative spectroscopic analysis for beryllium. In his concise but interesting paper, Sandell reported on the occurrence of beryllium in the sixteen analyzed groups of volcanic rocks and in some granitoid rock-forming minerals. He discusses particularly the form in which beryllium occurs in volcanic rocks; he derives its average content in the upper part of the lithosphere, as well as the average content in various rock types. The data he obtained were found to be very close to those of Goldschmidt and Peters.

After the war, systematic study of beryllium geochemistry began in the USSR in 1952 at the Laboratory of Mineralogy and Geochemistry of Rare

Elements, Academy of Sciences of the USSR (now known as the Institute of Mineralogy, Geochemistry, and Crystal Chemistry of Rare Elements, Academy of Sciences of the USSR). Research was undertaken in the determination of the peculiarities encountered in the entry of beryllium into the crystal structures of minerals (Beus, 1953b, 1956c), and in study of the laws governing the occurrence of beryllium in minerals, rocks, and deposits (Beus and Fedorchuk, 1955; Beus, 1956b; Beus and Sazhina, 1956; Borodin, 1956). The occurrence of beryllium in alkalic rocks was also studied at the IGEM AN USSR (L. L. Shilin *et al.*, 1956, 1957).

It should be noted that, since the 1930's, the achievements in the field of crystal chemistry have greatly contributed toward the success of investigations in beryllium geochemistry. The crystal-chemical role played by beryllium in silicates, as described in the papers by L. Pauling (1930), L. Pauling, H. Klug, and A. N. Winchell (1935), F. Machatschki (1928, 1932, 1938, 1948, 1953), and F. Machatschki and E. Stradner (1953), provides the basis for the treatment of a number of peculiarities in the isomorphous entry of beryllium into the structure of minerals. A tremendous contribution to the crystal-chemistry of beryllium and the detailed structure of beryllium minerals was made by the outstanding Soviet crystal-chemist N. V. Belov (1942, 1947, 1950, 1954a, 1954b), Belov and Tarkhova (1949, 1951), and by his pupils, Yu. A. Pyatenko *et al.* (1956). Certain peculiarities in the crystal-chemistry of beryllium, which enable one to understand the conditions of its migration and concentration in nature, were discussed in papers by V. S. Sobolev (1944, 1949, 1956), A. E. Ringwood (1955a, 1955b), and A. S. Povarennykh (1955a, 1955b).

The center of investigations in the geochemistry and mineralogy of beryllium in the USSR is the Institute of Mineralogy, Geochemistry, and Crystal Chemistry of Rare Elements, Academy of Sciences of the USSR. Work in this field is also conducted at many other university and departmental institutions of scientific research (IGEM AN USSR, the Far East Branch of the Academy of Sciences of the USSR, and the All-Union Institute of Scientific Research on Mineral Raw Materials). Further expansion of this research is highly desirable from both the theoretical and practical point of view; the rapid development of the Soviet rare-metal industry places before Soviet geologists, mineralogists, and geochemists serious problems related to the study of the relevant mineral sources.

In the Soviet Union, where an exceptional variety of geological structure exists, there are virtually all known types of beryllium deposits, as well as a number of extremely interesting occurrences that have no analogues in other countries. At the same time, a profound analysis of the laws of occurrence of beryllium deposits within the various geochemical provinces of the USSR entitles one to hope that large deposits of beryllium ores of various, perhaps even new, genetic types may be found soon. For, in order to be successful, this prospecting work should be conducted with full knowledge of the fundamental laws of the behavior of beryllium in the genesis of deposits of different types and the principal peculiarities of structure and mineralogical composition of these deposits.

No investigations can be found, either in Soviet or foreign geological and mineralogical-geochemical literature, that would present an up-to-date summary of all data relating to the known types of beryllium deposits and beryllium minerals. Since W. M. Goldschmidt's work, virtually no research has been done on the determination of the laws of the behavior of beryllium in the processes of mineral formation. At the same time, the abundant experimental data, accumulated by geologists during the long detailed study of beryllium deposits, commonly do not fit the known laws, but require for their explanation an intensive mineralogical-geochemical analysis of the facts. Such analysis became particularly important for determining the correct course of action in the large-scale geological prospecting and exploratory work for beryllium in the USSR.

In this book, the author tries to generalize the results of his own investigations, and all published data on the geochemistry of beryllium and the study of its deposits. Unlike his first book (Beus, 1956a),[8] which was destined exclusively for the practical work of Soviet geologists, the author believes the aim of the present book to be a deeper scientific analysis of the laws that allow the reconstruction of a more complete picture of the behavior of beryllium in the genesis of rocks and mineral deposits. It is obvious that the still limited factual and experimental data available did not enable the author to solve in this book all the problems posed. After additional facts are known, it will be possible to treat many phenomena with greater accuracy, or to introduce changes; but even now, it is already possible to reconstruct from the separate fragments, the history of the behavior of this unusual, highly individualistic element in the process of mineral formation. The author expects his book to assist geologists and geochemists and to act as a stimulus for gathering new factual data.

The author wishes to take this opportunity to express his deep gratitude to the workers of the Institute of Mineralogy, Geochemistry, and Crystal Chemistry of Rare Elements, Academy of Sciences of the USSR: V. S. Saltykova, S. N. Fedorchuk, and L. I. Sazhina, who made a large number of the analyses of beryllium minerals and the partial beryllium determinations of minerals and rocks used in this book; also, to D. N. Ustinov and A. A. Sitnin, who organized the technical layout of the book.

The author is very grateful to A. I. Ginzburg, N. E. Zalashkova, and L. S. Borodin for many valuable pieces of advice, which were substantially helpful in the work, and to K. A. Vlaslov who has edited it.

[8] English translation published for the Geochemical Society by W. H. Freeman and Company, San Francisco and London, 1962. Ed.

PART I

Chemical Properties and Mineralogy of Beryllium

CHAPTER 1

Position in the Periodic System, Atomic Structure, and Chemical Properties of Beryllium

In D. I. Mendeleev's periodic system of elements, beryllium is the first element of the second group, and the third element of the first (helium) period; these circumstances determine the special structural features of the beryllium atom. The ordinal number of the element, 4, indicates four positive particles in the nucleus and four electrons, two in each electron shell that correspond to the energy levels *K* and *L*. The four known beryllium isotopes have masses 7, 8, 9, and 10; only the Be^9 isotope is stable and occurs widely in nature.

The nucleus of this natural stable isotope Be^9 consists of nine particles (four protons and five neutrons) and it can be considered as a complex consisting of the nuclear residue Be^8, in the field of which moves the unpaired neutron (Kopaleishvili, 1956). The presence of one unpaired neutron allows us to assume an unequal energy distribution among the particles that constitute the beryllium nucleus (Mamasakhlisov, 1947). It has been clearly demonstrated that the unpaired neutron is bonded in the nucleus much more weakly than the other eight particles. This characteristic feature of the atomic structure makes it possible to use beryllium in practice as a neutron source, because the nuclear reaction between the beryllium nucleus and gamma-rays results in neutrons being emitted easily. This phenomenon is particularly useful in assaying the element in minerals and ores, and in prospecting for beryllium deposits.

The other beryllium isotopes, Be^7 and Be^{10}, were originally obtained by artificial methods but have been recently detected in nature during the

Table 1 Beryllium isotopes

Isotopes	Mass	Half-life period	Method of production (nuclear reaction)
Be^7	7.0192	52.9 days	Li^6 (d, n) Li^7 (p, n) Be^{10} (p, α) Be^{10} (d, α, n)
Be^8	8.0078	$< 5 \cdot 10^{-14}$ sec.	Be^9 (p, d) Be^9 (γ, n) Li^7 (d, n) O $(\gamma, 2\alpha)$
Be^9	9.0150	Stable	Occurs in nature
Be^{10}	10.0168	$2.7 \cdot 10^6$ years	Be^9 (α, p) Be^9 (d, p) Be^9 (n, γ) Be^{10} (n, p) C^{13} (n, α)

study of the products of secondary nuclear transformations caused by cosmic rays. Both of these radiogenic beryllium isotopes (especially Be^7) have half-life periods (Table 1) that are too short to allow them to accumulate in the earth's crust. At the same time, the half-life of Be^{10} is long enough so that this isotope can be used in the study of geological phenomena dating from the end of the Tertiary period, and in determining the rate of accumulation of marine sediments.

The occurrence of natural radioactive beryllium isotopes is presently being investigated by a large number of physicists and radiochemists in various countries; this study is certain to yield many interesting results soon.

It should be noted that, of the reactions listed in Table 1, the reaction $Be^9 (\gamma,n) Be^8$ is possible in the conditions of the lithosphere, where it can be caused by the radiation of some radioactive elements, radium in particular. The short-lived isotope Be^8, which forms in this reaction, disintegrates into two helium atoms according to the scheme $Be^8 \rightarrow 2He^4$. The probability of such a transformation is determined by the presence of components in the radium and thorium gamma-radiation whose energy exceeds the level required for two alpha particles to form from Be^9 (Crane and Lauritsen, 1935). Thus, besides Be^7 and Be^{10}, the natural nuclear reactions can be expected to produce also the shortlived Be^8. This is a partial explanation of the increased proportion of helium, so characteristic of beryllium minerals (Burkser, Kapustin, and Kondoguri, 1937; Khlopin and Abishev, 1941; Khlopin, 1949; Cherdyntsev and Kozak, 1949). Indeed, if the possibility of the radiogenic formation of helium in beryllium minerals is not taken into account, it is impossible to explain the unequivocally established direct relationships between the age of a mineral and its helium content. This possibility was not acknowledged in V. G. Khlopin's (1949) treatment of the phenomenon, where he explained the high helium content in beryllium, lithium, and boron minerals by the occlusion of helium from magma during their crystallization. The nuclear properties of beryllium point, with considerable certainty, to the occurrence of helium in beryllium minerals as a result of the disintegration of Be^9, caused by external gamma-radiation.

Along with the reaction referred to above, the nuclear reaction of the type $Be^9 + He^4 \rightarrow C^{12} + n_0$ is also probable in natural conditions. However, whereas the former reaction, caused by gamma-radiation, can take place under the effect of radioactive elements contained in rocks enclosing the beryllium mineral, the latter reaction, caused by the action of alpha particles, can be related, owing to the very short path of these particles, only to the effect of radioactive elements included in the lattice of the mineral itself.

It is known that gadolinite and beryllium-rich allanite are beryllium minerals containing radioactive elements. Although the presence of C^{12} in these minerals has not been specially studied, much of the analytic data available in the literature (*e.g.* Quensel, 1944) points to the occurrence of carbon or CO_2 in their composition. It appears desirable to study the occurrence of carbon in beryllium minerals containing radioactive elements.

The mass number of the only stable beryllium isotope, Be^9, is an exception to the rule of the predominance of isotopes with mass numbers equal to a multiple of 4. Elements with the atom type $4_q + 1$—beryllium, cesium, scandium, yttrium, niobium, tantalum, bismuth, and others,—constitute a group of elements that accounts (according to A. E. Fersman's calculations) for only 0.01 percent of the earth's crust. Beryllium differs from all other elements of this group in having an even number; indeed, it is the only even-numbered element in the periodic system whose nucleus is of the type $4_q + 1$.

On the curve of atomic volumes, beryllium, along with boron and carbon, occupies the lowest position, near the first minimum. Unlike the rock-forming elements that occupy an analogous position at the second (Al, Si) and third (Mn, Fe) minimuns, beryllium and boron are rare elements.

Without touching on the reasons that determine the occurrence of elements, we should point out that the rarity of beryllium is doubtless related to the lack of stability of the nuclei of all its isotopes (including Be^9). The low stability of the beryllium nucleus should manifest itself very clearly in stellar conditions, in the presence of a large number of free protons. According to R. Atkinson's (1931) calculations in stellar depths (40×10^6 deg) in the presence of up to 10 percent of free protons, the survival time of beryllium is 3.9 days. Using the results of Atkinson's calculations, A. E. Fersman (1933–1939) arrived at the conclusion that the scarcity of the lightest elements of the periodic system, including beryllium, on the curve of the mean contents, is the result of their primary instability, and not of their subsequent dissemination.

The properties of beryllium related to the structure of the electron shells of the atom are also distinctive. The atomic (metallic) radius of beryllium is 1.13Å. Increase in the mass and charge of the nucleus does not change the configuration of the electron shells but causes a sharp decrease in the length of the atomic and ionic radii of beryllium—much greater than in neighboring lithium ($r_a Li^7 = 1.52$ Å; $r_i Li = 0.60$ Å).

After the valency electrons have been removed, the beryllium atom forms an ion of the inert-gas type, which, like lithium, has only one electron shell, but is more compact and has smaller dimensions. The true radius of beryllium, 0.34 Å, is the smallest among the metals. Other conditions being equal, it is the indicator of the strengthened bond of the valency electron and, when this electron has been removed, is the measure of the greater strength of atomic structure (Fersman, 1933–1939, p. 77).

The ionization potentials for beryllium are (for the first, second, third, and fourth electrons, respectively): $I_1 = 9.28$; $I_2 = 18.12$; $I_3 = 153.1$; $I_4 = 216.6$ eV. On the curve of the ionization potentials of elements, beryllium occupies one of the top places in the series of metals. This position accounts for its low atomic radius and the fact that it does not give up its electrons very willingly, thus determining the element's degree of chemical activity and the stability of its compounds. The same factor is of decisive significance in determining which type of chemical bond will form when beryllium combines with other elements.

Also characteristic of beryllium is the sudden change of the ionization potential on transition to the inner electron shell (for the third electron). All this emphasizes the strength of the bond between electrons and the nucleus of the beryllium atom. The proximity of beryllium to zinc in regard to the ionization potential of the first electron (I_1) and the excitation potential of the second electron (i_2) (in eV) is very interesting:

	I_1	i_2	i_3
Be	9.28	8.84	134.98
Zn	9.37	8.67	21.96

G. S. Momdhzi (1955), who noticed this similarity, relates to it the distinct analogy found between a number of chemical properties of these elements.

A direct function of the ionization potential of an element is its electronegativity, which A. S. Povarennykh (1955b) defines as the energy of attraction of electrons by the given atom when combining with other atoms. The theory of electronegativity, as presently known, cannot be considered fully developed because the electronegativity values of elements, calculated with varying degrees of approximation by different authors (Pauling, 1940;[1] Nekrasov, 1946; Ringwood, 1955a; Povarennykh, 1955a, 1955b; and others), are still inconclusive. However, the application of this theory to the interpretation of the properties of compounds of chemical elements and their behavior in the processes encountered in nature was shown by A. E. Ringwood (1955a), A. S. Povarennykh (1955a, 1955b), and others to yield very important results: namely, it explained a number of crystal-chemical and geochemical phenomena which had been heretofore either inexplicable or controversial.

In particular, highly interesting results can be obtained by using the electronegativity of elements to characterize the type of their bonds in chemical compounds (Pauling, 1940;[2] Ormont, 1950; Povarennykh, 1955a, 1955b).

From this viewpoint, beryllium, along with aluminum and a number of other elements, can be considered as a typical transition element between the electropositive metal atoms, which give up their electrons readily, and the typical complex-forming elements, which have a tendency to form the covalent bond. The correctness of this assumption is borne out in particular by the fact that, in regard to the degree of dissociation, beryllium compounds occupy the transitional position between the typical cations and complex-formers, as mentioned by A. E. Fersman (1933–1939, pp. 214, 217).

Taking into account that beryllium is, to a certain extent, the boundary element between the typical electropositive atoms and the complex-formers, we see that its transitional character is definitely indicated in the table of relative electronegativity, in which the electronegativity of beryllium has been adopted as unity (Fig. 1). In this table, the regions of electropositive and electronegative elements, and the diagonal series of intermediate elements headed by beryllium are clearly shown.

It is known that the ability of a particular element to form complexes is determined by the degree of covalency in its oxygen bonding, which

[1] Given as 1947 in original, Ed.
[2] Given as 1947 in original, Ed.

							1 H 1^-1.36 *1.56* 1^+0.00 –										
2 He 1.22 –	3 Li 1^+0.68 *0.59*	4 Be 2^+0.34 *1.00*	5 B 3^+(0.20) *1.38*	6 C 4^+0.2 *1.81* 4^-(2.60) –	7 N 5^+(0.15) *2.9* 3^-(1.48) –	8 O 2^-(1.36) *2.52*	9 F 1^-(1.33) *2.93*										
10 Ne 0 1.60 –	11 Na 1^+0.98 *0.56*	12 Mg 2^+0.74 *0.83*	13 Al 3^+0.57 *1.05*	14 Si 4^+0.39 *1.29*	15 P 5^+0.35 *1.52* 3^+1.86 –	16 S 2^-1.82 – 6^+(0.29) *1.83*	17 Cl 1^-1.81 *2.17*										
18 Ar 0 1.92 –	19 K 1^+1.33 *0.48*	20 Ca 2^+1.04 *0.65*	21 Sc 3^+0.83 *0.95*	22 Ti 3^+0.69 *1.01* 4^+0.64 *1.24*	23 V 3^+0.69 *1.12* 5^+0.4 *1.50*	24 Cr 3^+0.64 *1.19* 6^+0.35 *1.76*	25 Mn 2^+0.91 *0.81* 7^+(0.46) *2.00*	26 Fe 2^+0.80 *0.88* 3^+0.67 *1.17*	27 Co 2^+0.78 *0.95* 3^+0.64 *1.24*	28 Ni 2^+0.74 *1.05*	29 Cu 1^+0.98 *0.85* 2^+0.80 *1.12*	30 Zn 2^+0.80 *0.99*	31 Ga 3^+0.62 *1.12*	32 Ge 2^+0.65 – 4^+0.44 *1.26*	33 As 3^+0.69 *1.05* 5^+(0.47) *1.45*	34 Se 4^+0.69 – 6^+0.39 *1.69*	35 Br 1^-1.96 *2.02*
36 Kr 0 1.98 –	37 Rb 1^+1.49 *0.46*	38 Sr 2^+1.20 *0.59*	39 Y 3^+0.97 *0.76*	40 Zr 4^+0.82 *0.95*	41 Nb 5^+0.66 *1.14*	42 Mo 4^+0.68 *1.12* 6^+0.65 *1.31*	43 Tc – *1.43*	44 Ru 4^+0.62 *1.29*	45 Rh 3^+0.75 – 4^+0.65 –	46 Pd 2^+ *1.09*	47 Ag 1^+1.13 *0.83*	48 Cd 2^+0.99 *0.93*	49 In 3^+0.99 *1.02*	50 Sn 2^+1.02 *0.81* 4^+0.67 *1.12*	51 Sb 3^+0.90 *0.93* 5^+0.62 *1.26*	52 Te 4^+0.89 *1.05* 6^+(0.56) *1.50*	53 J 1^-2.20 *1.79* 7^+(0.50) –
54 Xe 0 2.18 –	55 Cs 1^+1.65 *0.40*	56 Ba 2^+1.38 *0.55*	57-71 TR – ~*0.71*	72 Hf 4^+(0.78) *(0.88)*	73 Ta 5^+(0.66) *(1.02)*	74 W 4^+0.68 *0.98* 6^+0.65 *1.67*	75 Re 6^+0.52 *1.24* 4^+ *1.05*	76 Os 4^+0.65 –	77 Ir 4^+0.65 –	78 Pt 2^+ *0.95*	79 Au 1^+(0.37) *1.01*	80 Hg 2^+1.12 *1.02*	81 Tl 1^+1.49 *0.67* 3^+1.05 *1.09*	82 Pb 2^+1.26 *0.52* 4^+0.76 *1.17*	83 Bi 3^+1.20 *0.93* 5^+(0.74) *1.26*	84 Po – –	85 At – –
86 Rn – –	87 Fr – *(0.40)*	88 Ra 2^+1.44 *0.54*	89 Ac 3^+1.11 *(0.69)*	90 Th – *0.79*	91 Pa – *0.87*	92 U – *0.97*											

Fig. 1. Table of relative electronegativity. Beryllium heads the diagonal series of intermediate elements.

determines the strength of the complex. Unfortunately, we are still unable to make the correct approach to the quantitative evaluation of the state of the chemical bond in most compounds. The method suggested of determining the degree of covalency or of the ionic nature of the chemical bond, suggested in a number of papers (Pauling, 1940;[3] Ormont, 1950; Povarennykh, 1955a, 1955b) is based only on the difference of the electronegativities of the reacting atoms, which is decisive in a number of cases and therefore applicable only to neutral binary compounds. Generally, this method makes it possible only to estimate the qualitative tendency towards the formation of a particular type of bonding, which can change in some degree under the effect of external conditions.

At the same time, it is definitely the effect of external conditions that determines the dual (amphoteric) behavior of the intermediate elements, including beryllium. The main factor is apparently the concentration of atoms (or ions) with the low value of electronegativity, which determines the condition of the bond of the intermediate element in the compound, and its form in solution.

In the compounds, the essence of this relationship is determined by the fact that the atom of an element with a low value of electronegativity contained in the compound not only does not attract a part of the electron cloud of other atoms, but even gives up its electrons to oxygen atoms, partly "saturating" their electronegative energy. This equalizes the difference in electronegativities and increases the degree of covalency of the bond between oxygen and the atom of the intermediate element bonded to it that has a relatively high electronegativity. This rule was well illustrated by V. S. Sobolev (1949), who established that there is a decrease of the coordination number of aluminum when the concentration of alkali atoms in the minerals increases.

In neutral solutions the hydroxides of intermediate elements (amphoters), including beryllium, dissociate as follows:

$$M^{m+} + nOH^{1-} \rightleftarrows M(OH)_n \equiv H_nMO_n \rightleftarrows nH^{1+} + [MO_n]^{m-}.$$

It is natural that the preponderance of the basic or acidic properties depends wholly on the difference between the electronegativities of the amphoter and oxygen, which determines the proportion of covalency in the bond M — O and, consequently, the strength of the complex.

As an example, let us analyze from this standpoint the complexes $[BeO_4]$, $[AlO_4]$, $[SiO_4]$, and $[SO_4]$. The proportion of the bond covalency in these complexes, as calculated by A. S. Povarennykh's method for their isolated state, amounts in a neutral medium to 37, 40, 52, and 80 percent, respectively. These figures agree very well with the degree of stability of these complexes. It is known that $[SO_4]$ is a strong acidic complex anion; $[SiO_4]$ is a fairly stable complex with weakly expressed acid properties (these,

[3] Given as 1947 in original, Ed.

however, exceed the alkaline properties); finally, the complexes [AlO_4] and [BeO_4] are very unstable in a neutral medium, and therefore alkaline properties preponderate in the case of beryllium and aluminum hydroxides.

In alkaline solutions which contain the atoms of alkali elements that easily give up their electrons to the oxygen atoms, there arises the possibility of a more stable covalent bond between the anion and the atom of the amphoteric element. A complex is formed; its stability is determined by the concentration of elements with low electronegativity values, namely alkalies. A typical intermediate (amphoteric) element, beryllium behaves under these conditions as a complex-former.

In acid solutions containing a high concentration of hydrogen ions, the oxygen atoms are bonded mostly to anions with which they form stable complex ions. Like beryllium, intermediate elements with an average electronegativity value can occur under these conditions as free, positively charged ions; that is, they are cations.

The basicity properties of an element are also characterized by the magnitude of the ionic potential ω/r_i, which expressed the energy of the field of forces of the ion. As one would expect, the small beryllium atom has a considerable ionic potential, namely 5.88 (A. E. Fersman believed this high value of the ionic potential of beryllium to be anomalous), which unites this element with the group of metals-amphoters (aluminum, titanium, and zirconium). Aluminum is characterized by an ionic potential value (5.26) particularly close to that of beryllium.

Thus, because its chemical properties are completely determined by the structural features of the electron shells of the atom, beryllium is related to the typical amphoteric elements.

The element's behavior in melts and solutions and its function in compounds depend on the acidity of the medium (for solutions) and the nature of ambient atoms that affect essentially the nature of the bond between beryllium and oxygen or another highly electronegative element. It has been shown previously that alkalies exert the most interesting geochemical influence on the nature of the bond between beryllium and the electronegative atoms. Within definite concentration limits, the alkalies partly neutralize the electronegative energy of such atoms as oxygen, fluorine, etc., thus ensuring a high degree of covalency for the bond between these elements and beryllium and therefore also increasing the possibility of the formation of complex ions. In the presence of strong acidic complexes, without alkalies, beryllium behaves as an ordinary cation with weakly manifested alkaline properties.

The dual amphoteric character of beryllium is the outstanding peculiarity in the entire chemistry and geochemistry of this element.

As first element of the second group, beryllium differs from the adjacent magnesium by weaker alkaline properties and by the presence of weakly acidic properties not characteristic of magnesium. Considerable difference in the ionization potentials and, therefore, in the electronegativity, bring about certain differences in the chemical properties of these elements. On the contrary, boron, which succeeds beryllium on the horizontal line, is already characterized by distinct acidic properties and is a typical complex-forming element.

Beryllium metal dissolves easily in hydrochloric acid, yielding beryllium chloride; sulfuric and nitric acids dissolve beryllium less easily (the latter only on heating). The amphoteric properties of this element are shown in the reactions of beryllium metal with solutions of strong alkalies in which it dissolves with the evolution of hydrogen. Beryllium oxide and hydroxide also easily dissolve in strong alkalies. Beryllium hydroxide has distinct amphoteric properties and dissociates as follows:

$$Be^{2+} + 2\ OH^{1-} \rightleftarrows Be(OH)_2 \equiv H_2BeO_2 \rightleftarrows 2H^{1+} + [BeO_2]^{2-}.$$

The basic properties of beryllium hydroxide are more strongly expressed than the acidic ones; this is understandable because the greater covalency (consequently, also stability) of the bond between oxygen and hydrogen shifts the dissociation to the left. An aqueous solution of beryllium hydroxide, saturated at room temperature, contains about 3×10^{-3} g/l $Be(OH)_2$.

On reacting with alkalies, $Be(OH)_2$ yields beryllates having the general formula $M_2Be_2O_3$. Owing to the weakness of the acidic properties of beryllium hydroxide, the aqueous solutions of beryllates are strongly hydrolyzed and contain a considerable proportion of beryllium as hydroxide sol. Thus, sodium beryllate in aqueous solution is hydrolyzed to the extent of about 50 percent, as shown by its electrical conductivity (Bleshinskii and Abramova, 1955).

On dissolving in acids, beryllium hydroxide forms the corresponding salts. At the same time, the heat of solution drops from HF to H_2SO_4 and HCl as the covalency of the bond of the formed compound increases.

Of greatest interest, in regard to their possible role in natural processes, are the halides and carbonates of beryllium.

Beryllium fluoride and chloride are fairly stable compounds and they dissolve easily in water. They are easily fusible (Melting point of BeF_2 is 577°C (Ryss, 1956)[4] and of $BeCl_2$ is 405°C) and easily sublimated (BeF_2 at 800°C, $BeCl_2$ below about 400°C). At the same time, the neutral beryllium carbonate is almost insoluble in water (One mole $BeCo_3 \cdot 4H_2O$ dissolves in 278 moles of water) and is a highly unstable compound. On slight heating (to 100°C), $BeCO_3$ easily loses CO_2 and is converted into BeO (Nekrasov, 1954). At 200°C, the loss of CO_2 amounts to 50 percent.

In a weakly alkaline and weakly acid medium in the presence of a

[4] In other sources the melting-point of BeF_2 is given as 800°, 543°, 805°C (Ryss, 1956).

certain amount of electropositive atoms of alkali metals, beryllium forms complex compounds of the type

$$M^{1+}[BeF_3], \quad M_2^{1+}[BeF_4], \quad M_2^{1+}[BeCl_4], \text{ and } M_2^{1+}[Be(CO_3)_2].$$

With the exception of sodium tetrafluroberyllate, the properties of the complex compounds of beryllium have been studied very little (Table 2). However, the available data indicate the low melting point and good solubility of most compounds of this kind; these properties identify them as mobile and easily migrating substances.

It should be noted that complex beryllates are generally unstable compounds that can exist in solution only within certain ranges of alkalinity.

Table 2 Properties of complex beryllium compounds

Compound	Properties
$Na[BeF_3]$	Crystalline substance, sparingly soluble in water. Melts with decomposition at 360–370°C. Sublimates strongly at 1200–1300°C.
$Na_2[BeF_4]$	Crystalline substance, soluble in water. Melts at about 615°C. In boiling water dissolves at the ratio 2.94:100.
$K_2[BeF_4]$	Crystalline substance, soluble in boiling water at the ratio of 5.27:100.
$Li_2[BeF_4]$	Rhombohedral crystals soluble in water. Melts with decomposition at 461°C.
$Na_2[BeCl_4]$	Melts with decomposition at about 330°C. Eutectic with beryllium chloride melts at 215°C. The compound could not be isolated from aqueous solution.
$K_2[Be(CO_3)_2]$	Crystalline substance, readily soluble in water.
$M_2^{1+}[BeF_3(OH)]$ $M^{2+}[BeF_3(OH)]$	Studied insufficiently.

This fact is of considerable importance in geochemistry, because it determines, as the acidity-alkalinity conditions of solutions vary, the possibility of the formation, migration, and decomposition of the complex beryllium compounds in the processes of mineral formation.

Thus, for example, sodium tetrafluroberyllate $Na_2[BeF_4]$ disintegrates when the alkalinity of solution increases, and produces the precipitate $Be(OH)_2$ at pH 10.8–12 (Novoselova and Simanov, 1955). In normal conditions there is a ready hydrolysis of chloroberyllates and carbonateberyllates, which are even less stable compounds than fluroberyllates. Under high pressures, characteristic of endogenous processes, a substantially greater stability of the complex beryllium compounds is assumed, but even then there is no doubt that their existence depends on the pH of the mineral-forming solutions.

Thus, in this general survey of the chemical properties of beryllium, the following preliminary conclusions, which suggest the possible parts various beryllium compounds can play in the geochemical history of this element, can be drawn:

1. In a substantially acidic medium and when the concentration of the electropositive alkali atoms in solutions is low, beryllium, can most likely migrate in the form of very readily soluble and volatile compounds—fluorides and chlorides.
2. In a weakly acidic and weakly alkaline medium and in the presence of a sufficient quantity of electropositive alkali atoms, the migration of beryllium can occur in the form of various complex beryllates which are endowed with diverse stabilities depending on the nature of the medium.
3. A substantially alkaline medium can contribute to the migration of beryllium as beryllates or carbonate-beryllates which decompose easily as the alkalinity of solution decreases.
4. The migration of water-soluble beryllium compounds can take place in both true and supercritical solutions, because compounds soluble in water dissolve readily in the supercritical water phase, producing solutions which are not saturated with such compounds (Nikolaev, 1953).

To complete this discussion of beryllium's chemical properties, which must be considered if one is to understand its mineralogy and the peculiar features of its behavior in natural processes, we must note that the geochemical properties of many beryllium compounds have been studied insufficiently. Of particular importance to the geochemistry of beryllium would be a series of investigations on the solubility and stability of its complex compounds at various temperatures, and also of pressure as a function of pH and composition of solutions.

From such investigations, it would be possible to estimate, from a concrete standpoint, the possible state of beryllium during migration and its concentrations in various types of geochemical processes.

CHAPTER 2

Mineralogy of Beryllium

Most of the forty naturally occurring beryllium minerals known at present have not been adequately studied because the overwhelming majority of them are rare or very rare. Thus, for example, 64 percent of all beryllium minerals are known in only one or two deposits in the world.[1]

The distribution of beryllium minerals in the classes of chemical compounds is highly irregular (Table 3) and is determined by the lithophilic property of its atom, while chalcophilic properties are nonexistent. The principal minerals among the natural beryllium compounds are silicates (65 percent of the total number of minerals); phosphates and oxides (including compound oxides) are less important; single representatives of beryllium minerals are found among the antimonates, borates, and carbonates. The absence of sulfides among beryllium minerals confirms the lithophilic nature of this element.

Twenty-one elements combine with beryllium to form its natural compounds. The most important of these elements are oxygen, which is contained in all beryllium minerals, and silicon, which is in the structure of the anionic part of almost 65 percent of the beryllium minerals. There is a predominance of the inert-gas type ions (17 elements), whereas the transition-type ions (Mn, Fe) and those with 18-electron shells (Zn, Sb) are less abundant.

[1] The names in bold type refer to the most widely occurring minerals; those in normal type are common, and those in italics are very rare and found only in one or two deposits in the world.

I. OXIDES AND COMPOUND OXIDES

Bromellite
Chrysoberyl
Taaffeite

II. SILICATES

Epididymite
Eudidymite
Chkalovite

Helvite
Danalite
Genthelvite
Bavenite
Karpinskyite
Leucophanite
Meliphanite
Aminoffite
Trimerite

Gadolinite
Syanchualite
The bityite–bowelyite–beryllium-margarite group
Beryl
Milarite
Phenacite
Euclase
Barylite
Bertrandite
Gelbertrandite
Spherobertrandite
Beryllite

III. BORATES

Hambergite
Rhodizite

IV. ANTIMONATES

Swedenborgite

V. PHOSPHATES

Beryllonite
Hurlbutite
Herderite
Väyrynenite
Faheyite
Moraesite
Kolveckite

VI. CARBONATES

Beryllium-tengerite

Table 3 Distribution of beryllium minerals among the classes of chemical compounds

Class	Number of beryllium minerals	% of the total number of minerals
1. Oxides and compound oxides	3	7.5
2. Silicates	26	65.0
3. Borates	2	5.0
4. Phosphates	7	17.5
5. Antimonates	1	2.5
6. Carbonates	1	2.5

Because all beryllium minerals are oxygen-containing compounds, the structural position of beryllium in these minerals depends entirely on the nature of coordination between beryllium and oxygen. It is known that the coordination number of beryllium with respect to oxygen is 4, which is determined both by the ratio of ionic radii ($r_i\mathrm{Be}/r_i\mathrm{O} = 0.25$) and the nature of the beryllium-oxygen bond; in the natural compounds beryllium is always surrounded tetrahedrally by oxygen ions with which it forms compact tetrahedra $[BeO_4]^{6-}$. The part played by beryllium in the structure of beryllium minerals is determined in the first place by the small radius of the bivalent positive ion Be^{2+} (true $r_i = 0.34$ Å). This indicates a strengthening of the bond between its valency electrons and the nucleus as compared with the remaining elements of its group, and also is one of the causes of the high stability of lattices of natural beryllium compounds, of the increased electronegativity, and of the marked amphoteric properties of the element.

It should be noted that, with $Al^{(VI)}$ and $Zr^{(VIII)}$,[2] the size of the ion in the case of beryllium in tetrahedral coordination corresponds to the size of the cavity in the oxygen polyhedron, which also determines the increased stability of the lattice in its compounds.

The crystal structure of beryllium minerals as a whole has not been sufficiently studied. This fact renders it difficult to effect a crystal-chemical classification of beryllium minerals, especially of the silicate class, and in some cases it is possible to isolate the given groups of minerals only on the basis of their chemical composition and physical properties.

Beryllium minerals are formed in nature under extremely different conditions and are found in all types of mineral deposits except the true magmatic deposits. It can be seen from Table 4 that more beryllium minerals are found in pegmatites.

It is necessary to note the mineralogical resemblance between the beryllium silicate minerals in granitic pegmatites and the pneumatolytic-hydrothermal deposits formed in an alumino-silicate environment. Obviously, this is closely connected with the geochemical features of the

[2] Here and in the following text, Roman figures in brackets denote the coordination number.

types of deposits under consideration. At the same time, the geochemically different alkalic pegmatites and skarn formations each have a peculiar suite of beryllium minerals, which reflects, as shown below, the principal geochemical features of these types of mineral deposits.

Recently, there have been found a number of supergene beryllium minerals, which were formed by the superficial alteration of the unstable (in the supergene zone) beryllium minerals of the alkalic pegmatites (epididymite, gelbertrandite, possibly beryllite, and spherobertrandite). Some investigators such as A. I. Ginzburg, also suggest the possibility of phenacite forming (after danalite and helvite) under supergene conditions.

Table 4 Distribution of beryllium minerals among various types of mineral deposits (Italics denote the most characteristic minerals for the given type of deposit. The number of minerals is given in parentheses.)

Pegmatites		Pneumatolytic-hydrothermal formations	
Granitic (acid) (20)	Nepheline-syenitic (alkalic) (11)	In alumino-silicate environment (greisens and quartz veins) (9)	In carbonate environment (fluoritized skarns, fluoritic metasomatic strata in limestones) (13)
Compound oxides (1)	–	–	Oxides and compound oxides (3)
Chrysoberyl			Bromellite *Chrysoberyl* Taaffeite
Silicates (10)	Silicates (10)	Silicates (8)	Silicates (9)
Phenacite Euclase *Bertrandite* *Beryl* Beryllium-margarite-bityite Bowleyite *Gadolinite* Helvite Danalite Bavenite	Spherobertrandite *Chkalovite* *Eudidymite* *Epididymite* *Leucophanite* Melinophanite Genthelvite Beryllite Gelbertrandite Karpinskyite	Phenacite Euclase *Bertrandite* *Beryl* Milarite Helvite Danalite Bavenite	*Phenacite* Barylite *Helvite* *Danalite* Genthelvite Aminoffite Trimerite Bityite (?) Syanchualite
Borates (2)	Borates (1)	–	–
Hambergite Rhodizite	Hambergite	–	–
–	–	–	Antimonates (1)
			Swedenborgite
Phosphates (6)	–	Phosphates (1)	–
Beryllonite *Herderite* Vayrynenite Hurlbutite Faheyite Moraesite		Kolveckite	
Carbonates (1)	–	–	–
Beryllium-tengerite			

The beryllium minerals are described in the order of their chemical classification. Silicates, owing to the crystal-chemical features of this class of compound, are placed between the oxides and the salts of stronger acids (Sobolev, 1949). Special attention is paid to the specific chemical composition of the minerals.

The conditions of formation and of paragenesis of the minerals are considered only briefly; these problems will be discussed in detail in later chapters dealing with the behavior of beryllium in mineral deposits of various types. Also, the description of minerals does not include their detailed crystallographic features, which are sufficiently described in many reference books (Winchell, 1951; Dana *et al.*, 1944, 1951) and in mineralogical textbooks (A. G. Betekhtin, 1950).

OXIDES AND COMPOUND OXIDES

There are three natural beryllium minerals belonging to this class—bromellite, chrysoberyl, and taaffeite.

Bromellite: BeO

Bromellite, an almost pure beryllium oxide, is an extremely rare mineral, which so far has been found in only one deposit (Långban, Sweden).

The crystal structure of bromellite is of the wurtzite type and is characterized by a hexagonal lattice with a denser atom packing. This fact is reflected in the physical properties of the mineral, which has a high hardness and a relatively high (with respect to the low atomic weight of beryllium) specific gravity (Table 5).

The only available chemical analysis of bromellite (Aminoff, 1925) indicates that the BeO content is 98.02 percent, the remainder being impurities (in percent):

BeO	CaO	BaO	MgO	MnO	Sb_2O_3	Al_2O_3	Ignition	Total
98.08	1.03	0.55	0.07	traces	0.29	0.17	0.85	100.98

ORIGIN AND PARAGENESIS. It can be assumed that free breyllium oxide can be formed in nature under conditions of a great scarcity of silicon and aluminum with a simultaneous high concentration of beryllium in the mineral-forming solutions. Such conditions most probably resulted in the formation of bromellite in calcite veins and streaks that transgress the hematitic skarns and skarnized limestones of the Långban deposit, known for the abundant development of various beryllium minerals in the iron-manganese contact-metasomatic ores.

Table 5 Physical and optical properties of oxides and compound oxides of beryllium

Properties	Bromellite	Chrysoberyl	Taaffeite
System	Hexagonal	Orthorhombic	Hexagonal
Symmetry	Dihexagonal-pyramidal	Orthorhombic-dipyramidal	–
Dimensions of unit cell, Å	a_0=2.68; c_0=4.36	a_0=5.47; b_0=9.39; c_0=4.42	a_0=5.72; c_0=18.38
Form of segregation and crystal habit	Separate crystals of prismatic habit	Separate crystals usually thick-tabular on (001), sometimes short-prismatic on (100), less frequently on (001), trillings are characteristic	Idiomorphic fine crystals of hexagonal or lens-shaped habit, fine-granular aggregates
Color	White, colorless (transparent)	Green, of diverse hues, yellow, brown. Alexandrite in artificial illumination – red	Colorless, greenish, pink
Luster	Glassy	Glassy	Glassy
Cleavage	Moderate on (1010)	Imperfect on (011) and (010)	Not noted
Hardness	9	8.5	8–8.5
Specific gravity	3.017	3.57–3.83	3.60–3.613
Optical sign	(+)	(+)	(-)
Refractive indices:			Anderson / Huang Vei-Vei
γ =	1.733	1.756	1.720–1.723 / 1.736
β =	1.719	1.748	1.716–1.718 / 1.727
α =	–	1.746	
2V	–	67°–71°	Rarely biaxial, 2V not exceeding 15°
Pleochroism	–	γ – emerald-green β – orange-yellow α – purple	–
Optical orientation	–	Plane of optic axes (001): γ = *a*, β = *b*; α = *c*	–

The following minerals, in addition to calcite, were found in association with bromellite: swedenborgite, richterite, and manganophyllite. The last two minerals are probably postformational.

Chrysoberyl: Al_2BeO_4

Chrysoberyl is second only to beryl in the frequency of occurrence of beryllium minerals.

Chemically, this mineral is usually considered to be a compound oxide of beryllium and aluminum, having the formula $BeAl_2O_4$ (Betekhtin, 1950).

The structure of chrysoberyl is analogous to that of forsterite, so that the mineral can be represented also as aluminum beryllate (Al_2BeO_4, by analogy with Mg_2SiO_4). The elementary orthorhombic cell of chrysoberyl contains $4[Al_2BeO_4]$. The beryllium ions, like those of silicon in the forsterite lattice, are surrounded tetrahedrally by oxygen ions, whereas the aluminum ions, like magnesium ions in forsterite, are surrounded octahedrally. Sixteen oxygen ions in the unit cell are arranged according to the principle of the densest hexagonal packing, which is clearly seen from comparison of the parameters of the crystal lattice of chrysoberyl with the theoretically calculated values typical of the densest packing (Bragg, 1930).

	a_0	b_0	c_0
Chrysoberyl	5.47	9.39	4.42
Theoretically densest packing	5.40	9.36	4.41

As would be expected from the structural similarity between chrysoberyl and forsterite, almost all chemical analyses of chrysoberyl (Table 6) show the presence of small quantities of silicon and magnesium (an isostructural isomorphous impurity in forsterite).

The physical properties of chrysoberyl are summarized in Table 5. The high hardness and stability of chrysoberyl crystals, caused by the highly perfect compactness of the lattice, should be noted. The usual green or yellow coloration of the mineral are associated with the admixture of iron ions. The presence of a chromium impurity, in the proportion of a few tenths percent (Table 6, analysis 6), changes the color of the mineral to emerald-green, which becomes cherry-red in artificial light (the gem variety—alexandrite).

ORIGIN AND PARAGENESIS. The formation of chrysoberyl is associated with pegmatitic and hydrothermal-pneumatolytic processes and takes place under conditions of total or local enrichment of the mineral-forming melts and solutions in aluminum with the simultaneous scarcity of free silica.

The formation of accessory chrysoberyl, related to the disilication process, is noted on a small scale in the exo-contact reaction zones of beryl-bearing crossing-line pegmatites (the deposits of the emerald mines in the Urals USSR).

A secondary factor, which, in a number of cases, controls the formation of chrysoberyl in normal granitic pegmatites, is the process of aluminum contamination, associated with the assimilation of Al_2O_3 from the enclosing rocks which abound in alumina (pegmatites of the Yenisei Ridge, and many others).

Of greatest importance in the formation of chrysoberyl is the process of desilication, which is most distinctly manifest in some contact-metasomatic deposits where beryllium-containing fluoride solutions react with limestones.

Table 6 Chemical analyses of chrysoberyl

Components	1.[a] Golden, Colorado [b]			2. Colorless, Ghana [c]			3. Yellowish-green, Bershea Su [d]			Urals [e] 4			Urals [e] 5			Urals [e] 6			The Littoral [f]		
	%	Atomic quantities of Cations	Atomic quantities of Oxygen	%	Atomic quantities of Cations	Atomic quantities of Oxygen	%	Atomic quantities of Cations	Atomic quantities of Oxygen	%	Atomic quantities of Cations	Atomic quantities of Oxygen	%	Atomic quantities of Cations	Atomic quantities of Oxygen	%	Atomic quantities of Cations	Atomic quantities of Oxygen	%	Atomic quantities of Cations	Atomic quantities of Oxygen
SiO_2	—	—	—	2.24	037	074	1.12	018	036	—	—	—	1.90	032	064	2.43	040	080	—	—	—
BeO	19.15	765	765	18.56	742	742	18.80	752	752	18.05	722	722	19.05	761	761	18.74	790	790	20.69	830	830
Al_2O_3	76.34	1500	2225	76.40	1502	2228	74.86	1470	2205	78.88	1550	2325	76.00	1472	2208	75.26	1480	2220	77.66	1536	2299
Fe_2O_3	—	—	—	1.30	016	024	3.91	048	072	3.05	038	057	0.57	008	012	0.31	004	006	0.68	008	012
Cr_2O_3	—	—	—	—	—	—	—	—	—	—	—	—	0.08	—	—	0.30	004	006	—	—	—
FeO	3.60	050	050	—	—	—	—	—	—	—	—	—	1.39	019	019	0.41	006	006	—	—	—
MgO	—	—	—	0.40	010	010	0.76	018	018	0.35	008	008	0.65	016	016	—	—	—	—	—	—
TiO_2	0.55	007	014	0.22	003	006	0.19	003	006	—	—	—	0.34	004	008	—	—	—	—	—	—
MnO	—	—	—	—	—	—	—	—	—	0.12	—	—	—	—	—	—	—	—	—	—	—
CaO	—	—	—	0.48	009	009	—	—	—	—	—	—	0.27	005	005	1.51	027	027	—	—	—
H_2O^+	0.30	—	—	—	—	—	--	—	—	—	—	—	0.10	—	—	0.10	—	—	Washed	—	0.83
Total	99.94			99.60			99.64			100.45			100.35			100.10			99.86		
ΣO			3054			3093			3089			3112			3093			3135			3071
$\frac{\Sigma O}{4}$			763.5			773			772			778			773			784			770
Analyst or source	Schoder, in Dana (1944–1954)			Junner in Dana (1944–1954)						V. S. Saltykova			K. A. Vlasov and E. I. Kutukova, (1960)						M. E. Kazakova, from the collection of I. N. Govorov		

a. In this and in the subsequent tables of chemical analysis the figures denote the number of the analysis.

b. $(Al_{1.96}Fe_{0.06})BeO_4$

c. $(Al_{1.94}Fe_{0.02}Mg_{0.01}Ca_{0.01})(Be_{0.96}Si_{0.05})O_4$.

d. $(Al_{1.91}Fe_{0.06}Mg_{0.02})(Be_{0.98}Si_{0.02})O_4$

e. $(Al_2Fe_{0.05}Mg_{0.01})Be_{0.93}O_4$; $(Al_{1.96}Fe_{0.05}Mg_{0.03})(Be_{0.98}Si_{0.04})O_4$; $(Al_{1.91}Fe_{0.02}Ca_{0.03})(BeSi_{0.05})O_4$

f. $(Al_2Fe_{0.01})B_{1.08}O_4$

Such deposits contain most of the chrysoberyl distributed throughout the world; sometimes it accumulates in considerable quantities (in some fluoritized skarn-type formations of Kazakhstan and Central Asia, USSR).

The conditions of formation of chrysoberyl determine its normal paragenesis:

(*a*) In contact-metasomatic deposits—fluorite, magnetite, vesuvianite, micas, garnet, etc.

(*b*) In crossing-line (desilicated) pegmatites—corundum, spinel, chlorite, margarite, phlogopite, muscovite, plagioclase, fluorite, and apatite.

(*c*) In granitic pegmatites with obvious aluminum, contamination—kyanite, staurolite, garnet, muscovite, plagioclase, gahnite, beryl, quartz, etc.

Chrysoberyl occurs in numerous pegmatites, but it does not form important concentrations in the known deposits. The highest known concentrations of chrysoberyl are in fluoritized skarns.

Taaffeite: Al_4MgBeO_8

In 1951 Anderson and Claringbull described "taaffeite" as a cut gem from the private collection of Count Taaffe. The gem they had studied, on the basis of microchemical analysis, was a compound oxide of aluminum, beryllium, and magnesium (Anderson and Claringbull, 1951; Anderson, 1952a, 1952b).

The natural occurrence of taaffeite was corroborated in 1957 by the Chinese investigators, Huang Veng-Vei, Tu Shao-hua, *et. al.,*[3] who discovered and studied taaffeite in a peculiar contact-metasomatic deposit in the south of the Chinese People's Republic.

Table 7 Chemical analysis of taaffeite

Components	%	Atomic amounts of:		Number of atoms per O_8
		Cations	Oxygen	
Al_2O_3	70.0	1374	2061	3.7
Fe_2O_3	5.9	74	111	0.2
BeO	11.0	440	440	1.2
MgO	13.4	332	332	0.9
Total	99.3	2220	2944	6.0

The physical properties of this mineral (Table 5) show its similarity to spinel form which it differs by having double refraction.

On the basis of the special features of its chemical composition (Table 7), Anderson assumes taaffeite to be an intermediate mineral between

[3] Reference not available, Ed.

spinel and chrysoberyl, and to have a composition corresponding to the formula $BeMgAlO_8$.

The X-ray investigation (Anderson and Claringbull, 1951) yielded the hexagonal system of the mineral and the dimensions of the unit cell (a_0 = 5.72 Å and c_0 = 18.38 Å). The assumed densest hexagonal packing of oxygen atoms in taaffeite has a number of parameters in common with the spinel lattice. In particular, in both minerals the distances between the centers of oxygen atoms (2.86 and 2.85 Å) and between the adjacent oxygen layers of the lattice (2.30 and 2.32 Å) are almost identical. The similarity between the structures of spinel and taaffeite is also borne out by the resemblance of their X-ray diffraction patterns in which most of the lines are common.

It should be noted that, if one takes into account the substantial difference between the structures of spinel and chrysoberyl, the occurrence of natural transitions between these two minerals appears to be doubtful.

Most probably taaffeite is an individualized mineral, resembling spinel in structure and yet differing from the minerals of this group by the structural features that depend on the entry of very small ions of beryllium into the lattice along with magnesium ions. Because of the peculiar features of coordination of aluminum (VI), and of magnesium and beryllium (IV) in the mineral, the formula of taaffeite can best be represented as Al_4MgBeO_8. The structure of taaffeite should be further studied.

ORIGIN AND PARAGENESIS. Taaffeite was found in the south of the Chinese People's Republic in association with chrysoberyl and spinel in thin-banded metasomatic rocks in the exo-contact zone of a mass of greisenized beryllium-bearing granites in contact with a limestone-dolomite mass. The selvedges of the fluorite-zinnwaldite veins and streaks, which transgress the fluoritized carbonate rocks near their contact with granites, are also rich in taaffeite. With the taaffeite are usually found chrysoberyl, spinel, and cassiterite.

SILICATES

The silicates are the largest and most widespread group of beryllium minerals; the twenty-six mineral species (almost 65 percent of the total number of beryllium minerals) are characterized by a substantial variety of chemical composition and physical properties within the individual groups (Table 8, Figs. 2, 16).

It is still too early to establish a complete crystal-chemical classification of beryllium silicates; however, the work done by Soviet and other crystal-chemists (Belov and Tarkhova, 1951; Ito and West, 1932; Ito, 1947; Ito, Morimoto, and Sadanga, 1952; Pyatenko *et al.*, 1956), who have, during

Table 8 Tabulation of beryllium silicates on the basis of birefringence and hardness

Birefringence below 0.010		Birefringence above 0.010	
Eudidymite	0.002 – 0.003	Bertrandite	0.027
Milarite	0.003	Leucophanite	0.027
Chkalovite	0.005	Meliphanite	0.019
Epididymite	0.006	Euclase	0.020
Beryl	0.004 – 0.008	Bityite – bowleyite	0.020
Bavenite	0.005 – 0.010	Phenacite	0.016
Trimerite	0.010	Barylite	0.013
Aminoffite	0.010		
Gadolinite	0.010		
Hardness below 6		**Hardness above 6**	
Leucophanite	4	Phenacite	7.5 – 8
Meliphanite	5 – 5.5	Beryl	7.5 – 8
Bityite – bowleyite	5.5	Euclase	7.5
Bavenite	5 – 5.5	Barylite	6 – 7
Aminoffite	5.5	Gadolinite	6 – 7
Epididymite	5.5	Bertrandite	6 – 7
Eudidymite	6	Trimerite	6 – 7
Chkalovite	6	Syanchualite	6.5
Milarite	5 – 6		
Danalite	5.5 – 6		
Genthelvite	5.5 – 6		
Helvite	6		

the past decade, determined the structures of several complex and interesting beryliium minerals, makes it possible at least to outline such a classification based on experimental data.

The fundamental factor that determines the structure of beryllium minerals is the nature of the combination of the silicon-oxygen and beryllium-oxygen tetrahedra that form the basis of the crystal lattice of the mineral. A noteworthy feature of the beryllium-oxygen tetrahebron $[BeO_4]^{6-}$ is its structural analogy with the silicon-oxygen tetrahedron $[SiO_4]^{4-}$ whose parameters are very close to those of the former tetrahedron (Table 9). It is possible to exchange one or more oxygen ions in the beryllium-oxygen tetrehedral group for a hydroxyl $(HO)^-$, which is known to be an extremely rare phenomenon in a silicon-oxygen radical (Sobolev, 1949). There is a marked similarity between the beryllium-oxygen and aluminum-oxygen tetrahedral groups, although in the latter case the differences between the parameters of the two tetrahedra are somewhat larger (Table 9).

The crystal-chemical similarity among the groups $[BeO_4]^{6-}$, $[SiO_4]^{4-}$, and $[AlO_4]^{5-}$ determines the dual part played by beryllium in the crystal structure of silicates. It is known (Sobolev, 1949) that the silicon-oxygen tetrahedral complex occupies an intermediate position between the typical complex ions of the type [SO_4] or [PO_4] and the similar tetrahedral groups of some other oxides (for example, [MgO_4] in the spinels), which do not differ in general from the ordinary structural elements of the coordination lattice of minerals.

The lesser strength of valency bonds in the tetrahedral groups [AlO_4] and [BeO_4], compared with the group [SiO_4] and the greater cation-oxygen spacing, bring the analyzed tetrahedral groups nearer to the common cation-oxygen groups of the coordination lattice of minerals characterized by the minor role of the covalent bond between the cation and the surrounding oxygen ions.

It is known that the stability of bonds within the cation-oxygen complex increases with an increase in the degree of covalency of the bond between the central atom and the surrounding oxygen atoms. Moreover, the degree of covalency of the bonds between cations and oxygen is determined not only by the properties of the elements of which the complex consists, but also by the nature of the cations which surround the complex. In particular, cations with low electronegativity, which attract only an insignificant part of the electronic cloud of oxygen atoms, partly neutralizing their electronegative energy, should increase the degree of the bond covalency in a

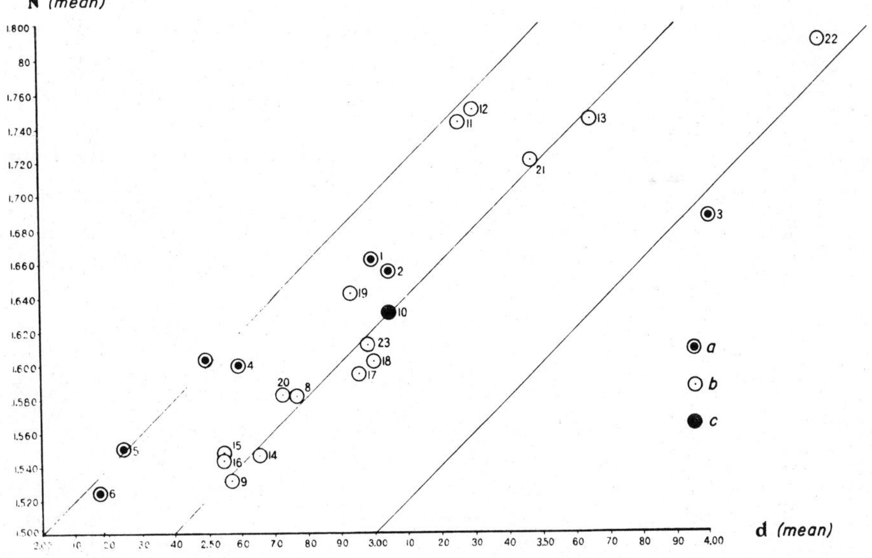

Fig. 2. Relation between the mean refractive index of beryllium silicates and their specific gravity. (a) nesosilicates; (b) textosilicates, probable tectosilicates and cyclosilicates; (c) layered silicates. (1) phenacite; (2) euclase; (3) barylite; (4) bertrandite; (5) beryllite; (6) helbertrandite; (7) spherobertrandite; (8) beryl; (9) milarite; (10) bityite-bowleyite; (11) helvite; (12) danalite; (13) genthélvite; (14) chkalovite; (15) eudidymite; (16) epididymite; (17) leucophanite; (18) miliphanite; (19) aminoffite; (20) bavenite; (21) trimerite; (22) gadolinite; (23) syanchualite.

cation-oxygen complex, in the center of which there is an atom with relatively high electronegativity. The effect of the surrounding atoms ought to be of special significance in complexes that are at the boundary between the conventional structural elements of the crystal lattice of minerals and the complex radicals whose properties are close to those of the true complex ions.

When studying the part played in the crystal structure of minerals by atoms with a low electronegativity, V. S. Sobolev (1949) noted that the increase of concentration of these atoms contributes to the formation of crystal structures with a lowered coordination of the more electronegative atoms. In other words, the increase of concentration of the alkali and the alkaline-earth atoms with a low electronegativity is a factor that determines

Table 9 Chrystal-chemical parameters of some tetrahedral groups

Tetrahedral groups	Complete charge	Charge per atom of oxygen	Spacing R-O, Å (mean)	Bond strength per atom of oxygen	Degree of covalency, %
$[SiO_4]$	-4	-i	Si-O = 1.6	1.0	48
$[AlO_4]$	-5	-1.25	Al-O = 1.74	0.75	40
$[BeO_4]$	-6	-1.5	Be-O = 1.65	0.5	37
[MgO]	-6	-1.5	Mg-O = 1.75	0.5	30

the increase of both the degree of covalency and the stability of the bond between the anion and the cation with a higher value of electronegativity.

The most striking example that corroborates this relationship is aluminum, which occupies the intermediate position between typical cations and complex-formers. The dual role of aluminum in the crystal structure of elements was discussed in detail in the papers of Soviet and other geochemists and crystal-chemists (Bragg, 1931,[4] Sobolev, 1949, *et. al.*). It should be stressed that, in almost 50 percent of the more than 250 aluminum-containing silicates, the aluminum occurs in octahedral coordination, functioning as a conventional cation of the coordination lattice. In the remaining aluminum-containing silicates all or part of the aluminum plays a part analogous to that of silicon, substituting for some ions of the latter in the silicon-oxygen radical. From the total number of aluminosilicates, more than 90 percent are alkali or alkaline-earth compounds. The entry of a small proportion of calcium into the lattice of the aluminum-containing silicates causes the transition of some of the aluminum ions from sixfold to fourfold coordination.

An increase in concentration of alkali cations has an even greater effect

[4] Given as 1937 in original, but reference omitted, Ed.

on the coordination of aluminum in silicates. Thus, depending on the alkalinity of the medium that determines the occurrence of alkali aluminosilicates, the amphoteric ion Al^{3+} can occur in the form of the complex $[AlO_4]^{5-}$, acquiring properties analogous to those of the complex radical $[SiO_4]^{4-}$.

Since the publication of the paper by Yu. A. Pytenko *et. al.* (1956), who studied the structure of chkalovite, the assumption advanced previously by a number of investigators (Fersman, 1939; Sobolev, 1949) has been accepted as proven—namely that along with aluminosilicates there also exist beryllosilicates in which beryllium, replacing some of the silicon ions, plays a part analogous to that of silicon in the structure of the complex beryllium-silicon-oxygen radical:

$$[Be_mSi_{n-m}O_{2n}]^{-2m} \quad m \leqslant 0.5n.$$

The nature of the radical can become more complex, owing to the possibility of replacing some of its oxygen ions (from the ions combined in the beryllium-oxygen tetrahedra) by hydroxyl or fluorine:

$$[Be_mSi_{n-m}O_{2n-l}(OH, F)_l]^{-2m+l} \quad m \leqslant 0.5n \quad l \leqslant m.$$

The peculiarities of the position of beryllium in the structure of silicates points up the question of the expediency of isolating, along with tectoaluminosilicates, tectoberyllosilicates among the tectosilicates. In connection with the isostructural position of $[AlO_4]$ and $[BeO_4]$ in the tectosilicates, there can also exist transitional representatives, in which both structurally close groups do occur.

On the basis of the available incomplete data, the beryllium-silicon radicals, together with the aluminum-silicon ones, can be looked on as the analogues of poly-silicon-oxygen radicals of the endless type. In the simplest case, lattices resembling those of any of the SiO_2 modifications should occur; these can indeed be observed with chkalovite.

The substitution of beryllium for silicon in the radical causes an increase in the overall negative charge by —2 for every beryllium ion. The large alkali ions, which neutralize the negative charge of the radical, are arranged in the cavities of the beryllium-silicon framework (chkalovites and other minerals), while in the helvite-danalite group, sulfur atoms are arranged in these cavities.

From the chemical aspect, the beryllosilicates, and similarly the aluminosilicates (Sobolev, 1949), can still be looked upon as double salts composed, on the one hand, of a strong and a very weak base and, on the other, of a very weak acid.

It can be assumed that beryllosilicates form a relatively alkaline medium, in which beryllium can occur as the complex $[BeO_4]^{6-}$. In compounds with cations whose strength of covalent bonds is $\geqslant 0.5$, beryllium plays the part of an ordinary cation of the coordination lattice; in compounds with alkalies (if one takes into account the low strength of their valence bonds) the beryllium-oxygen groups can play a role analogous to that of the silicon-oxygen complexes and take part in the structure of the beryllium-silicon framework of the mineral lattice.

The less amphoteric properties of beryllium (compared with those of aluminum) enable one to expect the occurrence of alkali beryllosilicates

CRYSTAL-CHEMICAL CLASSIFICATION OF BERYLLIUM SILICATES

I. BERYLLOSILICATES AND BERYLLOALUMINOSILICATES

A. *Tectoberyllosilicates and their analogues*

(1) with the group $[BeSi_3(O,OH)_8]^{1-}$
epididymite, eudidymite } $Na[BeSi_3O_7(OH)]$

(2) with the group $[BeSi_2O_6]^{2-}$
chkalovite $Na_2[BeSi_2O_6]$

(3) with the group $[BeSiO_4]^{2-}$
helvite $Mn_4[BeSiO_4]_3 \cdot S$
danalite $Fe_4[BeSiO_4]_3 \cdot S$
genthelvite $Zn_4[BeSiO_4]_3 \cdot S$

(4) with the group $[(Be,Al)_4Si_9(O,OH)_{26}]^{6-}$
bavenite $Ca_4[(Be,Al)_4Si_9(O,OH)_{26}](OH)_2$

B. *Probable tectosilicates and minerals of uncertain structure*

(1) with the group $[(Be,Al)Si_3(O,OH)_8]^{1-}$
karpinskyite $Na[(Al,Be,Zn,Si)_4(O,OH)_8]H_2O$

(2) with the group $[BeSi_2O_6]^{2-}$
leucophanite, meliphanite } $Na_{1-n}Ca[Be(Si,Al)_2O_6]F_{1-n}$
aminoffite $Ca_2[(Be,Al)Si_2O_6](OH)_2$

(3) with the group $[BeSiO_4]^{2-}$
trimerite $(Mn_2Ca)[BeSiO_4]_3$
gadolinite $(Y,Ca)_2Fe[BeSiO_4]_2(O,OH)_2$
syanchualite $Li_2Ca_3[BeSiO_4]_3F_2$

C. *Layered berylloaluminosilicates*

bityite–bowelyite–beryllium-margarite group $(Ca,Na)(Li,Mg)_{0.2\text{-}0.7}Al_2[(Be,Al)_2Si_2(O,OH,F)_{10}] \cdot (OH)_2$

II. BERYLLIUM SILICATES

A. *Meta- and dimetasilicates of cyclic structure*
 beryl $Al_2Be_3[Si_6O_{18}]$
 milarite $KCa_2 (Al,Be_2)[Si_{12}O_{30}]\cdot 0.5H_2O$

B. *Orthosilicates*
 (1) without additional anions
 phenacite $Be_2[SiO_4]$
 (2) with additional anions
 euclase $Al_2Be_2 (OH)_2[SiO_4]_2$

C. *Diorthosilicates*
 (1) without additional anions
 barylite $BaBe_2[Si_2O_7]$
 (2) with additional anions
 bertrandite $Be_4[Si_2O_7]OH_2$
 helbertrandite $Be_4[Si_2O_7] (OH)_2 \cdot nH_2O$
 spherobertrandite $Be_5[Si_2O_7] (OH)_4$
 beryllite $Be_5[Si_2O_7] (OH)_4\cdot 2H_2O$

---

where the medium is more alkaline than is required for the alkali alumino-silicates to be formed. In this connection, the formation of alkali beryllo-silicates in acid rocks where there is always an excess of SiO_2 can hardly be expected, but their occurrence would be fully understandable in the pegmatites of the alkalic magmas, which have a higher alkali concentration and a scarcity of SiO_2. The formation of the alkali and alkaline-earth beryllosilicates in acid rocks can apparently occur in the final stages of alakli metasomatism, which is characterized by a scarcity of SiO_2 and a high concentration of alkalies.

I. Beryllosilicates and berylloaluminosilicates

Tectoberyllosilicates and their analogues

Epididymite and eudidymite: $Na[BeSi_3O_7 (OH)]$

Epididymite and eudidymite are a relatively little studied polymorphous group of alkali beryllium silicates having an identical chemical composition and close physical properties
(Zacheriosen, 1929).

Until quite recently, both these minerals were considered to be very

Table 10 Physical and optical properties of epididymite and eudidymite

Properties	Epididymite	Eudidymite
System	Orthorhombic	Monoclinic
Dimensions of unit cell, Å	a_0=12.63; b_0=7.32; c_0=13.58	a_0=12.62; b_0=7.37; c_0=13.99; β_0=103°43'
Form of segregation and crystal habit	Lamellar on (001); twins on (001) turned through 60°; dense fine-grained masses.	Tabular to lamellar on (001); poly-synthetic twins on (001).
Color	White, colorless	White, colorless
Cleavage	Perfect on (001) and moderate on (100)	Eminent on (001) and imperfect along (110)
Luster	Glassy	Glassy
Hardness	5.5–6	6
Specific gravity	2.55	2.55
Optical sign	(-)	(+)
Refractive indices		
γ	1.569	1.551
β	1.569	1.546
α	1.565	1.544
2V	32°	29°55'
Optical orientation	Plane of optic axes (001)	Plane of optic axes (010)

rare, and their deposits were known only in the alkalic pegmatites of Norway and Greenland. In 1949 epididymite and eudidymite were found as accessory minerals in the pegmatites of the Lovozero alkalic mass (Shilin and Semenov, 1957), and later in the pegmatites of the Khibiny rock mass. It was found that epididymite is fairly widespread, whereas eudidymite is much rarer.

The physical properties and optical characteristics of epididymite and eudidymite are summarized in Table 10.

The chemical composition (Table 11) of epididymite and eudidymite is absolutely the same and can be expressed by the empirical formula $Na[Be\ Si_3O_7\ (OH)]$.

The structure of epididymite and eudidymite has not been satisfactorily solved. The treatment suggested by T. Ito (1947), based on the layered structures of epididymite and eudidymite, is not sufficiently convincing and is not borne out, in particular, by a number of physical properties of the minerals, which differ from the properties of layered silicates.

According to Ito, the structure of epididymite and eudidymite is built of complex $[Si_3O_8]$ groups that extend in the direction parallel to the *b* axis. These groups are connected by a common oxygen atom and yield, with the sodium atoms, layers having the composition $NaSi_3O_7$ which are arranged parallel to (001). Between the layers are the connecting beryllium atoms and OH groups. The silicon atoms in the structure are surrounded by

Table 11 Chemical composition of epididymite and eudidymite

Components	Epididymite															Eudidymite					
	1. Kuivchorr, Lovozero [a]			2. Yukspor, Khibiny [a]			3. Karnasurt, Lovozero [a]			4. Yukspor, Khibiny [b]			5. Alluaiv, Lovozero [b]			Southern Norway [c]					
																6.			7.		
	%	Atomic quantities		%	Atomic quantities		%	Atomic quantities		%	Atomic quantities		%	Atomic quantities		%	Atomic quantities		%	Atomic quantities	
		Cations	Oxygen		Cations	Oxygen		Cations	Oxygen		Cations	Oxygen		Cations	Oxygen		Cations	Oxygen		Cations	Oxygen
SiO_2	69.80	1162	2324	70.70	1177	2354	73.31	1220	2440	72.92	1214	2428	72.94	1214	2428	72.19	1202	2404	73.11	1217	2434
Al_2O_3	1.51	030	045	0.60	012	018	0.51	010	015	0.45	010	015	0.57	012	018	—	—	—	—	—	—
Fe_2O_3	0.05	—	—	—	—	—	0.08	002	003	0.05	—	—	0.29	004	006	—	—	—	—	—	—
BeO	12.90	516	516	12.15	486	486	10.39	415	415	10.42	402	402	11.20	448	448	11.15	446	446	10.12	406	406
CaO	0.29	005	005	0.25	005	005	0.23	004	004	0.16	003	003	0.44	008	008	—	—	—	—	—	—
MgO	0.11	003	003	0.10	003	003	—	—	—	—	—	—	—	—	—	—	—	—	—	—	—
Na_2O	11.61	374	187	11.81	380	190	11.83	380	190	11.91 [d]	378	189	10.56	342	171	12.66	408	204	12.24	394	192
H_2O^+	4.00	444	222	4.50	500	250	3.96	440	220	4.01	444	222	4.07	496	248	3.84	428	214	3.79	422	211
H_2O^-	—	—	—	—	—	—	-	—	—	0.14	—	—	0.35								
Total	100.27		3080 [d]	100.11		3056 [e]	100.31		3067 [e]	100.06		3037 [e]	100.42		3079 [e]	99.84		3064 [e]	99.76		3032 [e]
Analysts	V. S. Saltikova						M. E. Kazakova						G. I. Bocharova			Flink			Nordenskjold		

a. Shilin and Semenov, 1957
b. From the collection of I. P. Tikhonenkov
c. Brögger, 1890
d. Without H_2O
e. Including 0.43 % K_2O

four oxygen atoms, whereas the sodium atoms are in the center of the more or less distorted octahedral oxygen groups. The beryllium atoms in epididymite are in the center of tetrahedra consisting of two oxygen atoms and two OH groups; in eudidymite the Be tetrahedra are constructed of three oxygen atoms and one OH group. The difference between the structures of these two minerals also is determined by the arrangement of sodium atoms which, in epididymite, are in the center of symmetry, whereas, in eudidymite, they are arranged on the twofold axis. The difference in the arrangement of the OH groups in the structure of these minerals determines, according to Ito, the difference in the nature of cleavage of epididymite and eudidymite (Fig. 3).

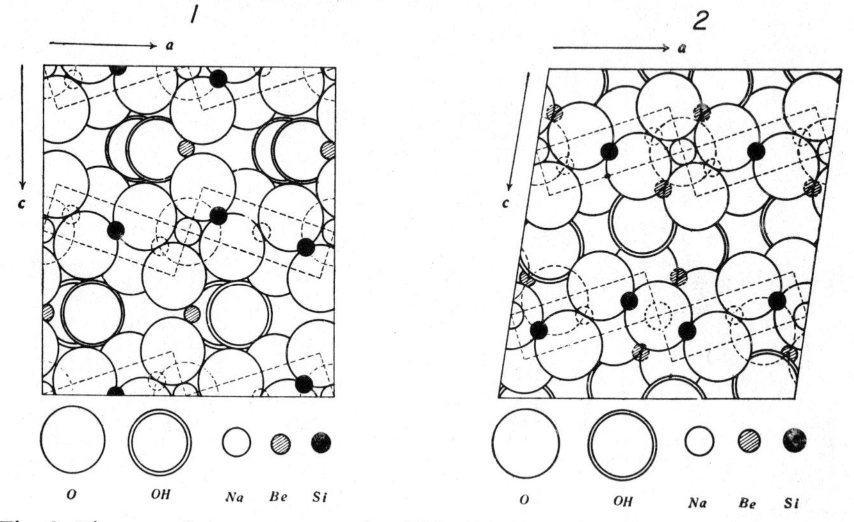

Fig. 3. Diagram of the structures of epididymite (1) and eudidymite (2).

If the structures of epididymite and eudidymite are analyzed from general considerations, the controversial point is Ito's treatment of the part played by beryllium; according to this treatment, both minerals are layered silicates (Ito, 1947). A more rational solution to the problem of epididymite and eudidymite structures can apparently be found in the possibly analogous structural roles of beryllium and silicon in the lattice of the alkali beryllium silicates. Then the structures of epididymite and eudidymite can be considered to be beryllium-silicon frameworks, resembling to a certain extent the aluminum-silicon framework of feldspars, in which one-fourth of the oxygen atoms in the beryllium-oxygen tetrahedra have been replaced by OH. The difference between some properties of epididymite and eudidymite (in particular cleavage) can be explained by the difference in the positions of Be—OH groups in the structures of the minerals; these positions determine the direction and nature of the planes of weakened bonding in crystals.

Table 12 Conversion of the chemical analyses of epididymite and eudidymite for Si + Be + Al = 4

Elements and groups	Number of atoms						
	1[a]	2	3	4	5	6	7
Si	2.78	2.81	2.97	2.99	2.90	2.94	3
Al	0.07	0.03	0.02	0.02	0.02	—	—
Be	1.20	1.16	1	0.99	1.08	1.06	1
Na[b]	0.92	0.95	0.92	0.94	0.87	1	0.96
O	6.82	6.7	7	7	6.9	7	7
(OH)	1.1	1.2	1	1	1.1	1.04	1

Formulae:

1. $Na_{0.92}[Be_{1.2}(Si, Al)_{2.85}(O, OH)_8]$
2. $Na_{0.95}[Be_{1.16}(Si, Al)_{2.84}(O, OH)_8]$
3. $Na_{0.92}[Be(Si, Al)_{2.99}O_7(OH)]$
4. $Na_{0.94}[Be_{0.99}(Si, Al)_{3.01}O_7(OH)]$
5. $Na_{0.87}[Be_{1.08}(Si, Al)_{2.92}O_{6.9}(OH)_{1.1}]$
6. $Na_{1.00}[Be_{1.06}Si_{2.94}O_7(OH)]$
7. $Na_{0.96}[BeSi_3O_7(OH)]$

[a] Both here and in subsequent conversion tables the numbers correspond to the numbers of analyses in the tables of chemical compositions of the minerals described.

[b] Including very small proportions of Ca and K.

The physical properties of epididymite and eudidymite make it possible to relate, with considerable certainty, these minerals to the subclass to tectoberyllosilicates. This subclass corresponds also to the (Be + Si)/(O + OH) ratio of 1 to 2.

On the basis of these considerations it is possible to represent the formula of epididymite and eudidymite as $Na[BeSi_3O_7(OH)]$.

The conversion of analyses of epididymite and eudidymite to the sum Si + Be + Al = 4 (Table 12) agrees fairly well with the formula, and the substitution of aluminum for a part of the silicon, which occurs here to a very slight extent, is apparently compensated by the substitution of OH for the corresponding part of oxygen. A substantial part of water evolves from epididymite in the short temperature interval 700 to 800°C (Fig. 4).

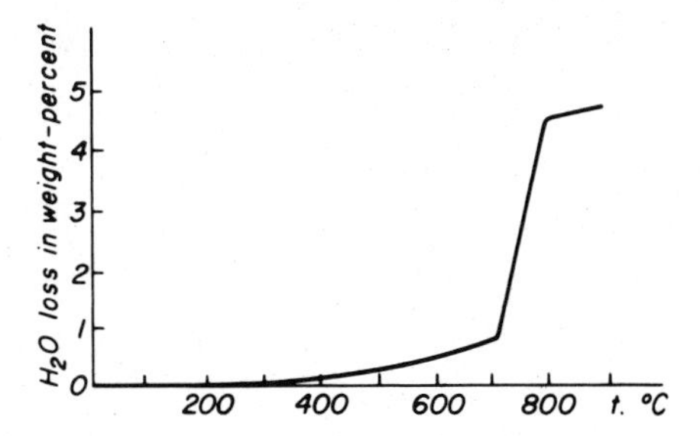

Fig. 4. Dehydration curve of epididymite (according to M. V. Kyz'menko, 1954).

Table 13 Physical properties of chkalovite

Properties	Characteristic
System	Orthorhombic
Dimensions of unit cell, Å	$a_0=b_0=21.1$; $c_0=6.87$
Form of segregation and crystal habit	Irregular monocrystalline segregations
Color	Semitransparent, white
Luster	Glassy
Cleavage	Perfect in one direction
Hardness	6
Specific gravity	2.662
Refractive indices	
γ	1.549
α	1.544
$\gamma-\alpha$	0.005
Optical sign	(+)
2V	78°

Thus epididymite and eudidymite apparently can be considered to be peculiar beryllium analogues of albite $Na[AlSi_3O_8]$, in which beryllium is substituted for aluminum and, correspondingly, the OH group is substituted for one oxygen atom from those combined in the beryllium-oxygen tetrahedra.

ORIGIN AND PARAGENESIS. Both minerals are representatives of the ultimate stages of alkali metasomatism of the pegmatites of nepheline syenites. They usually occur as crystals in cavities or as dense masses in albitized central portions of the zoned alkalic pegmatites in association with albite, elpidite, natrolite, analcime, and fluorite, which form in the process of substitution of the primary pegmatitic minerals—nepheline or potassium feldspar.

Chkalovite: $Na_2[BeSi_2O_6]$

Chkalovite is an extremely rare mineral, which has been found, so far in insignificant quantities, only in the pegmatites of the Lovozero alkalic rock mass.

Physical properties of chkalovite are listed in Table 13. The low refractive indices and weak birefringence are characteristic of this mineral.

The chemical analysis of chkalovite (Gerasimovskii, 1939b) is easily converted to the empirical formula $Na_2BeSi_2O_6$ (Table 14).

The structure of chkalovite (Yu. A. Pyatenko, 1956) has been found to be close to that of high-temperature β-cristobalite, in which one-third of

Table 14 Chemical composition of chkalovite

Components	%	Atomic quantities of		Numbers of atoms
		Cations	Oxygen	
SiO_2	56.81	946	1892	1.95 ≈ 2
Al_2O_3	—	—	—	
Fe_2O_3	0.30	004	006	
FeO	0.12	002	002	
BeO	12.67	506	506	1.05 ≈ 1
CaO	0.37	—	—	
Na_2O	28.93	900	450	1.92 ≈ 2
K_2O	0.13	20	10	
H_2O^+	—	—	—	
H_2O^-	0.23	—	—	
F	—	—	—	
SO_3	0.22	—	—	
Total	99.78		2866	

the silicon atoms have been replaced by beryllium, whereas the sodium atoms, which compensate this substitution, are arranged in large cavities in the beryllium-silicon framework, filling two-thirds of the cavities of the elementary cell. The peculiarities of the composition of chkalovite determine the difference between its structure and that of cristobalite, which is expressed by the trebling of the periods *a* and *b* of chkalovite compared with the edge of the elementary cell of β-cristobalite (subfixes refer to *cr*istobalite and *chk*alovite, Ed.):

$$a_{cr} = 7.16\ \text{Å}; \quad a_{chk} = b_{chk} = 21.1\ \text{Å} \pm 0.1 \approx 3a_{cr}$$
$$c_{chk} = 6.87\ \text{Å} \pm 0.03 \approx a_{cr}.$$

Besides, a different orientation of the oxygen tetrahedra in the framework of chkalovite, in comparison with their position in β-cristobalite, has been noted.

The results of structural analysis assign chkalovite, with good reason, to the subclass of tectoberyllosilicates with the radical $[BeSi_2O_6]^{2-}$ and the formula $Na_2[BeSi_2O_6]$.

The elementary cell of chkalovite contains $24Na_2[BeSi_2O_6]$.

ORIGIN AND PARAGENESIS. Chkalovite was found in the aegirine-ussingite-eudialyte pegmatites within the southwestern part of the Lovozero alkalic rock mass (Mt. M. Puankaruaiv) as large irregular monocrystalline segregations in ussingite. In association with chkalovite were the following minerals: schizolite, steenstrupine, erikite, natrolite, and sphalerite.

Helvite, danalite, and genthelvite:

$Mn_4[BeSiO_4]_3S$, $Fe_4[BeSiO_4]_3S$, $Zn_4[BeSiO_4]_3S$

Helvite and danalite are the end members of the isomorphous series

Table 15 Physical properties of helvite, danalite, and genthelvite

Properties	Helvite	Danalite	Genthelvite
System	Cubic	Cubic	Cubic
Dimensions of unit cell, Å	a_0=8.27–8.20	a_0=8.20–8.15	a_0=8.15–8.11
Form of segregation and crystal habit	Separate tetrahedral crystals, round accumulations	Separate octahedral crystals, irregular segregations, fine grains	Fine tetrahedral crystals
Color	Sulfur-yellow, yellow-green, gray to brown, sometimes semi-transparent	Light-red, red, gray, lemon-yellow, fallow[a]	Pink, pink-brown, gray, bluish-green, emerald-green (manganese genthelvite)
Luster	Glassy to resinous	Glassy to resinous	Glassy to resinous
Cleavage	Poor or (111)	—	No Cleavage
Hardness	6	5.5–6	5.5–6
Specific gravity	3.17–3.37	3.34–3.46	3.55–3.66
Refractive index (N)	1.728–1.747	1.755–1.771	1.742–1.745

[a] Cinnamon or dark brown with a tinge of gray (Ed.)

$Mn_4[BeSiO_4]_3S$–$Fe_4[BeSiO_4]_3S$, whose members are relatively widespread beryllium minerals. In a number of places they form quite large accumulations, which may be of considerable industrial importance.

The third member of the isomorphous group, genthelvite, $Zn_4[BeSiO_4]_3S$, is, unlike the two other minerals, an extremely rare mineral encountered only at three localities in the world.

The relatively well-studied minerals of the helvite-danalite-genthelvite group clearly illustrate the close relation between the chemical composition

Table 16 Theoretical composition of helvite, danalite, and genthelvite (in percent)

Components	Helvite	Danalite	Genthelvite
MnO	51.12	—	—
FeO	—	51.44	—
ZnO	—	—	54.54
BeO	13.52	13.43	12.58
SiO_2	32.46	32.25	30.19
S	5.78	5.74	5.37
Total	102.88	102.86	102.68
−O = S	2.88	2.86	2.68
	100.00	100.00	100.00

of the minerals in an isomorphous series and their physical properties. This relationship is shown by the regular variation of the parameters of the unit cell, of the refractive index, and of the specific gravity of the individual representative of the isomorphous series (Table 15, Fig. 5*a,b*). With these data it is possible to determine precisely the minerals of the group under consideration.

Table 16 shows the theoretical chemical composition of helvite, danalite, and genthelvite. However, as can be seen from the chemical analyses listed in Tables 17 and 18 the end members of the isomorphous series are virtually unknown in nature. Also, the available data do not allow the determination, based on sound reasons, of the continuity and limits of the isomorphous series. An abrupt discontinuity of data designates the field of genthelvite and a less distinct discontinuity is noted for the series helvite-danalite. The continuity of the isomorphism can be traced in the following parts of the isomorphous series:

For helvite–helvite 53 to 96 percent, danalite 4 to 36 percent, genthelvite 0 to 30 percent;
For danalite–helvite 10 to 13 percent, danalite 55 to 80 percent, genthelvite 8 to 34 percent;
For genthelvite–helvite 2 to 19 percent, danalite 11 to 13 percent, genthelvite 71 to 85 percent.

The middle members of the isomorphous series (Fig. 5), containing 19 to 52 percent helvite, 37 to 54 percent danalite, and 35 to 70 percent genthelvite (Table 19) are unknown. Further studies of the individual members of this group, obtained form various types of deposits, will enable the problem of discontinuity or lack of it in this isomorphous series to be solved more accurately.

The crystal structure of helvite was determined by Pauling, who demonstrated its fundamental similarity to that of the tectoaluminosilicate—sodalite (Pauling, 1930). Beryllium is arranged in helvite in the place where aluminum is found in sodalite and with silicon forms a cubic beryllium-silicon framework consisting of cation-oxygen tetrahedra. The sulfur ions are found in positions where chlorine occurs in sodalite, and occupy the free cavities in the corners and in the center of the cube. Each sulfur ion is surrounded by four manganese ions, two beryllium-oxygen tetrahedra, and two silicon-oxygen tetrahedra. On the whole, the structure of helvite is denser than that of sodalite. Even more compact are the structures of danalite and genthelvite; this is especially evident in a comparison of the parameters of their unit cells:

Sodalite	$a_0 = 8.89$ Å
Helvite	$a_0 = 8.27$ Å
Danalite	$a_0 = 8.18$ Å
Genthelvite	$a_0 = 8.10$ Å

Table 17 Chemical composition of helvite (in percent)

Components	1. Central Asia [a]	2. Amelia, Virginia, U.S.A.	3. Amelia, Virginia, U.S.A.	4. Southern Norway	5. Schwarzenberg, Saxony	6. Schwarzenberg, Saxony	7. Kazakh, S.S.R.	8. U.S.S.R. in Europe	9. Sigteso, Iceland
SiO_2	31.04	25.48	31.42	33.13	33.33	33.26	31.74	30.34	32.85
BeO	13.01	12.63	10.97	11.46	14.92	12.03	8.90	10.46	11.19
Al_2O_3	—	—	—	—	—	—	4.16	—	—
Fe_2O_3	—	—	—	—	—	—	—	—	—
FeO	0.68	2.03	2.99	4.00	4.45	8.00	5.97	10.37	13.02
MnO	50.65	50.24	51.64	49.10	44.43	41.76	41.48	37.88	39.68
CaO	—	—	—	—	—	—	1.70	—	—
ZnO	1.33	—	—	—	—	—	3.80	—	—
TiO_2	—	—	—	—	—	—	—	—	—
MgO	—	—	—	—	—	—	—	0.68	—
S	6.77	4.96	4.90	5.71	5.03	5.05	4.50	5.95	5.71
H_2O^+	—	—	—	—	—	—	—	—	—
Other [b]	—	5.10	0.36	—	0.77	1.15	—	4.92	1.40
Total	103.48	100.44	102.28	103.40	102.93	101.25	102.25	100.60	103.85
−O = S	3.38	2.48	2.45	2.85	2.51	2.52	2.25	2.97	2.85
	100.10	97.96	99.83	100.55	100.42	98.73	100.00	97.63	101.00
Analyst or source	S.T. Badalov (1956)	J. J. Glass et. al. (1944)					From the collection of M.S. Tsybulskaya	From the collection of E.F. Ziv	J. J. Glass et. al. (1944)

Components	10. Ilmen Mountains Urals	11. Sierra de Cordoba, Argentina	12. Kazakh, S.S.R.	13. Hörtekollen, Norway	14. Mt. Francisco, Western Australia	15. Kazakh, S.S.R.	16. Iron Mt., New Mexico, U.S.A.	17. U.S.S.R. in Europe
SiO_2	32.49	32.65	30.10	31.95	31.82	30.00	31.54	30.48
BeO	13.52	12.20	13.10	13.17	13.90	14.00	13.60	14.00
Al_2O_3	—	—	2.60	—	—	0.03	—	1.53
Fe_2O_3	—	—	5.05	—	—	—	—	18.30
FeO	15.12	14.75	—	15.55	15.80	15.90	18.02	—
MnO	35.41	30.79	30.10	28.46	28.00	28.40	26.51	21.80
CaO	—	—	trace	—	—	trace	—	—
ZnO	—	4.89	15.00	7.65	7.76	7.80	5.61	9.00
TiO_2	—	—	—	—	—	0.30	—	—
MgO	—	2.24	—	—	—	—	—	—
S	5.77	6.01	4.97	5.68	5.75	5.27	5.34	5.04
H_2O^+	—	—	—	—	—	0.10	—	—
Other [b]	0.77	—	—	—	—	—	2.06	—
Total	103.08	103.53	100.92	102.64	103.03	101.80	102.68	100.15
−O = S	2.88	3.00	2.48	2.93	2.87	2.63	2.67	2.52
	100.20	100.53	98.44	99.71	100.16	99.27	100.01	97.63
Analyst or source	J. J. Glass et. al. (1944)		From the collection of M.D. Dorfman	J. J. Glass et. al. (1944)		From the collection of M.D. Dorfman	J.J. Glass et. al. (1944)	From the collection of M.D. Dorfman

a. Figures are the numbers of analyses.

b. CaO, Al_2O_3, Na_2O, K_2O, TiO_2, H_2O

Table 18 Chemical composition of danalite and genthelvite (in percent)

Components	18. Danalite, wine-red, U.S.S.R., Europe	19. Danalite, Cornwall, U.K.	20. Danalite, Gloucester, Massachusetts, U.S.A.	21. Danalite, Rockport, Massachusetts, U.S.A.	22. Genthelvite, West Cheyenne Canyon, Colorado, U.S.A.	23. Genthelvite, West Cheyenne Canyon, Colorado, U.S.A.	24. Manganese-genthelvite, Lovozero, Kola Peninsula, U.S.S.R.
SiO_2	29.40	29.48	29.88	31.73	30.26	—	27.35
BeO	14.20	14.17	14.72	13.83	12.70	—	12.00
Al_2O_3	2.00	—	—	—	—	—	—
Fe_2O_3 }		—	—	—	—	—	6.70
FeO }	39.40	37.53	28.13	27.40	6.81	6.1	—
MnO	5.25	11.53	5.71	6.28	1.22	1.5	10.21
ZnO	5.10	4.87	18.15	17.52	46.20	46.0	40.00
S	5.32	5.04	4.82	5.48	5.49	—	5.74
Other [a]	—	—	0.83	—	0.51	—	—
Total	100.67	102.62	102.24	102.24	103.19	—	102.00
-O = S	2.66	2.52	2.41	2.74	2.74		2.87
	98.01	100.10	99.83	99.50	100.45		99.13
Analyst or source	From the collection of E. F. Ziv	J. J. Glass et. al. (1944)			J. J. Glass et. al. (1953)		E. M. Es'kova (1957)

[a] CaO, Al_2O_3, Na_2O, K_2O, TiO_2, H_2O.

The structural formula for the minerals of the helvite–danalite–genthelvite group can be represented as $M_4[BeSiO_4]_3S$ or, taking into account the position of sulfur in the structure of these minerals, as $M_4S[BeSiO_4]_3$, where M is manganese, iron, or zinc, the unit cell of helvite, danalite, or genthelvite contains $2M_4S[BeSiO_4]_3$; this enabled many investigators to represent their structural formula as $M_8[BeSiO_4]_6S_2$.

The remark of V. S. Sobolev (1949), who objected to including helvite in the subclass of tectosilicates because of the relatively high density of its structure, is not well-founded, as the high density of structure of this member of the tectoberyllosilicates (in comparison with the analogous type of aluminosilicate structure is entirely probable.

ORIGIN AND PARAGENESIS. The minerals of the helvite group are formed under a wide range of natural conditions and occur in the most diverse types of deposits. The main factors that determine the possibility of occurrence of helvite, danalite, or genthelvite instead of other, more common beryllium silicates, are these:

1. Shortage of silicon or aluminum at a certain stage of the process.

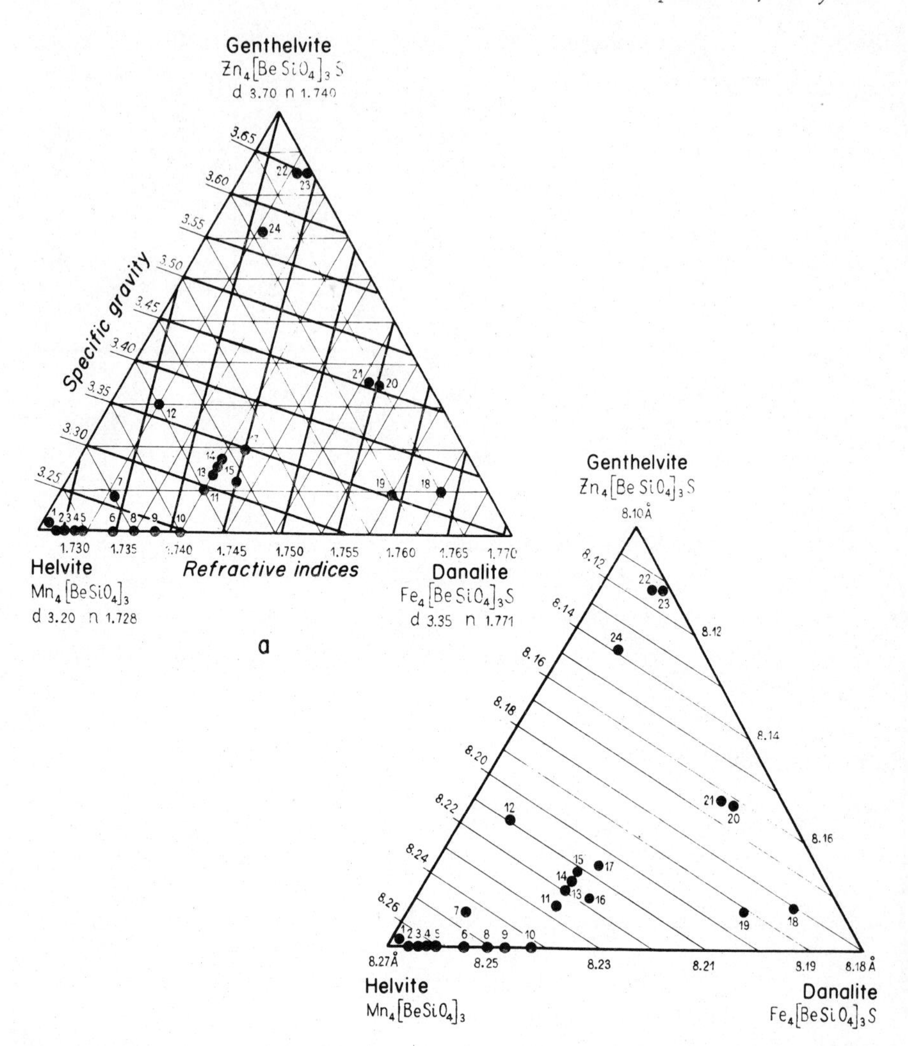

Fig. 5. Diagrams showing the dependence of (a) physical properties and of (b) the dimensions of the elementary cells of minerals in the helvite-danalite-genthelvite groups on their chemical composition. The numbers in the diagrams correspond to the numbers for analyses in Tables 17 and 18.

2. High concentration of sulfur, combined with high concentrations of iron, manganese, or zinc, in the mineral-forming solutions.

When minerals of this group are formed, usually both factors are involved simultaneously, the more important being the latter, which is related to the peculiarities of composition of the mineral-forming solutions.

Different conditions of formation determine also the diversity of the paragenesis of minerals of the helvite group in the different types of deposits given below:

Table 19 Ratios of the helvite, danalite, and genthelvite molecules in the helvite-group minerals (in percent)

No. of analysis	Deposit	$Mn_4[BeSiO_4]_3S$	$Fe_4[BeSiO_4]_3S$	$Zn_4[BeSiO_4]_3S$
		Helvite		
1*	Central Asia	96.4	1.3	2.18
2	Amelia, Virginia, U.S.A.	96.0	4.0	–
3	Amelia, Virginia, U.S.A.	94.5	5.5	–
4	Southern Norway	92.5	7.5	–
5	Schwarzenberg, Saxony	92.0	8.0	–
6	Schwarzenberg, Saxony	84.0	16.0	–
7	Kazakh SSR	80.0	12.0	8.0
8	USSR in Europe	79.0	21.0	–
9	Sigteso, Iceland	75.0	25.0	–
10	USSR in Europe	70.0	30.0	–
11	Sierra Cordoba, Argentina	60.0	30.0	10.0
12	Kazakh SSR	60.0	10.0	30.0
13	Hörtekollen, Norway	56.0	30.0	14.0
14	Mt. Francisco, Western Australia	55.0	30.0	15.0
15	Kazakh SSR	54.0	30.0	16.0
16	Iron Mountain, New Mexico, U.S.A.	52.0	36.0	12.0
17	USSR in Europe	47.0	34.0	19.0
		Danalite		
18	USSR in Europe	10.0	80.0	10.0
19	Cornwall, United Kingdom	21.0	70.0	9.0
20	Gloucester, Massachusetts, U.S.A.	11.0	54.0	35.0
21	Rockport, Massachusetts, U.S.A.	13.0	52.0	35.0
		Genthelvite		
22	Colorado, U.S.A.	3.0	12.0	85.0
23	Colorado, U.S.A.	2.0	13.0	85.0
		Manganese genthelvite		
24	Lovozero, Kola Peninsula, USSR	18.0	11.0	71.0

*The numbers of the analyses correspond to Tables 17 and 18

1. As an accessory mineral in coarse-grained and block quartz-amazonite granitic pegmatites:

(a) helvite, topaz, spessartite, monazite, and phenacite (Ilmen Mountains, Urals, USSR; Amelia County, Virginia, U.S.A.);

(b) helvite (danalite), flourite, lepidolite, and tantaloniobates (Rockport and Gloucester deposits, Massachusetts, U.S.A.).

2. In albitized granitic pegmatites–danalite, albite, and cassiterite (eastern Siberia, USSR) (I. F. Grigor'ev, 1944).

3. As an accessory mineral in syenite and nepheline-syenite pegmatites:

(a) helvite, microcline, and corundum (Ilmen Mountains, Urals, USSR);

(b) helvite, microcline, albite, and zircon (southern Norway);

(c) helvite, aegirine, nepheline, and feldspar (Sigteso, Iceland; Langesund Fjord, southern Norway);

(d) genthelvite, feldspar, sodalite, manganoilmenite, and zircon (Kola Peninsula, Lovozero, USSR).

4. In greisen formations:

(a) helvite, danalite, hematite, quartz, bertrandite, fluorite, and garnet (Kazakh SSR);

(b) helvite, muscovite, zinnwaldite, quartz, sulfides, and earlier beryl (Chinese People's Republic).

5. In contact-metasomatic formations: magnetite-fluorite skarns–helvite, danalite, magnetite, fluorite, vesuvianite, pyroxene, and others (Kazakh SSR; Central Asia; Iron Mountain, New Mexico, U.S.A.).

6. In hydrothermal veins:

a) helvite, quartz, wolframite, and feldspar (veins in limestone, Kazakh SSR);

b) helvite, quartz, cassiterite, and sulfides (Kazakh SSR);

c) helvite, quartz, wolframite, hematite, and sulfides (Kazakh SSR);

d) helvite, quartz, tourmaline, cassiterite, and sulfides (eastern Siberia);

e) helvite, calcite, quartz, sphalerite, galena, etc. (Central Asia; Grandview deposit, New Mexico, U.S.A.);

f) helvite, rhodonite, rhodochrosite, sphalerite, galena, and pyrite (Silverton deposit, Colorado, and Butte deposit, Montana, U.S.A.);

g) danalite, quartz, arsenopyrite, and chlorite (Cornwall, United Kingdom).

The most widespread types of helvite and danalite deposits are the magnetite-fluorite and vesuvianite-fluorite skarn formations on the contact of beryllium-bearing granites with limestone.

The nature of the deposit of genthelvite in the Cheyenne Canyon, Colorado, remains unknown. The crystals of genthelvite are described in association with astrophyllite and quartz. It appears possible that the specimens originated from the pegmatites of alkalic granites.

Bavenite: $Ca_4[(Be,Al)_4Si_9(O,OH)_{26}](OH)_2$

Bavenite was found and studied for the first time in 1901 by Artini in specimens from Baveno, Italy. In the first chemical analysis of this mineral, beryllium was not detected; thus the empirical formula established by Artini, $6SiO_2 \cdot Al_2O_3 \cdot 3CaO \cdot H_2O$,[5] did not correspond to the real composition of the mineral.

Thirty years later, while analyzing bavenite from the Mesa Grande, California, deposit, Fairchild found 2.67 percent of beryllium oxide (Schaller and Fairchild, 1932). On the basis of this analysis, he suggested a new formula for bavenite—$Ca_4Al_2BeSi_9O_{25}(OH)_2$.

Fairchild's results were confirmed by two subsequent analyses of bavenite from Baveno, carried out by Pagliani (3.12 percent BeO) and Bianci (2.48 percent BeO) (E. Grill, 1941; quoted in Fleischer and Switzer, 1953). However, in 1946, E. I. Kutukova published the results of two chemical analyses of bavenite from the emerald mines of the Urals, USSR, by V. S. Saltykova and M. E. Kazakova that showed a BeO content of 6.60 and 6.33 percent respectively. In both analyses of bavenite from the Urals, the completeness of beryllium precipitation was checked spectrographically.

In 1948 Rowledge and Hayton described as duplexite a mineral containing 7.14 and 7.72 percent BeO, which, after being tested by means of X-rays, was found to be identical with bavenite (Rowledge and Hayton, 1948).

While investigating the problem of the correct chemical composition of bavenite, Fleischer and Switzer (1953) carried out a comparative study of a series of bavenite specimens from both old and new deposits; on comparing the results obtained with those of earlier authors, they concluded that no great differences could be found in the BeO content of bavenite and that, perhaps in the earlier analyses, part of the beryllium had been determined as aluminum. Thus, for example, a repeated chemical analysis of a bavenite specimen from Mesa Grande, previously analyzed by Fairchild (Schaller and Fairchild, 1932), yielded 7.66 percent BeO.

Recalculation of the latest analyses of bavenite (Numbers 4 and 5 in Table 21) yielded the following formulae for this mineral:

Analysis 4: $Ca_{3.87}Be_{2.57}Al_{1.24}Si_{8.88}O_{26} \cdot 1.23H_2O$

Analysis 5: $Ca_{4.11}Be_{2.95}Al_{1.22}Si_{9.22}O_{26} \cdot 1.90H_2O$.

It should be noted that the principle of basing the calculation on oxygen may result in serious errors, in the case of a water-containing mineral, when the structure is unknown and there are no objective data relating to the form in which water is combined in the mineral. In particular, the variable content of aluminum and beryllium in bavenite, and the fact that their sum is more or less constant, allow the preliminary assumption re-

[5] AlO_3 in text—in error for Al_2O_3, Ed.

Table 20 Physical properties of bavenite

Properties	Characteristic
System	Orthorhombic
Dimensions of unit cell, Å	a_0=19.34; b_0=23.06; c_0=4.95
Form of segregation and crystal habit	Fibrous and radiating segregations, rarely separate crystals elongated along the c axis and flattened along (010)
Cleavage	Perfect on (100), medium on (001)
Color	White, rose
Luster	Glassy
Hardness	5.5
Specific gravity	2.71–2.74
Optical sign	(+)
Refractive indices:	
γ	1.583–1.593
β	1.579–1.585
α	1.578–1.586
γ–α	0.005–0.011
2V	from 22° to 60° ❦
Optical orientation	Plane of optic axes (010); =α

❦ From various sources

garding the isomorphism of these elements. This, in turn, permits the assumption that one or more oxygen ions in the lattice of the mineral may be replaced by hydroxyl for compensating the heterovalent substitution between aluminum and beryllium. As shown in thermal investigations carried out in A. I. Tsvetkov's laboratory, water in bavenite is of the high-temperature nature, and separates in the range of 900 to 1000° (Fig. 6)

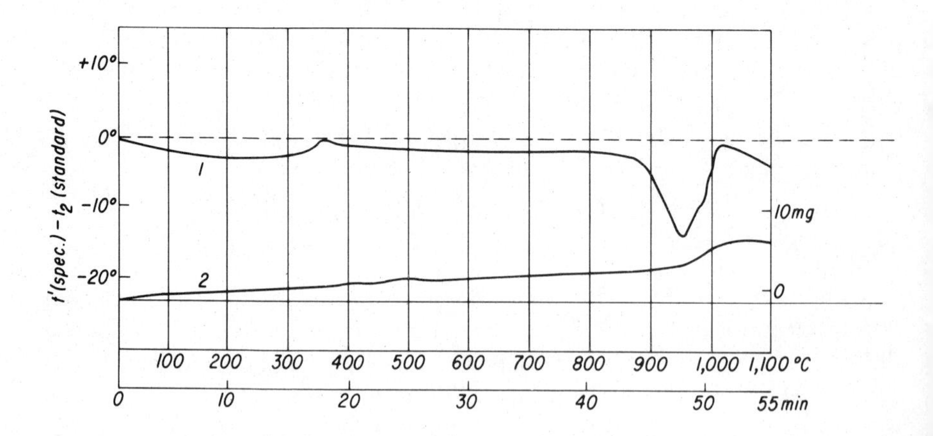

Fig. 6. (1) Heating and (2) dehydration curves of bavenite.

Table 21 Chemical analyses of bavenite

Components	Emerald Mines						Western Australia			Londonderry			Mesa Grande, California			Sinsiang, Chinese People's Republic		
	1.			2.			3.			4.			5.			6.		
	%	Atomic quantities of		%	Atomic quantities of		%	Atomic quantities of		%	Atomic quantities of		%	Atomic quantities of		%	Atomic quantities of	
		Cations	Oxygen		Cations	Oxygen		Cations	Oxygen		Cations	Oxygen		Cations	Oxygen		Cations	Oxygen
SiO_2	57.11	951	1902	57.25	952	1904	58.92	981	1962	59.13	984	1968	57.64	960	1920	55.25	920	1840
Al_2O_3	9.60	188	282	9.89	194	291	6.88	136	204	7.00	138	207	6.46	128	192	8.26	162	243
Fe_2O_3	0.11	002	003	0.10	002	003	0.07	002	003	—	—	—	—	—	—	1.18	14	21
BeO	6.60	264	264	6.3	253	253	7.72	309	309	7.14	286	286	7.66	307	307	7.00	280	280
CaO	24.30	433	433	24.35	434	434	23.26	415	415	23.90	426	426	23.90	427	427	24.15	431	431
MnO	—	—	—	—	—	—	0.01	—	—	0.01	—	—	—	—	—	—	—	—
MgO	—	—	—	—	—	—	0.13	003	003	0.05	—	—	—	—	—	—	—	—
Na_2O	—	—	—	—	—	—	0.44	014	007	0.10	004	002	—	—	—	—	—	—
H_2O^+	1.87	208	104	1.90	212	106	2.41	266	133	2.46	270	135	3.56	394	197	4.00	444	222
Others	0.31[a]			0.31[a]			0.01[c]			0,16[d]						0.74[d]		
Total	99.90		2884	100.13			99.94		3036	100,01		3024	99.60		3043	100.58		
Analyst or source	V. S. Saltykova			M. E. Kazakova			Hayton, in H. P. Rowledge and J. D. Hayton, 1948						Carron, in M. Fleischer and G. Schwitzer, 1953			M. E. Kazakova		

a. B_2O_3.
b. K_2O. (None indicated in Russian text. Ed.)
c. Cl — 0.02%, CO_2 -- 003%, C — 0.11%
d. H_2O^-.

Thus, the recalculation of the analyses of bavenite, based on the assumed number of oxygen atoms, cannot be considered correct. But the relatively stable numbers of silicon atoms (9) and calcium atoms (4) permit use of one of these elements as the basis of recalculation.

The recalculation of the analyses of bavenite, based on Ca_4 (See Table 22), yields the following general empirical formula of the mineral, which is consistent with the ability of OH to replace oxygen in beryllium tetrahedra:

$$Ca_4(Be,Al)_4Si_9O_{26-n}(OH)_{2+n}.$$

The available chemical analyses of bavenite indicate the existence of the series:

$$Ca_4[(Be_2Al_2)Si_9O_{26}](OH)_2 - Ca_4[(Be_3Al)Si_9O_{25}(OH)](OH)_2.$$

The suggested formula differs from the formula $Ca_4BeAl_2 \cdot Si_9O_{25}(OH)_2$ (Betekhtin, 1950), calculated most probably on the basis of the earlier inaccurate analyses. The elementary cell of the mineral, determined first by Ksanda (Ksanda and Merwin, 1933), and later G. F. Claringbull (1940), contains 4 molecules.

Bavenite crystallizes in the orthorhombic system. Its physical properties are listed in Table 20. The crystal structure of the mineral has not been

Table 22 Recalculation of the analyses of bavenite based on Ca_4

Deposit	Formula	Total	
		Al+Be+Si	Al+Be
1,2. Emerald Mines (Urals)	$Ca_4Al_{1.76}Be_{2.44}Si_{8.8}O_{25.74}(OH)_2$	13	4.20
3. Londonderry (Australia)	$Ca_4Al_{1.27}Be_{2.86}Si_9O_{25.5}(OH)_{2.5}$	13.13	4.13
4. Londonderry (Australia)	$Ca_4Al_{1.27}Be_{2.66}Si_{9.05}O_{25.5}(OH)_{2.5}$	12.98	3.93
5. Mesa Grande (California)	$Ca_4Al_{1.20}Be_{2.86}Si_{8.95}O_{24.8}(OH)_{3.3}$	13.01	4.06
6. Sinsiang (?) (China)	$Ca_4Al_{1.66}Be_{2.64}Si_{8.7}O_{25}(OH)_3 \cdot 0.5H_2O$	13	4.3

studied. On the strength of the silicon/oxygen ratio, A. G. Betekhtin (1950) tentatively relates the mineral to the silicates with cyclinal structure.

The physical properties of bavenite and the (Si + Be + Al)/O ratio in the formula (1 to 2) relates bavenite to the tectosilicates.

ORIGIN AND PARAGENESIS. Bavenite is a secondary hydrothermal accessory mineral in some beryl-containing pegmatites and greisen deposits. It metasomatically replaces beryl or forms aggregates of thin crystals in leached cavities in feldspars.

The substitution of bavenite for beryl is probably the result of the reaction between beryl and late-hydrothermal calcium-containing alkaline solutions, which in many cases are characteristic of the final stages of the pegmatitic process (Ginzburg, 1955a, 1955b). Calcium, silicon, and (OH) are added when bavenite forms after beryl. Aluminum passes from the octahedral to tetrahedral coordination; some aluminum is possibly subtracted.

Probable Tectosilicates and Minerals of Uncertain Structure

Karpinskyite: $Na[(Be,Al,Zn)(Si,Zn)_3(Si,Al)_3(O,OH)_8]\cdot H_2O$

Karpinskyite is a new beryllium mineral found in alkalic pegmatites and discovered by L. L. Shilin in 1955 in the pegmatites of the Lovozero rock mass (Shilin, 1956).

The physical properties of this mineral are listed in Table 23.

Table 23 Physical properties of karpinskyite

Properties	Characteristic
System	Hexagonal
Dimensions of unit cell, Å	a_0=14.24; c_0=4.83
Form of segregation and crystal habit	Acicular prismatic crystals, collected in radiating aggregates
Color	White
Luster	Glassy to pearly
Cleavage	Perfect prismatic
Hardness	About 2 (?)
Specific gravity	2.545
Refractive indices	
ε	1.518
ω	1.511
Optical sign	(+)

The chemical composition of the mineral is fairly complicated, as can be seen from the results of the only analysis available (Table 24).

The high-temperature water, detected analytically, apparently separates from the mineral at 540°C, according to the rather obscure results of the thermal investigation (Shilin, 1956).

The first to study this mineral, L. L. Shilin, suggested a formula calculated on the basis of $(O,OH)_{18}$ and corresponding to a tectocyclosilicate:

$$(Na,K)_{1.99}(Be,Zn,Mg)_{0.98}Al_{1.94}Si_{5.71}(O,OH)_{18}$$

or

$$Na_2(Be,Zn,Mg)Al_2Si_6O_{16}(OH)_2.$$

Such a formula, based on the arbitrary choice of the number of oxygen atoms, may be correct, provided it is assumed that the chemical analysis

Table 24 Chemical composition of karpinskyite

Components	%	Atomic quantities of		Number of atoms per		Number of atoms per
		Cations	Oxygen	$(O,OH)_{18}$	$(Na,K)_1$	$\Sigma R^{(IV)} = 4$
SiO_2	56.68	9447	18894	5.71	2.86	2.64
Al_2O_3	16.40	3216	4824	1.99 (Al, Fe)	0.98	0.90
Fe_2O_3	0.06	0008	0012			
BeO	2.58	1031	1031	0.62	0.31	0.29
ZnO	3.26	0400	0400	0.24	0.12	0.11
MgO	0.78	0195	0195	0.12	0.06	0.06
Na_2O	9.18	2962	1481	1.79	1 (Na, K)	0.92
K_2O	1.55	0330	0165	0.20		
H_2O^+	5.00	5556	2778			
H_2O^-	2.50		1389			
Total	99.99	17589[a]	27002[a]	10.67	5.33	

[a] Without H_2O

is not accurate; otherwise it is impossible to explain the appreciable silicon deficiency (5.71 compared with the required 6). Further doubt is caused by the regular grouping of (Be, Zn, Mg) in isolation from Al and Si.

The ratio of cations of various coordination and of oxygen in the empirical formula of the mineral corresponds well with the typical formula:

$$R^{VIII-X}:R^{IV}:O = 1:4:8.$$

Recalculation of the analysis of karpinskyite on the basis of the sum $R^{IV} = 4$ results in this formula:

$$(Na,K)_{0.92}Be_{0.29}Zn_{0.11}Mg_{0.06}Al_{0.90}Si_{2.64}O_7\,(OH)$$

or

$$Na[\,(Al,Be,Zn,Si)_4\,(O,OH)_8]\cdot H_2O.$$

This formula resembles that of the minerals of the epididymite-eudidymite group.

Some similarity between the structures of karpinskyite and the minerals of the epididymite-eudidymite group is also indicated by the coincidence of all principal lines of the powder patterns of the analyzed minerals. Virtually all strong lines found in the powder patterns of karpinskyite correspond to the strong lines of epididymite or eudidymite.

The final structural formula of karpinskyite can be derived only when the results of the X-ray investigation of the mineral are known.

ORIGIN AND PARAGENESIS. Karpinskyite is one of the latest assessory minerals of the hydrothermal stage of the process of formation of natrolite-albite alkalic pegmatites of the Lovozero rock mass. Radiating aggregates of karpinskyite form in the cavities and cracks in albite and, more rarely, in those in natrolite. Karpinskyite has been observed to replace albite.

The mineral is encountered in association with albite, natrolite, karnasurtite, and occasionally with epididymite.

Leucophanite and meliphanite: $Na_{(1-n)}Ca[BeSi_2O_6]F_{(1-n)}$

Leucophanite and meliphanite are extremely rare minerals which present polymorphous varieties of the empirical composition $NaCaBeSi_2O_6F$; they were discovered by Brögger in the pegmatites of nepheline syenites of Langesund Fjord, and subsequently described by him in 1890 (Brögger, 1890). Recently, leucophanite was also found in the alkalic pegmatites of the Lovozero rock mass (Semenov, 1957b).

On the basis of crystallographic and optical investigations of both minerals, Brögger referred leucophanite to the orthorhombic system, and meliphanite to the tetragonal system. Brögger's results were later confirmed by W. H. Zachariasen (1930, 1931).

The physical properties of leucophanite and meliphanite as well as those of the analogous aminoffite are listed in Table 25. We should note the high birefringence value and relatively low hardness of both leucophanite and meliphanite.

The chemical composition of leucophanite and meliphanite is given by the analyses in Table 26. Brögger (1890) gave the following empirical formulae of these minerals:

Meliphanite: $(Ca,Na)_2Be\,(Si,Al)_2\,(O,F)_7$;
Leucophanite: $(Ca,Na)_2BeSi_2\,(O,OH,F)_7$.

Having corrected the results of Brögger, Zachariasen (1930) concluded that the chemical composition of meliphanite and leucophanite is almost identical, the only difference being the presence of some aluminum replacing silicon in meliphanite. He suggested the following formulae for meliphanite and leucophanite:

Meliphanite: $Ca_4Na_2Be_4Si_6O_{20}F$;
Leucophanite: $Ca_3Na_3Be_3Si_6O_{18}F_3$.

The recalculation of the chemical analyses of meliphanite and leucophanite for $Si + Be + Al = 3$ (Table 27) enables one to draw the following conclusions about the peculiarities of their chemical composition:

1. The chemical composition of leucophanite and meliphanite is identical; the isomorphous admixture of aluminum, which replaces silicon, can occur in both meliphanite and leucophanite; for instance, the leucophanite from the pegmatites of the Lovozero rock mass, studied by E. I. Semenov (analysis 1), contains 2.32 percent Al_2O_3.

2. The calcium content is highly constant in all cases (0.99 to 1.08)

Table 25 Physical properties of leucophanite, meliphanite, and aminoffite

Properties	Leucophanite	Meliphanite	Aminoffite
System	Orthorhombic	Tetragonal	Tetragonal
Dimensions of unit cell, Å	a_0=7.38; c_0=9.96	a_0=10.58; c_0=9.88	a_0=13.8; c_0=9.8
Form of segregation and cryatal habit	Pseudotetragonal tabular crystals. Under the microscope-compound polysynthetic twins	Short-pyramidal and prismatic crystals	Well-developed individual crystals of dipyramidal form
Color	White, green, yellow	Yellow	Colorless
Luster	Glassy	Glassy	Glassy
Cleavage	Perfect on (001) and medium on (100) and (010)	Medium on (001)	Imperfect on (001)
Hardness	4	5–5.5	5.5
Specific gravity	2.96–2.98	3.0	2.94
Optical sign	(-)	(-)	(-)
Refractive indices:			
γ	1.596–1.598	–	–
β	1.594–1.595	1.612	1.647
α	1.570–1.571	1.593	1.637
Birefringence	$\gamma-\alpha=0.027$	$\beta-\alpha=0.019$	$\beta-\alpha=0.010$
Axiality and 2V	2V = 39°	Uniaxial. Sometimes biaxial with 2V up to 36°	Sometimes biaxial with 2V up to 15°
Pleochroism	–	α–green-yellow β–honey-colored to fallowish-yellow	–
Optical orientation	Plane of optic axes (100)	–	–

and has no obvious relation to sodium content, which is subjected to considerable variations (0.91 to 0.65).

3. The fluorine content varies in noticeable limits (0.7 to 0.88) and shows a constant direct relationship to the sodium content (Fig. 7).

4. The beryllium content is relatively constant (0.98 to 1.1), while aluminum apparently replaces silicon in all cases.

The general empirical formula of meliphanite and leucophanite can be represented as follows:

$$Na_{0.6\text{-}1}CaBe(Si,Al)_2O_6{\cdot}F_{0.6\text{-}1}.$$

The substitution of aluminum for a part of silicon can, as appears from analysis 1, be compensated by the substitution of the OH group for the corresponding part of oxygen.

Table 26 Chemical composition of leucophanite and meliphanite

Components	Mt. Nepkha, Lovozero Leucophanite			Langesund Fjord, Norway, Leucophanite												Langesund Fjord, Norway, Meliphanite		
	1.			2.			3.			4.			5.			6.		
	%	Atomic quantities of		%	Atomic quantities of		%	Atomic quantities of		%	Atomic quantities of		%	Atomic quantities of		%	Atomic quantities of	
		Cations	Oxygen		Cations	Oxygen		Cations	Oxygen		Cations	Oxygen		Cations	Oxygen		Cations	Oxygen
SiO_2	45.98	766	1532	47.03	783	1566	48.38	806	1612	47.82	796	1592	48.50	808	1616	43.60	721	1442
Al_2O_3	2.32	046	069	1.03	020	030	—	—	—	—	—	—	0.45	008	012	4.61	090	135
Fe_2O_3	0.22	002	003	—	—	—	—	—	—	—	—	—	—	—	—	—	—	—
BeO	11.52	461	461	10.70	430[a]	430[a]	11.97	485[b]	485[b]	11.51	461[c]	461	10.03	400	400	9.80	392	392
CaO	23.65	422	422	23.37	417	417	23.37	417	417	25.01	446	446	22.94	409	409	29.56	427	427
MgO	0.30	007	007	0.17	005[d]	005	—	—	—	—	—	—	0.27	007	007	0.16	005	005
MnO	—	—	—	—	—	—	—	—	—	1.01	014	014	—	—	—	—	—	—
Na_2O	10.79	348	174	11.26	364	182	10.27	331	166	10.20	330	165	12.42	400	200	7.98	258	129
K_2O	0.70	014	007	0.30	006	003	0.30	006	003	0.31	006	003	—	—	—	0.23	004	002
F	7.04	—	370	6.57	—	350	6.77	—	356	6.17	—	325	5.94	—	309	5.43	—	282
H_2O	0.83	—	046	—	—	—	—	—	—	—	—	—	1.08	—	061	—	—	—
Total	103.36		2675[e]	100.43		2633[f]	101.06		2683[g]	102.02		2681[e]	101.63		2644[e]	101.37		2532[e]
*Total	100.40			97.68			98.23			99.44			99.15			99.08		
Source	E. I. Semenov, 1957			W. G. Brögger, 1890														

*Total less correction for fluoride to oxide equivalent.

a. Corrected – original text has 403.

b. Corrected – original text has 458.

c. Corrected – original text has 561.

d. Corrected – original text has 750.

e. Without H_2O and F.

f. Corrected – original text has 2606 without H_2O and F.

g. Corrected – original text has 2656 without H_2O and F.

Table 27 Conversion of chemical analyses of leucophanite and meliphanite for Si + Be + Al = 3

Elements and groups	Number of atoms					
	1	2	3	4	5	6
Si	1.81	1.95	1.92	1.90	1.99	1.80
Al	0.11	0.05	—	—	0.02	0.22
Be	1.08	1	1.08	1.1	0.99	0.98
Ca[a]	1	1.05	0.99	1	1	1.08
Na[b]	0.85	0.91	0.79	0.8	0.99	0.65
F	0.85	0.88	0.84	0.78	0.76	0.7
OH	—	—	—	—	0.24	—
O	6.3	6.5	6.3	6.4	6.5	6.3
$O - \frac{F + OH}{2}$	5.8	6	5.9	6	6	6

Formulae:

Leucophanite:

1. $Na_{0.85}Ca\,[Be_{1.08}(Si, Al)_{1.92}O_{5.8}OH_{0.2}]\,F_{0.85}$ or $Ca\,[Be\,(Si, Al)_2\,(O, OH)_6]\,0.85\,(NaF)$;
2. $Na_{0.9}Ca\,[Be\,(Si, Al)_2\,(O,OH)_6]F_{0.88}$ or $Ca\,[Be\,(Si, Al)_2\,(O, OH)_6]\,0.9\,(NaF)$;
3. $Na_{0.79}Ca\,[Be_{1.08}Si_{1.92}O_6]\,F_{0.84}$ or $Ca\,[BeSi_2O_6]\,0,8\,NaF$;
4. $Na_{0.8}Ca\,[BeSi_{1.9}O_6]\,F_{0.78}$ or $Ca\,[BeSi_2O_6]\,0.8\,(NaF)$;
5. $Na_{0.99}Ca\,[Be\,(Si, Al)_2O_6]\,(F_{0.76}OH_{0.24})$ or $Ca\,[BeSi_2O_6]\,Na\,(F, OH)$

Meliphanite 6. $Na_{0.65}Ca\,[Be\,(Si, Al)_2O_6]F_{0.7}$ or $Ca\,[Be\,(Si, Al)_2O_6]\,0.7\,(NaF)$

General formula $Na_{1-n}Ca[Be\,(Si, Al)_2O_6]\,F_{1-n}$

[a] Including a small proportion of Mn and Mg.

[b] Including a small proportion of K

The previously stressed peculiarities of the chemical composition of meliphanite and leucophanite do not allow one to agree with Zachariasen (1930) and Winchell (1951), who consider both minerals to be the representatives of the isomorphous series between tetragonal $Ca_2BeSi_2O_7$ (akin to melilite) and orthorhombic $Na_2BeSi_2O_5F_2$. In the latter case, there should be a direct relationship not only between the sodium and fluorine content, but also between the sodium and calcium content; this has not been observed.

The structure of meliphanite and leucophanite has not been studied. The physical properties of the minerals do not permit definite designation

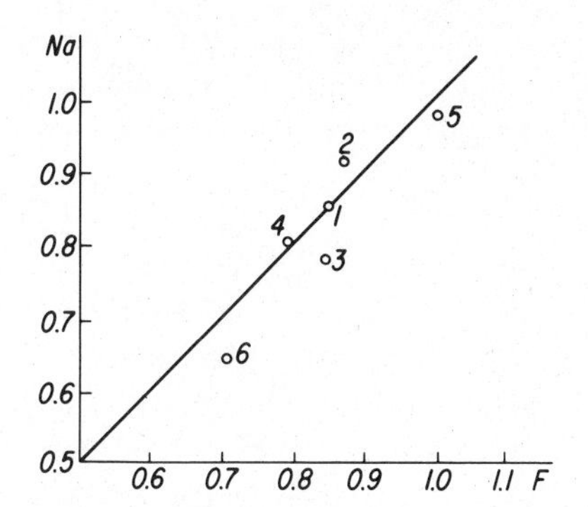

Fig. 7. Relation between the number of atoms of fluorine and sodium (for Si + Be + Al = 3) in the minerals of the leucophanite-meliphanite group. Numbers in the graph correspond to the numbers for analyses in Table 27.

to a particular subclass of silicates. For example, both minerals are characterized by a low hardness, which is characteristic of the tectoberyllosilicates and is not typical of the beryllium orthosilicates and diorthosilicates (Table 8). The high birefrigence (meliphanite–0.019; leucophanite–0.027) indicates that care should be taken in considering the possibility of placing them in the tectoberyllosilicates.

Zachariasen (1930) designates meliphanite and leucophanite as diorthosilicates with isolated twinned tetrahedra $[Si_2(O,F)_7]$, structurally similar to the melilite-group minerals: melilite $(Ca,Na)_2(Mg,Al)[(Si,Al_2O_7]$, åkermannite $Ca_2Mg[Si_2O_7]$, and hardystonite $Ca_2Zn[Si_2O_7]$. This is apparently borne out by the structural investigation of the artificial beryllium analogue of åkermannite $Ca_2Be[Si_2O_7]$ Goria, 1953–1954). This investigation disclosed a structural analogy between Be-åkermannite and the minerals of the melilite group, which is expressed by the similarity of dimensions of their elementary cells (in Å).

		a_0	c_0	c/a	Number of molecules in elementary cell
Be-åkermannite	$Ca_2Be[Si_2O_7]$	7.50	4.93	0.657	2
Åkermannite	$Ca_2Mg[Si_2O_7]$	7.73	5.01	0.648	2
Hardystonite	$Ca_2Zn[Si_2O_7]$	7.83	4.99	0.637	2

At the same time, the comparison of the parameters of the elementary cells of the melilite-group minerals with leucophanite, meliphanite, and the related aminoffite points to the existence of fundamental structural differences.

		a_0	c_0	c/a	Number of molecules in elementary cell
Leucophanite	$Na_{1-n}CaBeSi_2O_6F_{1-n}$	7.38	9.96	1.35	4
Meliphanite		10.58	9.88	0.933	8
Aminoffite	$Ca_2BeSi_2O_6(OH)_2$	13.8	9.8	0.710	12

Thus, it is impossible to agree with Zachariasen and Goria, who believe that the large-scale isomorphous substitution of fluorine and hydroxyl for oxygen is the fundamental cause of the lowering of the symmetry of pseudotetragonal (orthorhombic) leucophanite, compared with tetragonal meliphanite. The lowering of symmetry is not observed, in particular, in the case of aminoffite, although in this mineral (from the point of view of the hypothesis of the authors referred to above), one oxygen atom has been completely substituted by the OH group.

Thus, the inclusion of meliphanite and leucophanite in the melilite group and the presence of twinned $[Si_2(O,F,OH)_7]$ tetrahedra in the structure of the investigated minerals remains unproved. In particular, considerations supporting these ideas cannot explain the structural difference between Be-åkermannite and the highly analogous (by composition) aminoffite (see below).

The dependence of fluorine content on sodium content, referred to above, would indicate that fluorine does not enter into a radical, but is an additional anion, loosely bonded in the structure. On the other hand, in minerals of the epididymite-eudidymite group, where the entry of the OH group into the beryllium-silicon radical is highly probable, there is no analogous relationship between sodium content and OH content.

The ratio $(Be + Si):O = 1:2$ and the alkaline nature of the compounds make it possible to place, with some degree of certainty, leucophanite and meliphanite in the group of beryllosilicates having the following formula:

$$Na_{1-n}Ca[BeSi_2O_6]F_{1-n}.$$

The features of the crystal structure of both minerals, which determine the nature of their physical properties and chemical composition, should be explained by the results of detailed structural analysis.

ORIGIN AND PARAGENESIS. Leucophanite and meliphanite form during the final stages of formation of alkalic pegmatites in the cavities leached in minerals of both the early crystallization stages (microcline, nepheline) and the replacement stages (natrolite). The paragenesis of meliphanite, as described by Brögger (1890) for the Langesund Fjord pegmatites, is highly interesting. Meliphanite appears here as tabular rosette-shaped segregations several centimeters in diameter, localized in specific parts of the biotite-nepheline-feldspar pegmatites in close association with homilite, which is found only in association with meliphanite. Later, zeolites are associated with meliphanite and homilite and fill the central portions of geodes.

In the pegmatites of the Lovozero rock mass, leucophanite was detected in the central natrolite zone of the pegmatite on Mt. Nepkha (Semenov, 1957b). The leucophanite spherolites are rare in cavities of the rose natrolite.

Aminoffite: $Ca_2[Be, Al)Si_2O_6](OH)_2$

Aminoffite is one of the extremely rare beryllium minerals.

The physical properties of aminoffite are listed in Table 25.

The chemical analysis of this mineral (Table 28) is easily converted to the empirical formula $Ca_2(Be,Al)Si_2O_6{\cdot}(OH)_2$.

The structure of aminoffite has not been investigated; only the dimen-

Table 28 Conversion of the chemical analysis of aminoffite

Components	Wt-% from Hurlbut's analysis	Atomic quantities of		Number of atoms
		Cations	Oxygen	
SiO_2	42.49	708	1416	1.98
Al_2O_3	4.41	086	129	0.24 } 0.93
BeO	6.20	248	248	0.69 }
Fe_2O_3	0.31	004	006	–
MnO	0.19	003	003	–
CaO	40.27	718	718	2
H_2O	6.45	714	357	2
Total	100.32		2877	8

sions of the elementary cell (a_o = 13.8 Å; c_o = 9.8Å) and the number of molecules (12) in it have been determined (Hurlbut, 1937).

For this reason, and in view of the absence of data relating to the form in which water is present in the mineral, the formula of aminoffite can be interpreted in various ways, depending on the possible structure of the mineral:

1. $Ca_2[(Be, Al)Si_2O_6](OH)_2 \ \frac{O}{R^{IV}} = 2$ beryllo-silicon-oxygen framework;
2. $Ca_2(Be, Al)[Si_2O_7]H_2O$ groups of joined tetrahedra.

The former version appears to be more probable, as the physical properties of aminoffite make it impossible to assume the occurrence of zeolitic water or water of crystallization in the mineral. Characteristic also is the essential structural difference between aminoffite and the artificial compound $Ca_2Be[Si_2O_7]$ (Be-åkermannite), which has much smaller cell dimensions (Goria, 1953–1954).

ORIGIN AND PARAGENESIS. Aminoffite has been found only in the deposit of Långban, Sweden (Hurlbut, 1937), in the form of well developed small (0.5 to 1 mm) tetragonal dipyramids, which were in the cavities of calcite veins that transgress massive magnetite skarn with limonite. Besides calcite, the veins also contain fluorite and barite. If we judge from the paragenesis, we may call aminoffite a typical hydrothermal mineral.

Trimerite: $(Mn_2Ca)[BeSiO_4]_3$

Trimerite is one of the extremely rare beryllium minerals, found only in the deposits of Långban and Paisberg, Sweden.

Physical properties of the mineral are listed in Table 29.

Table 29 Physical properties of trimerite

Properties	Characteristic
System	Monoclinic
Dimensions of unit cell, Å	a_0=16.11; b_0=7.60; c_0=27.86; β=90°09′.
Form of segregation and crystal habit	Pseudo-hexagonal prismatic crystals. The pseudo-hexagonal habit of crystals is caused by twinning
Color	Pale-rose to colorless
Luster	Glassy
Cleavage	Distinct on (001)
Hardness	6–7
Specific gravity	3.47
Refractive indices:	
γ	1.725
β	1.720
α	1.715
Optical sign	(-)
Optical orientation	Plane of optic axes almost perpendicular to (100) and forms with (001) an angle of ca. 20°

The chemical composition corresponds to the empirical formula $(Mn,Ca)BeSiO_4$ or $Mn_2CaBe_3Si_3O_{12}$ (Table 30).

The structure of trimerite was investigated by H. Strunz (1937). It is based on the framework of SiO_4 and BeO_4 tetrahedra, in the cavities of which are arranged atoms of calcium and manganese. Structural features permit the placing of trimerite in the subclass of tectoberyllosilicates with the formula $(Mn,Ca)[BeSiO_4]$ or $(Mn_2Ca)[BeSiO_4]_3$. The elementary cell of trimerite contains $16(Mn_2Ca)[BeSiO_4]_3$.

ORIGIN AND PARAGENESIS. The crystals of trimerite were detected in calcite nests occurring among fine-grained biotite in the contact-metasomatic formations of the Långban deposit (Aminoff, 1926). If we judge from the paragenesis, the mineral seems to be the hydrothermal product of the late stages of contact metasomatism.

Table 30 Chemical composition of trimerite

Components	%	Atomic quantities of		Number of atoms per O_4
		Cations	Oxygen	
SiO_2	39.77	662	1324	1
BeO	17.08	683	683	1.02
FeO	3.87	054	054	} 0.1
MgO	0.61	015	015	
MnO	26.86	380	380	0.56
CaO	12.44	222	222	0.33
Total	100.63		2678	

Gadolinite: $(Y,Ca)_2Fe[BeSiO_4](O,OH)_2$

Gadolinite is a relatively rare mineral found mostly in granitic pegmatites; it stands out among beryllium minerals owing to the peculiarities of chemical composition which determine the specific physical properties of the mineral (Table 31).

Especially characteristic of gadolinite are the refractive indices (highest among the beryllium minerals), a high specific gravity (See Fig. 2.), the dark (up to black) color, and a relatively low birefringence (Table 31).

Table 31 Physical properties of gadolinite

Properties	Characteristic
System	Monoclinic
Dimensions of unit cell, Å	a_0=4.65; b_0=7.53; c_0=9.87; β=96°33'
Form of segregation and crystal habit	As irregular segregations and dense masses. Rarely coarse prismatic crystals
Color	Reddish-brown, black, greenish-black
Luster	Glassy to pitchy
Cleavage	None
Hardness	6.5–7
Specific gravity	4.0–4.65
Refractive indices:	
γ	1.777–1.785
β	1.78
α	1.722–1.780
$\gamma-\alpha$	0.010
Optical Sign	(+)
Pleochroism	In thick plates; $\gamma=\beta$ – grass-green; α – olive-green
2V	85°
Optical orientation	Plane of optic axes (010)

The first investigation of the Russian gadolinites was carried out by G. P. Chernik (1900, 1905a, 1905b).

Gadolinite is a compound silicate of beryllium, bivalent iron, and rare earths with the empirical formula $Y_2FeBe_2Si_2O_{10}$. Cerium with yttrium usually occurs and reaches a maximum in the essentially cerium variety, cerium-gadolinite. Small amounts of thorium also are usually present (Table 32).

A substantial proportion of the rare earths in some gadolinites is replaced by calcium (calciogadolinite) (Nakai, 1938). This replacement apparently is associated with the parallel substitution of the OH^- group for the corresponding proportion of oxygen (Table 32).

The structural similarity between gadolinite and homilite $Ca_2FeB_2Si_2O_{10}$ points to the analogous role of beryllium and boron in the structure of these minerals.

Let us analyze the function of boron in borosilicate minerals similar to homilite or datolite; from the standpoint of crystal chemistry, we must admit the possibility that boron along with silicon enters into the anionic

Table 32 Chemical composition of gadolinite

Components	Kola Peninsula			Japan, calcio-gadolinite
	West Keivy	Keivy	Kanozero	
SiO_2	24.75	24.05	24.68	23.89
BeO	10.13	10.97	10.30	10.73
Al_2O_3	1.22	0.08	—	1.68
Fe_2O_3	0.57	8.17	0.21	7.65
FeO	12.27	5.71	11.52	11.24
MgO	—	0.04	0.01	0.14
MnO	0.29	—	0.33	0.84
CaO	0.99	0.82	0.53	11.91
Na_2O	0.07	0.30	0.18	—
K_2O	—	—	0.07	—
Ce_2O_3	2.27	2.22	0.67	4.69
La_2O_3	3.71	4.94	0.86	24.47
Y_2O_3	42.58	42.23	49.06	—
ThO_2	0.60	0.38	0.27	0.80
U_3O_8	—	0.30	0.10	0.10
TiO_2	—	0.06	—	
H_2O^+	0.16	—	1.20	2.05
H_2O^-	0.05	0.04	0.10	0.14
Total	99.96	100.31	100.09	100.34
Analyst or source	M. E. Kazakova	Z. M. Gileva from I. B. Bel'kov's collection	Z. I. Goroshchenko	T. Nakai (1938)

radical.[6] The structural analogy between the borosilicate homilite and the beryllosilicate gadolinite suggests that gadolinite $(Y,Ca)_2Fe[BeSiO_4]_2(O,OH)_2$ has a framework pattern in the structure.

Such an interpretation agrees, in particular, with the ratio (Si + Be):O = 1:2 and the relatively low birefringence of the mineral, which is not characteristic of nesosilicates.

The occurrence of additional oxygen anions in the structure of gadolinite is confirmed by the relatively easy replaceability of these anions with the OH group when rare earths are replaced by calcium (calciogadolinite).

The complex structure and composition of gadolinite, especially the occurrence of a large proportion of the heavy rare-earth atoms and the occurrence of radioactive elements, determines the low stability of the crystal lattice of gadolinite and its easy transition into a metamict state.

ORIGIN AND PARAGENESIS. Gadolinite is an extremely rare accessory mineral of biotite-quartz-microcline pegmatites containing high concentrations of beryllium, yttrium, and iron (Kola Peninsula, USSR; Iveland, southern Norway; Baringer Hill, U.S.A.). The mineral usually gravitates to the zone of the coarse-grained or block pegmatite, where it is found along with microcline (amazonite), biotite, garnet, zircon, and the rare-earth minerals (allanite, yytrialite, rowlandite, fergusonite, etc.). The highest concentrations of gadolinite in pegmatites are usually related to locally pronounced albitization (Kola Peninsula, Baringer Hill, etc.). In places gadolinite is replaced by beryllium tengerite and tengerite (Baringer Hill).

As a great rarity gadolinite occurs in the form of well developed crystals in Alpine veins (Switzerland) in association with quartz, adularia, albite, hematite, chlorite, and xenotime (Parker and Quervain, 1940).

Syanchualite: $Li_2Ca_3[BeSiO_4]_3F_2$

Syanchualite is the beryllium mineral, discovered and investigated in 1957 by the Chinese mineralogists Yun-Hui Huang, Shao-Hua Tu, K'ung-Hai Wang, Ch'un-Lin Chao, and Cheng-Ch'ih Yu.[7]

Physical properties of the mineral, whose transparent polished sections are very similar to garnet, are listed in Table 33. Syanchualite has a relatively high refractive index, and a higher specific gravity, which distinguishes it from the remaining alkaliberyllium minerals.

[6] The degree of covalency and the related bond strength is greater in the complex BO_4^{5-} than in the complex BeO_4^{4-}, which determines the more acidic nature of the boron-oxygen complex compared with the silicon-oxygen one.

[7] Report read at the All-China Geological Conference in 1958. (*Chem. Abst.* 1959, 53, No. 20, 18766d, Ed.)

Table 33 Physical properties of syanchualite

Properties	Characteristic
System	Cubic
Dimensions of unit cell, Å	a_o=12.897
Form of segregation and crystal habit	Idiomorphic crystals of pentagonal-dodecahedral and rhombo-dodecahedral form. Fine-grained masses, spherical segregations
Color	Milky white, colorless
Luster	Glassy
Cleavage	None
Hardness	6.5
Specific gravity	2.97–3.00
Refractive index (N)	1.613

Table 34 Chemical composition of syanchualite

Components	1.				2.			
	%	Atomic quantities of Cations	Atomic quantities of Oxygen	Number of atoms per Si_3	%	Atomic quantities of Cations	Atomic quantities of Oxygen	Number of atoms per Si_3
SiO_2	35.66	604	1208	3	36.64	606	1212	3
CaO	34.60	618	618	3.07	35.18	627	627	3.08
BeO	15.78	630	630	3.13	16.30	650	650	3.2
Li_2O	5.85	393	196	1.95	5.60	378	189	1.85
Al_2O_3	0.50	012	018	—	—	—	—	—
Fe_2O_3	0.22	—	—	—	0.06	—	—	—
MgO	0.18	—	—	—	0.17	—	—	—
Na_2O	0.13	—	—	—	0.03	—	—	—
K_2O	0.06	—	—	—	0.03	—	—	—
F	7.81	—	401	2	7.27	—	382	2.06
	1.28	—	—	—	—	—	—	—
Total	102.07	–	—	—	101.28	—	–	—
$-O = F/_2$	3.2	—	—	—	3.06	—	—	—
	98.87	—	—	—	98.22	—	—	—

[a] Report read at the All-China Geological Conference in 1958

The chemical composition of this mineral corresponds to the empirical formula $Li_2Ca_3Be_3Si_3O_{12}F_2$ (Table 34). The structure of the mineral has not yet been studied. Because of its compositional features, syanchualite possibly belong to the beryllosilicates. If so, its formula might be represented as $Li_2Ca_3[BeSiO_4]_3F_2$ or $Ca_3[BeSiO_4]_3 \cdot (LiF)_2$. However, because of its high refractive index, the mineral is not related to the tectosilicates; thus, pending a special structural investigation, the crystal-chemical formula of syanchualite remains problematic.

ORIGIN AND PARAGENESIS. Syanchualite is a characteristic mineral of the zinnwaldite veins developed among the fluoritized carbonate rocks of the exocontact zone of the beryllium-bearing granitic rock mass in the south of the Chinese People's Republic. In fluoritized limestones at the contact with the syanchualite-zinnwaldite veins, there are developed fluorite-spinel metasomatic rocks that contain chrysoberyl and taaffeite.

Layered berylloaluminosilicates

Bityite–bowelyite–beryllium-margarite group:

$$(Ca,Na)(Li,Mg)_{0.2-0.3}Al_2[(Be,Al)_2Si\,(O.OH,F)_{10}]\,(OH)_2$$

Bityite belongs to the still insufficiently studied beryllium-containing minerals. It was first discovered by Lacroix in the lepidolite-albite pegmatites on Mt. Bity in the Maharitra region, Madagascar, and was described by Lacroix in 1908 (Lacroix, 1908). This paper contains the only analysis of bityite—made by Pisani (Table 36).

H. P. Rowledge and J. D. Hayton (1948) discovered, in the lithium pegmatites of the region of Londonderry, Western Australia, and described as bowleyite a mineral very similar to bityite, from which it differed by a much higher beryllium content.

The possibility of bityite being identical with bowleyite was first indicated by M. Fleischer (1950), who assumed that the beryllium content given for bityite was too low, owing to the inaccuracy of the chemical analysis.

When interpreting the chemical composition of the minerals under consideration, A. I. Ginzburg (1957) demonstrated, by recalculation of the analyses of bityite and bowleyite, that both these minerals belonged to the margarite group. This also is borne out by the usual occurrence of distinctive proportions of beryllium in margarites from various deposits. Notwithstanding the insufficient number of complete analyses of the beryllium-containing margarites, it is apparent that there is a continuous series from the beryllium-margarite, containing 0.5 to 1 percent BeO, to bityite, which contains more than 2 percent BeO.

The physical properties of minerals of the group bityite–bowleyite–beryllium-margarite, as shown in Table 35, point to their almost complete

Table 35 Physical properties of minerals of the beryllium-margarite–bityite–bowleyite group

Properties	Beryllium-margarite	Bityite	Bowleyite
System	Monoclinic (pseudo-hexagonal)	Monoclinic (?) (pseudo-hexagonal)	?
Form of aggregation and crystal habit	Mica-like thin-lamellar formations, more rarely short-prismatic crystals	Fine thin-lamellar crystals of hexagonal habit	Dense mica-like aggregates
Color	Pearly-white to green and brownish	White to yellowish	Brownish-white
Cleavage	Perfect along (001)	Perfect along the pinacoid	Perfect along the pinacoid
Hardness	3.5–5.5	5.5	?
Specific gravity	3.0–3.08	3.05	3.02–3.03
Refractive indices:			
γ	1.635–1.645	1.64	1.66
β	1.630–1.643	1.63	–
α	1.620–1.632	1.62	1.65
Optical sign	(-)	(-)	(-)
Angle of optical axes	Small	Small	Small
Optical orientation	(010)	–	The optic axial plane is almost normal to the plane of the cleavage

analogy. It is still necessary to check the probable increase of the hardiness of these minerals as a function of the beryllium content.

The chemical composition of the minerals of this group is subjected to fairly substantial variations (Table 36). It can be seen from the available analyses and their recalculations (Tables 36, 37) that the relatively constant constituents in the composition of all representatives of this group are calcium + sodium and silicon. At the same time, the Li_2O content varies from 0.47 to 2.61 percent, that of BeO from 1.18 to 8.05 percent, and that of Al_2O_3 from 35.58 to 47.35 percent.

Although not all the available analyses are completely comparable,[8] they yield, after recalculation, a fairly regular picture of the variation in composition of the minerals as a function of the Li:Be:Al ratio. Because all minerals of this group belong to layered silicates and there exists the possibility of compensatory substitution of OH for some oxygen atoms in the beryllium-oxygen tetrahedra; the recalculation was carried out for $O + OH = 12$ (Table 37). The constant number of atoms $Ca + Na = 1$

[8] In analysis 3 it is obvious that F (or water) has not been completely determined; in analysis 6 Li has not been determined (it is included in Na_2O) and water and F have not been determined separately; in analysis 4 the determination of Be raises some doubts. Apparently the most accurate are analyses 1, 2, and 7.

Table 36 Chemical composition of beryllium-margarite, bityite, and bowleyite

Components	Bowleyite, Londonderry (Western Australia)						Beryllium-margarite, Urals			Bityite, Maharitra, Madagascar			Beryllium-margarite, Urals								
	1.			2.			3.			4.			5.			6.			7.		
	%	Atomic quantities of		%	Atomic quantities of		%	Atomic quantities of		%	Atomic quantities of		%	Atomic quantities of		%	Atomic quantities of		%	Atomic quantities of	
		Cations	Oxygen		Cations	Oxygen		Cations	Oxygen		Cations	Oxygen		Cations	Oxygen		Cations	Oxygen		Cations	Oxygen
SiO_2	32.22	537	1074	33.37	555	1110	30.44	507	1014	31.95	532	1064	30.16	502	1004	28.63	476	952	29.84	497	994
Al_2O_3	35.58	698	1047	36.24	710	1065	45.56	896	1344	41.75	818	1227	45.07	884	1326	46.45	912	1368	47.35	929	1393
Fe_2O_3	—	—	—	—	—	—	0.38	006	009	—	—	—	0.13	002	003	0.70	008	012	0.81	010	015
FeO	—	—	—	0.17	002	002	—	—	—	—	—	—	—	—	—	—	—	—	—	—	—
BeO	8.05	322	322	7.30	292	292	3.26	130	130	2.27	091	091	2.40	096	096	1.88	075	075	1.18	047	047
CaO	15.35	274	274	14.42	257	257	13.48	241	241	14.30	255	255	13.18	235	235	12.58	225	225	11.70	209	209
MgO	—	—	—	0.04	—	—	0.67	016	016	0.13	003	003	1.06	026	026	1.84	046	046	1.22	030	030
Na_2O	0.55	018	009	0.29	010	005	0.57	018	009	0.40	012	006	1.08	036	018	2.00[a]	064	032	1.93	062	031
K_2O	0.09	002	001	0.04	—	—	0.25	005	002	0.16	004	002	0.52	010	005	0.86	020	010	0.55	011	005
Li_2O	2.61	174	087	2.39	160	080	0.78	052	026	2.73	182	091	0.72	040	020	—	—	—	0.47	032	016
S	—	—	—	—	—	—	0.11	003	—	—	—	—	—	—	—	—	—	—	—	—	—
Cl	—	—	—	—	—	—	0.20	005	—	—	—	—	0.13	003	—	—	—	—	—	—	—
F	—	—	—	—	—	—	0.36	019	—	—	—	—	1.64	086	—	—	—	—	0.70	—	—
H_2O^+	5.80	644	322	5.72	636	318	3.98	444	222	6.50	361	722	3.80	—	—	—	—	—	4.48	498	249
H_2O^-	—	—	—	—	—	—	0.32	—	—	—	—		0.70	—	—	—	—	—	0.12	—	—
Total	100.25			99.98			100.40[b]			100.19			100.99[c]			100.31[d]			100.35		
—O=$F/_2$							0.20						0.72						0.28		
							100.20						100.27						100.07		
Analyst and source	Hayton (H. P. Rowledge, J. D. Hayton, 1948)						K. A. Vlasov, E. I. Kutukova 1959			Pisani (A. Lacroix, 1908)			K. A. Vlasov, E. I. Kutukova, 1959			From the collection of E. I. Nefedov			V. S. Saltykova		

a. Including Li_2O
b. Including 0.04% BaO
c. Including 0.40% Cr_2O_3
d. Including 5.35% of losses

Table 37 Recalculation of analyses of beryllium-margarite, bityite, and bowleyite for O+OH=12

Components	Number of cation atoms per O + OH = 12						
	1	2	3	4	5	6	7
Ca	1.1	0.98	0.95	1	0.94	0.90	0.83
Na	} 0.08	0.04	0.09	0.02	0.14	0.05[a]	0.25
K		—	0.02	—	0.04	0.08	0.04
Li	0.67	0.61	0.20	0.70	0.15	0.20[a]	0.13
Mg	—	—	0.06	—	0.10	0.18	0.12
$Al^{(VI)}$	1.94	1.98	2.0	1.59	1.91	1.86	1.92
$Al^{(IV)}$	0.70	0.75	1.48	1.59	1.62	1.80	1.83
Be	1.24	1.12	0.52	0.35	0.38	0.30	0.19
Si	2.06	2.13	2	2.06	2	1.90	1.98
Total	7.79	7.61	7.32	7.31	7.28	7.27	7.29
Sum of valencies of cations by groups:							
A (Ca, Na), Li, $Al^{(VI)}$	8.77	8.55	8.32	7.49	8.14	8.07	8.08
B $Al^{(IV)}$, Be, Si	12.82	13.01	13.48	13.71	13.62	13.60	13.79
A+B	21.59	21.56	21.80	21.20	21.76	21.67	21.87

[a] Sodium and lithium in analysis 6 are separated conventionally.

and Si = 2, obtained for all analyzed representatives of the group, confirms the fundamental correctness of the adopted method of recalculation.

It can be seen from these results (Table 37) that beryllium always replaces aluminum, which is in tetrahedral coordination. Yet no relationship is noted between the content of lithium and that of aluminum in octahedral coordination. Consequently, the entry of lithium into the margarite structure apparently cannot be explained by the occurrence of a heterovalent isomorphism between lithium and aluminum. Except bityite, in all recalculated analyses the number of Al^{VI} atoms equals or nearly equals 2, whereas that of Li + Mg atoms varies from 0.25 to 0.70.

The formulae of bowleyite (1,2), bityite (4), and beryllium-margarite (3,5,6,7) are presented as follows:

1. $Ca_{1.18}Li_{0.67}Al_{1.84}[(Be_{1.24}Al_{0.70})Si_2(O,OH)_{10}](OH)_2$
2. $Ca_{1.02}Li_{0.61}Al_{1.98}[(Be_{1.12}Al_{0.75})Si_{2.13}(O,OH)_{10}](OH)_2$
3. $Ca_{1.06}(Li,Mg)_{0.26}Al_2[(Al_{1.48}Be_{0.52})Si_2(O,OH)_{10}](OH)_2$
4. $Ca_{1.02}Li_{0.7}Al_{1.59}[(Al_{1.59}Be_{0.35})]Si_{2.06}(O,OH)_{10}(OH)_2$
5. $Ca_{1.12}(Li,Mg)_{0.25}Al_{1.91}[(Al_{1.62}Be_{0.38})Si_2(O,OH)_{10}](OH)_2$
6. $Ca_{1.03}(Li,Mg)_{0.38}Al_{1.86}[(Al_{1.80}Be_{0.30})Si_{1.90}(O,OH)_{10}](OH)_2$
7. $Ca_{1.2}(Li,Mg)_{0.25}Al_{1.92}[(AL_{1.83}Be_{0.19})Si_{1.98}(O,OH)_{10}](OH)_2$.

The total number of the cation atoms (depending on the content of Li and Mg) in the formula varies from 7.27 to 7.79. The compensation of the isomorphous substitution of Be^{2+} for Al^{3+} can be accomplished in two ways:

1. By the entry into the structure of the mineral of supplementary Li cations in a quantity equivalent to beryllium, that is by the substitution of Be + Li for Al.
2. By the substitution of the OH group, equivalent to beryllium, for a part of the oxygen (substitution of $BeO_3(OH)^{5-}$ for AlO_4^{5-}).

In the former example, the general formula of the minerals should be

$$CaLi_nAl_2[(Be_nAl_{2-n})Si_2O_{10}](OH)_2;$$

in the latter,

$$CaAl_2[Be_nAl_{2-n})Si_2(O_{10-n}OH_n)](OH)_2.$$

On the basis of the analyses, we can say that the combination of both occur in nature. Thus the general formula of the minerals of the group bowleyite–bityite–beryllium-margarite can be represented as follows:

$$(Ca,Na)(Li,Mg)_nAl_2[(Be_mAl_{2-m})Si_2(O,OH)_{10}](OH)_2$$

Here, n = 0.25 to 0.70; m = 0.1 to 1.24; the number of oxygen atoms in the radical is $0_{9.5}$ to $0_{9.9}$, and the corresponding number of the hydroxyl groups in the radical is $(OH)_{0.5}$ to $(OH)_{0.1}$.

The main difference between beryllium-margarite and bityite, on the one hand, and bowleyite, on the other, is the considerably lower beryllium content (1.18 to 3.26 percent BeO compared with 7.30 to 8.05 percent). At the same time, the Li content (2.39 to 2.73 percent Li_2O) in bityite and bowleyite considerably exceeds that in beryllium-margarites[9] (0.47 to 0.78 percent Li_2O).

The simplified formulae of the minerals of this group can be expressed as follows:

Bowleyite: $CaLi_{0.6}Al_2[(Be,Al)_2Si_2(O,OH)_{10}](OH)_2$;
Bityite: $CaLi_{0.7}Al_{1.6}[(Al,Be)_2Si_2(O,OH)_{10}](OH)_2$;
Beryllium-margarite: $(Ca,Na)Li_{0.25}Al_2[(Al,Be)_2Si_2(O,OH)_{10}](OH)_2$.

The structural analogues of bowleyite, bityite, and beryllium-margarite, which do not contain beryllium, are apparently xanthophyllite $Ca(Mg,Al)_{3,2}[Al_2Si_2O_{10}](OH)_2$, and margarite $CaAl_2[Al_2Si_2O_{10}](OH)_2$.

ORIGIN AND PARAGENESIS. Bowleyite and bityite are late minerals of the substitution stage of lithium pegmatites; they form under conditions of relative enrichment of residual solutions in calcium, leached out of the earlier minerals (Ginzburg, 1957).

[9] If the Be content in the analysis of bityite is too low, the divergence between bowleyite and bityite is completely eliminated.

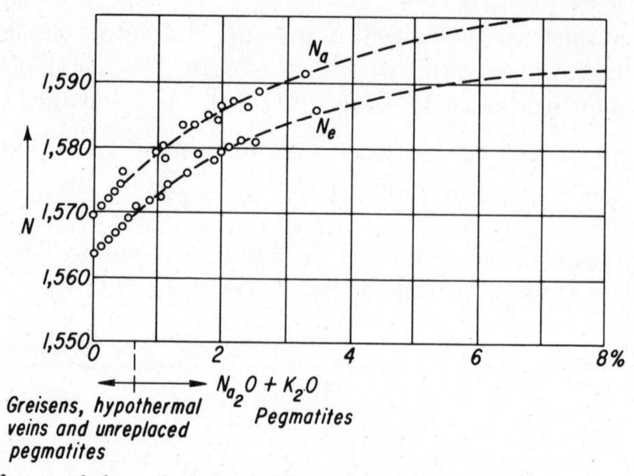

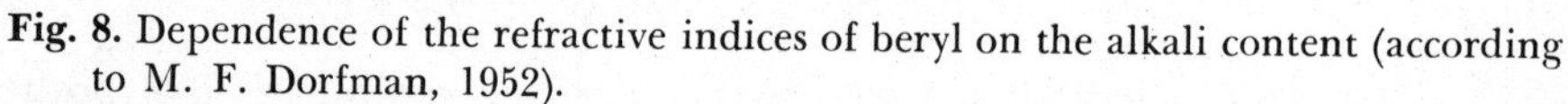

Fig. 8. Dependence of the refractive indices of beryl on the alkali content (according to M. F. Dorfman, 1952).

Late lithium micas, bavenite, and cassiterite are in paragenetic association with bowleyite and bityite. The earlier minerals of the same pegmatites are petalite, alkali beryl, albite, and alkali tourmaline.

Apparently, beryllium-margarite is not characteristic of the normal granitic pegmatites; it is the typical mineral of beryllium-bearing pegmatites of the "crossing line", where it is found in close association with plagioclase, phlogopite, and beryl.

Beryllium silicates

Meta- and dimetasilicates of cyclic structure

Beryl: $Al_2Be_3[Si_6O_{18}]$

Beryl is the most widespread beryllium mineral; it occurs in highly diverse types of deposits. So far it is the only beryllium mineral that is used on a large scale in industry to obtain beryllium and its compounds.

PHYSICAL PROPERTIES. The physical properties of beryl are highly characteristic and provide a clear illustration of a close relationship among the peculiarities of the structure, the chemical composition, and the principal physical properties of the mineral (Fig. 8, 9, Table 38).

Beryl's chemical composition is a metasilicate of beryllium and aluminum with the empirical formula $Al_2Be_3Si_6O_{18}$. Only rarely, however, does the true composition of the mineral correspond to this ideal formula. The usual impurities, which make up a substantial part of the many varieties of beryl, are the alkalies (Na, Li, Cs, Rb, K); of lesser importance are Ca, Mg, Mn, Fe^{2+}, Fe^{3+}, Cr, H_2O, CO_2. Some beryls have a high content of helium and, sometimes, of argon.

Depending on the content and composition of alkalies, four main varieties of beryl may be distinguished:

1. Alkali-free beryl	total	$R_2O \leqslant 0.5$ percent
2. Sodium beryl	total	$R_2O > 0.5$ percent
3. Sodium-lithium beryl	total	$R_2O > 1$ percent
4. Lithium-cesium beryl	total	$R_2O > 1$ percent.

Each of these varieties has specific physical properties that vary regularly, as one passes from one variety to another, with the variation in the alkali content.

CRYSTAL HABIT. The crystal habit of beryl is highly diverse, varying from thin-prismatic to tabular, with gradual transitions between these two extreme varieties (Fig. 10).

The alkali-free beryl and the kindred varieties of sodium beryl have a total R_2O content of less than 0.5 percent, or slightly in excess of this figure; they form crystals of thin-prismatic, long-prismatic, and prismatic

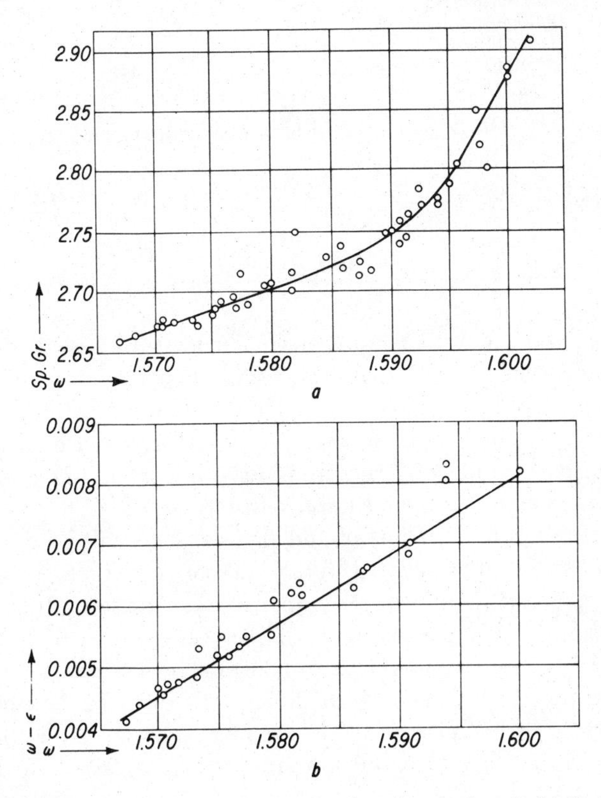

Fig. 9. (a) Relation of specific gravity and refraction in beryl. (b) Relation of birefringence and refringence in beryl.

Table 38 Physical properties of beryl

Properties	Alkali-free beryl, $R_2O < 0.5\%$	Sodium beryl, $R_2O > 0.5\%$	Sodium-lithium beryl, $R_2O > 1\%$	Lithium-cesium beryl, $R_2O > 1\%$
System	Hexagonal	Hexagonal	Hexagonal	Hexagonal
Crystal habit	Well-developed crystals of prismatic, long-prismatic, slender prism-matic habit, sometimes with well-defined cap	Poorly developed crystals of prismatic, truncated-pyr-amidal, coniform habit. Skeletal ("stuffed") crystals	Poorly developed crystals of coniform habit or irregular segregations. Less often short-prismatic, well-developed crystals	Irregular segrega-tions, also short-prismatic to tab-ular crystals
Color	Green, yellow-green—common beryl; greenish-blue to blue—aquamarine; wine-yellow, wine-brownish, golden—heliodor; emerald-green—emerald	Bright-green, yellow-green, yellow	Greenish-white to white, seldom blue	Pink—vorobyevite; colorless—rosterite. Rarely green
Hardness	7.5–8	7–7.5	7–7.5	7–7.5
Specific gravity	For the relationship between specific gravity, refractivity, and birefringence see Figs. 8, 9a, and 9b			
Refractive indices:				
Optical sign	(-)	(-)	(-)	(-)
Optical orientation	–	$c = \alpha$	–	–

habit, the ratio of width to length varying from 1:15 to 1:2. The crystals are usually well-formed; in individual cases, when free growth is possible, they have a pinacoid as a cap and a combination of pyramidal faces. A pinacoid is usually the preponderant face of the crystal cap. Rarely, however, the main part of the cap structure is a group of diverse pyramidal faces, and the cap then becomes very complex in structure.

In pegmatites, the long-prismatic and prismatic crystals of this variety of beryl are usually found as isolated individuals or in pockets; only rarely do they form intergrowths of two (Fig. 10) or more crystals. In general, the crystals in pegmatites are coarse and of prismatic habit, with dimensions exceeding 0.5 × 4 cm. Crystals with dimensions of 5 to 10 × 20 to 30 cm are quite common, and crystals with dimensions of 50 to 80 cm along the long axis and 15 to 20 cm across are not rare. The largest well-developed crystals of alkali-free beryl are more than 1 m across and 5 to 8 m along the axis.

Unlike pegmatites, the pneumatolytic-hydrothermal deposits are characterized by slender-prismatic crystals with dimensions below 0.5 × 4 cm

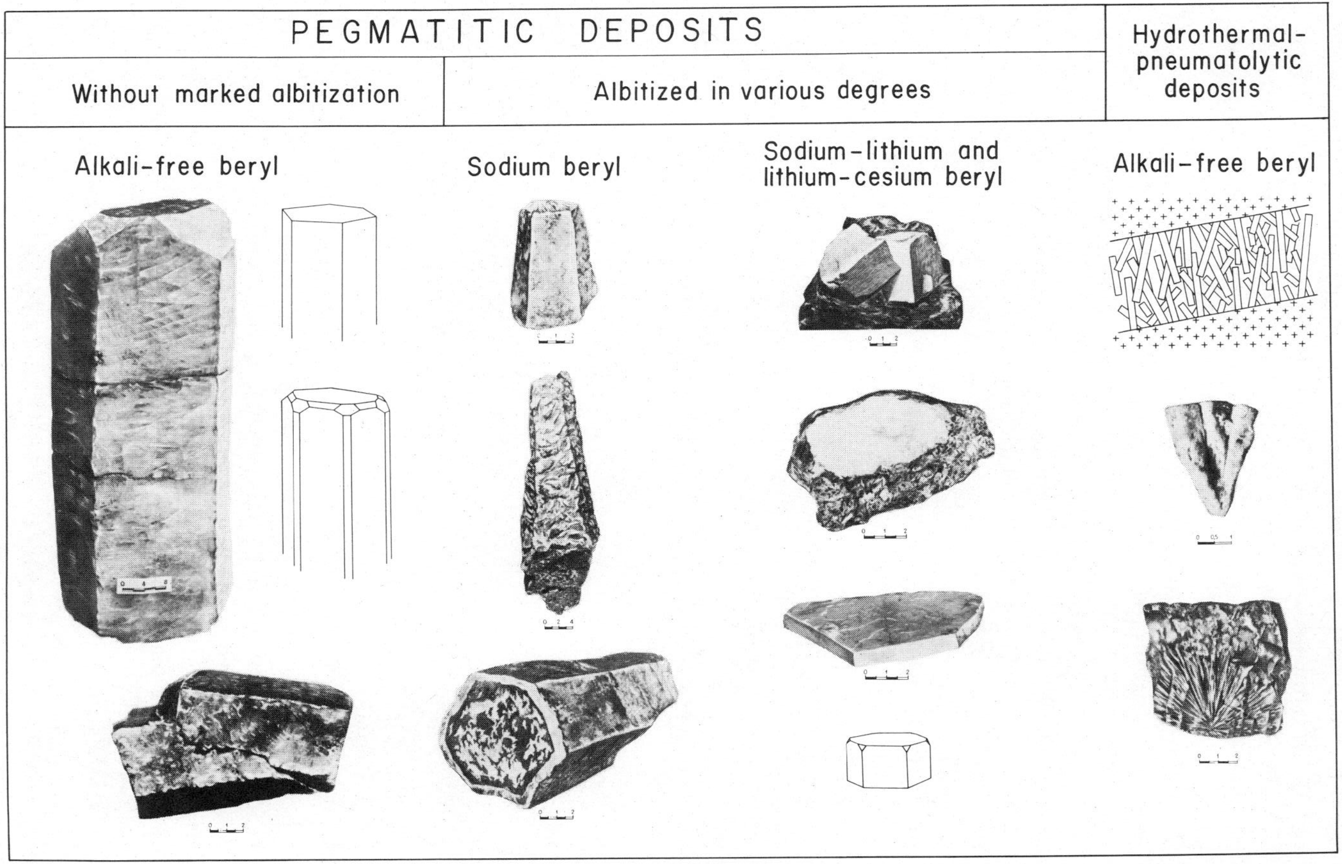

PEGMATITIC DEPOSITS

Without marked albitization

Albitized in various degrees

Hydrothermal-pneumatolytic deposits

Alkali-free beryl

Sodium beryl

Sodium-lithium and lithium-cesium beryl

Alkali-free beryl

Fig. 10. Typomorphic features of beryl crystals. Scale in cm.

(as a rule, larger crystals are very rare). In such deposits, the dimensions of beryl crystals usually are measured in fractions of a centimeter. Deposits of this nature are characterized especially by dense intergrowths of crystals in radiating growths ("beryl stars") (Fig. 10) or dense, even massive, aggregates. The dimensions of crystals vary within very wide limits.

In addition to the usual prismatic crystals, sodium beryl is usually in crystals of a truncated-pyramidal, conical, and the odd "skeleton-like" habit. Unlike the alkali-free beryl, the sodium variety does not form, as a rule, hexagonal crystals with well-defined faces. The crystals of prismatic habit are usually bounded by very uneven faces, which are separated from each other by smoothed, poorly defined edges; or else, on the contrary, they have a ribbed, "fluted" surface. The same applies to the truncated-pyramidal and coniform crystals which, as a rule, have no well-developed faces of the hexagonal prism. The crystals of this variety are usually complex parallel intergrowths of a large number of single crystals, clad in a single crystal form. It is this factor that apparently determines, as a rule, the poor development of faces in the crystals of sodium beryl (fluted surface, etc.). When broken up, such composite crystals produce a series of slender single crystals bounded by irregular faces. Thus, the composite crystals of sodium beryl are actually dense clusters of slender crystals that radiate from one common point or plane (Fig. 11).

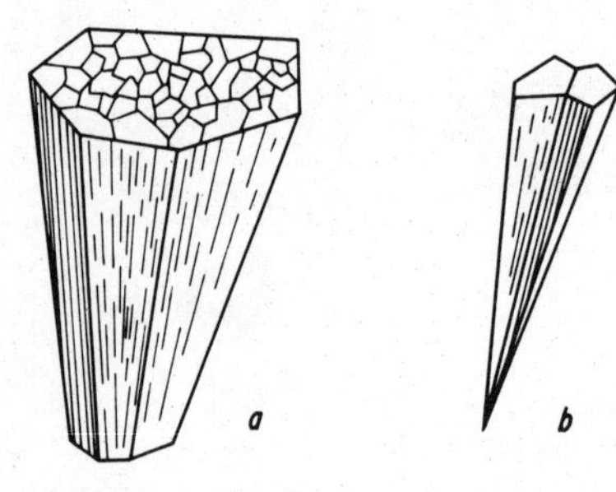

Fig. 11. (a) Composite crystal of sodium beryl with pyramidal habit. (b) Single crystals, formed after the composite crystal has been broken up.

The so called "stuffed" crystals also commonly occur with the massive varieties. The main feature of the crystals is the occurrence of inclusions of albite, quartz, less common muscovite, tourmaline, and microcline, which penetrate into the beryl and in many places form the core of its crystals. In a number of places, such crystals present a thin beryl shell filled with an albite or albite-quartz aggregate. Usually, in the core of the "stuffed" beryl crystals there is the partially albitized, medium-grained pegmatite of apographic structure, which does not differ at all from the pegmatite that surrounds the beryl crystals. If a later albitization is superposed on the crystals of "stuffed" beryl, there occurs the substitution of later saccharoidal albite or cleavelandite for beryl. A change also takes place at the same time in the core of the "stuffed" crystal, which is transformed into an aggregate

Fig. 12. Transverse sections of "stuffed" (skeletal) beryl crystals. (1) Microcline; (2) quartz; (3) muscovite; (4) albite; white beryl.

of saccharoidal albite or cleavelandite, in which muscovite and spessartite inclusions may be dispersed.

As in the case of the dense coniform beryl, the "stuffed" crystals of beryl are complex formations consisting of a series of uniformly oriented, closely intergrown single crystals of a peculiar tabular form, caused by the development of only two opposite prismatic faces which bound the outer and inner surfaces of "stuffed" crystals (Fig. 12).

When large composite crystals are studied in detail, one clearly discerns separate flat crystals that form the shell of "stuffed" beryl. In a number of places, the composite crystals form parallel intergrowths of albite and a series of flat beryl plates bounded on both sides by the lustrous faces of the prism. As a rule, such a skeleton-like aggregate has the form of a hexagonal beryl crystal (Fig. 12).

Fig. 13 shows a large composite crystal of "stuffed" coniform beryl with albitized apographic pegmatite in the core. The crystal is built from a large number of regularly oriented, tabular single crystals, in parallel intergrowth with albite. Very characteristic also are the growths of the "cone in a cone" type, which present two or three hollow conical crystals of beryl,

Fig. 13. Composite "stuffed" crystal of coniform beryl (Altai).

arranged zonally, one inside another, and separated from one another by albite. It is necessary to stress that such hollow cones usually have on the inner side well-developed idiomorphic lustrous faces, and they are peculiar negative crystals.

The dimensions of the sodium beryl crystals also vary within wide limits, as do those of the alkali-free variety. However, usually the dimensions of crystals do not exceed 10 to 15 cm along the axis, and 5 to 6 cm across. The largest known crystal, discovered in the Bumpus mine, Albany county, Maine, U.S.A., had a conical form, was 9 m along the long axis, the transverse dimension being 1.5 m at the base and 0.25 m at the top; it yielded 27 tons of beryllium concentrate.[10]

The sodium-lithium beryls form three crystal types:

1. of coniform habit, without clearly developed faces
2. of an isometric irregular form, without marked crystal outlines
3. well-developed hexagonal crystals, of short-prismatic (to tabular) habit (the width/length ratio varying from 1:1.5 to 1:0.5) with a well-

[10] Largest beryl crystal, *Mineralogist*, 1953, No. 9.

developed pinacoid (the pyramid faces are usually absent or are only rudimentary).

Types 2 and 3 are also characteristic of the lithium-cesium beryl variety. These crystal forms are inherent in this variety, namely tabular to lamellar, the ratio of the width of the crystal to its length along the *c*-axis attaining 15:1.

COLOR. Beryl proper is a colorless mineral. The variegated coloration of its varieties is determined entirely by the admixture of very small quantities of element-chromophores, especially iron. The largest number and variety of colors and hues is found in the alkali-free variety of beryl. The following varieties are distinguished: blue and greenish-blue aquamarine; pale-green, green, and yellowish-green common beryl; yellow, wine-yellow, and golden beryl (the transparent variety being heliodor); bright-green emerald.

The blue, green, and brownish-yellow colorations of beryl are probably caused by the admixture of iron in various degrees of oxidation. The bright-green coloration of emerald is caused by the infinitesimal (only hundredths of one percent) admixture of chromium.

The variations of color that can be observed when heating the beryl (Kurbatov and Kargin, 1927; Grum-Grzhimailo, 1940: Gavrusevich and Sarapulov, 1941; Frondel, 1955) are interesting. The golden and wine-yellow colors are stable only to 250°C. Within the temperature range 250 to 280°C, the color changes to green, and above 280 to 300°C, to blue. The blue varieties are stable up to 1000 to 1025°C; above this temperature beryl becomes cloudy and disintegrates. The intensity of the high-temperature blue coloration of beryl corresponds to the intensity of the initial yellow or green coloration. The chemical investigation of specimens of the typical heliodor showed that all iron in it was present in the trivalent form, whereas most of the iron in blue aquamarine was in ferrous form. It is very possible that the occurrence of all intermediate colors of beryl—greenish-blue, green, and yellow-green—is determined by the quantitative ratio of iron atoms, with a varying degree of oxidation, found in the mineral. Attempts at finding chromophores in beryl other than iron, vanadium, and chromium were fruitless (Frondel, 1955).

Most sodium beryls have pale greenish, bluish-green, and yellowish-green colors, and the intensity usually decreases as the alkali content increases.

The colorless and white varieties of sodium-lithium beryl predominate; sometimes they have a weak bluish or greenish hue. The colorless water-clear, short-prismatic, and tabular crystals of this variety are usually called rosterite. Similar colorless crystals are also characteristic of lithium-cesium beryl. However, the chief feature of the latter variety is the beautiful pink color, apparently caused by a very small addition of manganese in a high degree of oxidation. The pink lithium-cesium beryls are known under the name of vorobyevite or morganite, and, provided the quality of the crystals is suitable, they yield very good material for jewelry. More rare are the green, yellow-green, and yellow lithium-cesium beryls, colored by the admixture of iron.

SPECIFIC GRAVITY AND REFRACTIVE INDICES. The specific gravity and refractive indices of beryl vary regularly, depending on the content of alkalies. The lowest values of specific gravity and refractive indices are found in the alkali-free beryls, the highest in the lithium-cesium beryl (Fig. 8).

However, the relationship of the total alkali content of beryl to its refractive indices and specific gravity is somewhat more complex than is shown in Fig. 9, drawn up on the basis of data obtained by R. Böse (1936). In particular, in regard to specific gravity, it is not only the total alkali content that is important, but also the qualitative composition of the alkalies. For instance, the alkali beryl high in lithium has a specific gravity very close to that of the alkali-free varieties, in some cases, in spite of a high lithium content. At the same time, the occurrence of sodium and, especially, of cesium in the composition of beryl results in a marked increase of specific gravity. The specific gravity of beryl also depends largely on the

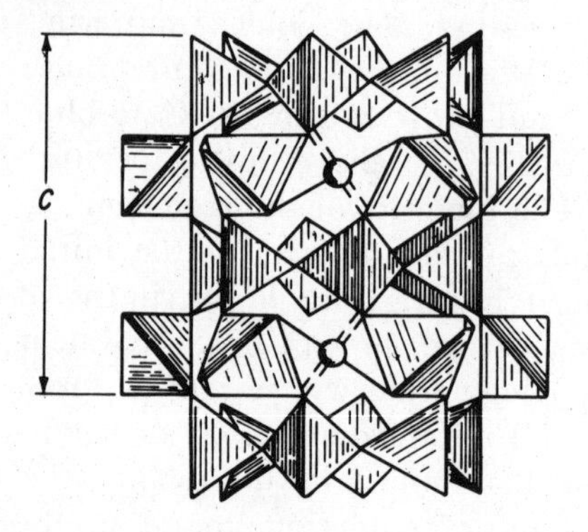

Fig. 14. Vertical projection of beryl structure.

water content of the mineral and on the extent to which the crystals are saturated with gas-liquid inclusions.

The magnitude of the refractive index is determined not only by the alkalies, but also, to a lesser extent, by the iron content and apparently by its degree of oxidation. Thus, for instance, the refractive indices of the wine-brown transparent heliodor, colored with Fe^{3+} and containing no alkalies (Table 39, analysis 1), are $\omega = 1.578$, $\varepsilon = 1.572$, which usually corresponds to a beryl with about 1 percent R_2O.

STRUCTURE. Beryl is the typical representative of the cyclosilicates. The structural patterns of the mineral are determined by the occurrence of

Table 39 Chemical composition of alkali-free beryls from pegmatites with total $R_2O < 0.5\%$ (in percent)

Components	1. Heliodor from a pegmatite cavity, Sinsiang, China	2. Greenish-gray from pegmatite, Kazakh SSSR	3. Bluish from pegmatite, Kazakh SSSR	4. Yellowish-cream from pegmatite, Kazakh SSSR	5. Bluish-green from pegmatite cavity, eastern Siberia	6. Bright green from pegmatite, USSR in Europe	7. Olive green from pegmatite cavity, USSR in Europe	8. Emerald Puuna, Australia	9. Greenish-blue from pneumatolytes, Kazakh SSSR	10. Blue from pneumatolytes, eastern Siberia	11. White from pneumatolytes, Kazakh SSSR	12. Bright green from pneumatolytes, eastern Siberia
SiO_2	64.31	65.48	65.48	65.54	66.49	64.80	65.33	64.42	65.18	64.20	65.20	64.60
BeO	13.98	13.70	13.60	12.38	13.04	13.36	13.90	14.28	14.00	14.26	12.00	13.34
Al_2O_3	18.71	18.46	17.46	19.63	18.08	18.26	17.66	18.03	19.80	20.00	19.10	17.75
Fe_2O_3	0.64	0.80	1.72	0.63	0.40	0.28	0.82	0.05	traces	0.20	0.57	1.37
FeO	none	0.13	0.40	0.13	0.48	0.52	—	traces	—	0.10	—	none
MnO	0.01	traces	none	—	0.02	traces	—	0.19	—	—	—	—
MgO	0.08	0.07	0.11	0.18	—	0.05	0.04	0.52	0.80	0.13	0.11	0.48
CaO	0.18	0.55	0.22	0.46	0.08	0.21	0.56	0.16	0.02	0.46	1.40	0.45
Na_2O	traces	0.07	0.14	0.15	0.22	0.46	0.23	0.48	—	—		
Li_2O	—	—	—	—	—	traces	—	traces	—	—	} 0.46	0.41
K_2O	—	0.27	0.20	0.36	—	0.04	0.25	0.14	—	—		0.25
Cs_2O	—	—	—	—	—	traces	—	—	—	—	—	—
H_2O^+	2.22	0.42	0.16	0.36	1.04	1.85	1.20	1.60	0.80	1.05	0.57	not. det.
P. p. p.	—	—	—	—	—	—	—	—	0.90	1.20	—	1.75
Total	100.13[a]	99.95	99.49	99.82	99.92	99.70[b]	100.80	100.53[c]	99.97[c]	100.42	99.41	100.4
Analyst or source	S. N. Fedorchuk	A. I. Ponomarev			From the collection of G. A. Topunova	Yu. K. Knipovich	S. N. Fedorchuk	E. Simpson (1948)	V. S. Saltykova	V. S. Saltykova	V. S. Saltykova	From the collection of M. M. Povilaitis

Including:
a. TiO_2 —0.03%;
b. Cl —0.02%; SO_3— traces; H_2O^-—0.04%;
c. Cr_2O_3—0.23%;
V_2O_3 —0.09%.

$[Si_6O_{18}]$ rings, which are united by the Be and Al ions arranged between the rings. In the vertical projection, the layers of the beryllium-oxygen tetrahedra and the aluminum ions, arranged in octahedral coordination, alternate with the layers of silicon-oxygen rings $[Si_6O_{18}]$ (Fig. 14). The latter, disposed one on top of the other, from hollow channels with a radius of 2.55 Å, highly characteristic of the beryl structure.

If we consider the beryllium-oxygen tetrahedra to be equivalent to the silicon-oxygen tetrahedra, the structure of beryl is either a tecto-structure $O/(Si + Be) = 2$, or a tectocyclo structure.

The dimensions of the elementary cell of alkali-free beryl are $a_0 =$ 9.21 Å, $c_0 =$ 9.17 Å. When alkalies enter into the structure of beryl, the above parameters change but very little; the "*c*" parameter increases as the alkali content rises to as much as 9.23 with 4.13 percent Cs_2O, 2.50 percent Na_2O, and 0.60 percent Li_2O, according to T. A. Sosedko, (1957), whereas the "*a*" parameter either-remains constant or has a tendency to decrease. The change of the *c*:*a* ratio (from 0.9966 for the alkali-free beryl varieties to 1.0030 for the lithium-cesium beryls) is apparently the main cause of the change in the crystal habit of beryl as a function of the alkali content.

CHEMICAL COMPOSITION. The chemical composition of beryl is usually represented by the structural formula $Al_2Be_3[Si_6O_{18}]$. The elementary cell of the mineral contains $2Al_2Be_3[Si_6O_{18}]$.

Numerous analyses (Tables 39, 40, 41) have shown that the maximum content of the sum of the oxides of alkali metals in the composition of beryls attains 7.23 (Table 41, analysis 38), whereas the maximum number of atoms of alkali metals per Si_6, depending on the Na:Li:Cs ratio, attains $R_{1.3}^{1+}$ (A. I. Ginzburg, 1955a). In the alkali varieties of beryl, the Na_2O content varies from 0.5 to 2.74 percent ($Na_{0.5}$ per Si_6), Li_2O from traces to 2 percent ($Li_{0.75}$ per Si_6), and Cs_2O from O to 4.13 percent ($Cs_{0.16}$ per Si_6).

The occurrence of noticeable concentrations of potassium and rubidium is not characteristic of alkali beryl. The detailed analysis of the ratio of various alkali elements in beryl (Table 42) enables one to draw the conclusion that the occurrence of potassium is most characteristic of the alkali-free beryl varieties which contain less than 0.5 percent of the total R_2O. Rubidium is not generally recorded in the analyses of beryl. An exception is the analysis of pink beryl from Maharitra, Madagascar, which contains 1.34 percent Rb_2O (Doelter, 1914–1925), and the white beryl from the Turkestan range, containing 1.09 percent Rb_2O (Table 41, analysis 32). The special investigation of the occurrence of rubidium in beryl, carried out by L. I. Sazhina and A. A. Sitnin (1954), showed that its content in various types of beryl varies from 0.001 percent (in the alkali-free varieties) to 0.13 percent (in the lithium-cesium beryl from Sin'tszyan).

The natural grouping of beryls as a function of the ratio of atomic quantities of the alkalies is shown in the tetrahedral diagram (Fig. 15).

Table 40 Chemical composition of sodium beryls from pegmatites, $R_2O > 0.5\%$ (in percent)

Components	13. Pale blue, China	14. Greenish-blue, China	15.	16. Pale green, China	17. Bright yellow, China	18. Bluish-green, China	19. Light green, Urals	20. Yellowish pink, eastern Siberia	21. USSR in Europe	22. Yellow, Central Asia	23. Light green, China	24. Yellowish-green, China	25. Pink, China	26. White, China
SiO_2	65.40	64.70	64.34	64.00	64.60	64.40	64.99	63.64	65.32	65.50	66.36	64.16	63.81	62.73
BeO	13.80	13.80	13.64	13.32	13.24	12.78	13.83	13.32	12.64	13.34	13.46	12.48	12.40	12.06
Al_2O_3	18.62	17.74	17.88	17.94	18.21	18.52	18.38	20.61	17.77	17.95	17.94	17.84	18.70	17.57
Fe_2O_3	0.22	0.40	0.75	0.74	0.63	0.35	0.23	0.13	0.13	} 1.30	} 0.35	0.84	0.20	0.48
FeO	—	—	—	—	—	—	—	—	—			—	—	—
MnO	0.03	0.05	—	—	—	—	—	0.03	—	0.03	—	tr	0.10	—
MgO	0.16	0.06	0.23	0.21	0.13	0.13	—	0.16	0.25	0.15	0.20	0.21	0.28	0.24
CaO	0.20	0.15	0.12	0.76	0.40	0.20	0.40	tr	0.26	0.24	0.26	0.28	0.55	0.61
Na_2O	0.64	0.69	0.70	0.82	0.86	0.91	1.16	1.18	1.27	1.32	1.45	1.54	1.51	2.74
Li_2O	0.04	0.09	0.14	—	—	0.26	0.30	0.45	0.30	—	—	0.36	0.40	0.40
K_2O	}					0.05	—	0.11	—	—	—	}	}	}
Rb_2O	} 0.34	1.35	0.08	—	—	—	—	—	—	—	—	} 0.19	} 1.04	} 0.47
Cs_2O	}		—	—	—	—	—	nil	0.27	—	—	}	}	}
TiO_2	—	—	0.01	—	—	0.01	—	—	—	—	—	0.01	—	0.05
H_2O^+	0.65	1.20	2.02	2.00	1.94	2.38	0.90	0.29	1.76	0.20	0.15	2.30	0.84	2.59
H_2O^-	0.09	0.07	—	—	—	—	—	—	—	—	—	—	0.09	—
Total	100.19	100.30	99.91	99.79	100.01	99.99	100.19	99.92	100.02	100.03	100.17	100.21	99.92	99.94
Analyst or source	M.E. Kazakova		S.N. Fedorchuk				M.E. Kazakova	V.S. Saltykova	E.H. Egorova	From the collection of Ibadullaev		S.N. Fedorchuk	M.E. Kazakova	S.N. Fedorchuk

Table 41 Chemical composition of sodium-lithium and lithium-cesium beryls from pegmatites, $R_2O > 1\%$ (in percent)

Components	27. Smoky, China	28. Yellowish-green, Central Asia	29. Pink, USSR in Europe	30. Light green, USSR in Europe	31. Water-clear, China	32. White, Central Asia	33. Colorless, Kazakh SSR	34. USSR in Europe	35. Pink transparent, China	36. White, China	37. Pink, Urals	38. Pink, USSR in Europe
SiO_2	65.08	66.39	63.55	62.66	63.60	65.74	62.62	64.17	62.76	64.46	62.84	61.68
BeO	13.00	12.20	11.35	11.93	11.74	12.96	12.80	11.82	12.66	11.84	11.45	10.54
Al_2O_3	18.44	17.74	19.17	16.77	18.53	16.79	20.03	17.42	19.75	18.36	18.34	17.10
Fe_2O_3	0.25	0.94	} 0.35	1.39	0.16		0.07	0.12	0.06	0.27	trace	0.08
FeO	—	—		—	—	0.19	—	—	—	—	—	—
MnO	0.04	trace	—	trace	none	0.03	trace	—	0.05	0.04	0.04	—
MgO	0.10	—	—	0.20	0.07	0.02	trace	0.21	trace	0.06	0.24	0.22
CaO	0.15	0.63	0.17	0.43	0.18	0.71	0.07	0.44	trace	0.30	—	0.44
Na_2O	0.98	1.27	1.25	2.42	2.43	0.07	1.18	1.39	1.27	1.44	trace	2.50
Li_2O	0.36	0.77	1.08	0.68	0.78	0.66	0.63	1.23	0.83	0.54	1.39	0.60
K_2O	—	—				0.05	—	—	—		—	—
Rb_2O	} 1.12	—	} 0.25	} 0.67	} 0.44	1.09	—	—	—	} 1.66	—	—
Cs_2O		—				—	0.92	0.67	1.14		3.10	4.13
TiO_2	—	—	—	—	0.02	0.05	—	0.01	—	—	—	0.01
H_2O-	0.70	0.21	2.52	2.34	2.44	2.44	1.45	1.88	1.35	1.00	1.92	2.26
H_2O-	0.08	0.08	0.05	—	—	0.04	—	0.60	—	0.08	—	0.16
P. p. p.	—	—	—	—	—	—	2.54	—	2.40	—	—	—
Total	100.30	100.23	99.99	99.53	100.37	100.80	99.77	99.96	99.87	100.05	99.32	99.92
Analyst or source	M. E. Kazakova	V. V. Shibaeva	M. I. Volkova	S. N. Fedorchuk	S. N. Fedorchuk	A. F. Fioletova (M. F. Strelkin, 1938)	S. Saltykova	E. N. Egorova	V. S. Saltykova	M. V. Kazakova	K. E. Nenadkevich (1911)	E. N. Egorova

When analyzing the problem of the location of the alkali metal atoms in the structure of beryl, A. I. Ginzburg (1955a) criticizes correctly the assumption of A. G. Betekhtin (1950), who thought that the entry of cesium into the structure of beryl is associated with the parallel substitution of the corresponding part of silicon with aluminum in tetrahedral coordination, and who suggested the formula $CsBe_3Al_2[Si_5AlO_{18}]$ for vorobyevite. Taking into consideration that the proportion of alkalies increases, Ginzburg concludes that the entry of alkali metals into the beryl structure is caused by the substitution of $2R^{1+}$ for beryllium, where R^{1+} = Na, Li, K, and Cs. The replacement of one small beryllium atom by two large ions of alkali elements becomes possible, according to Ginzburg, owing to the presence in the beryl structure of hollow channels with a radius of 2.55Å. In this case, the chemical formula of beryl should be

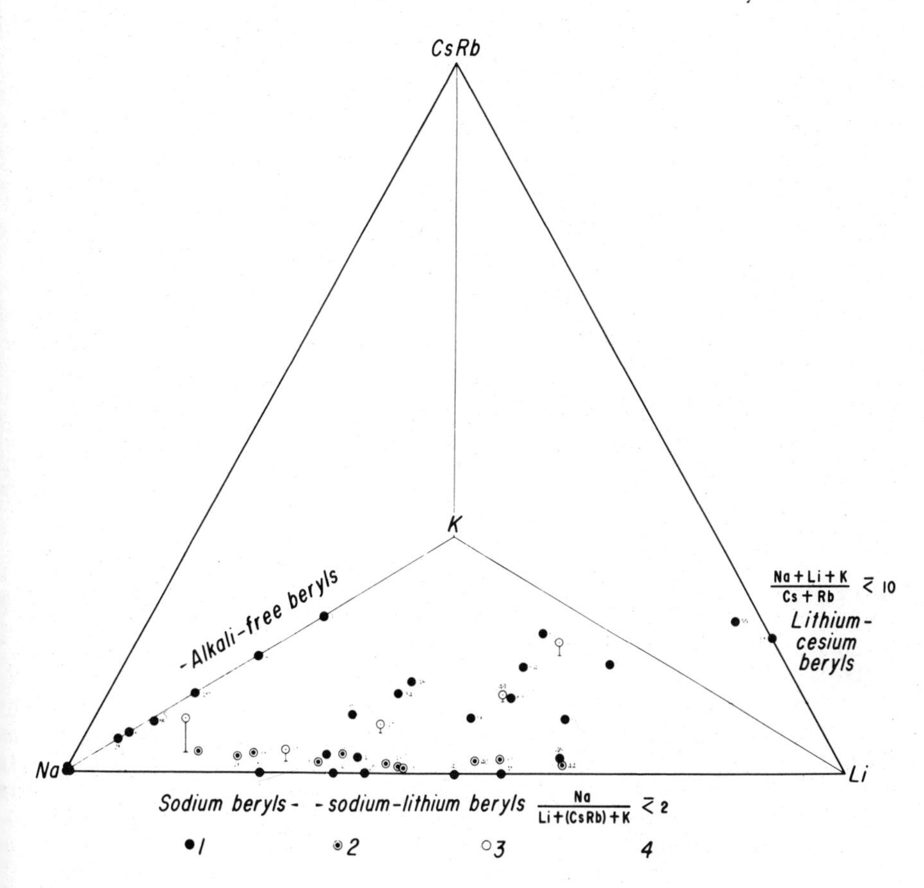

Fig. 15. Diagram of the ratio of the number of atoms of alkali metals [Na, li, (Cs, Rb), and K] in beryl. (1) Points disposed on the plane Na-Li-(Cs, Rb) (base of the tetrahedron); (2) projection of points disposed on the faces of the tetrahedron; (3) projection of points disposed inside the tetrahedron; (4) vector showing the relative K content. Numbers in the diagram correspond to analyses in Table 42.

Table 42 Chemical composition of beryls

No. of analysis	Locality	Color of Beryl	R_I		
			K	Na	Li
			Alkaline bery[illegible]		
1 (9)[a]	Kazakhstan	Greenish-blue	—	—	—
2 (10)	Eastern Siberia	Blue	—	—	—
3 (11)	Kazakhstan	White	—	0.08	—
4 (12)	Eastern Siberia	Light-green	0.03	0.06	—
5	Muso, Colombia	Emerald	—	0.08	—
			Alkali-fr[illegible]		
6 (1)	Sinsiang, China	Heliodor	—	—	—
7 (3)	Kazakhstan	Greenish-gray	0.03	—	—
8 (3)	Kazakhstan	Bluish	0.02	0.02	—
9 (4)	Kazakhstan	Yellowish-creamy	0.04	0.02	—
10 (5)	Eastern Siberia	Bluish-green	—	0.03	—
11 (6)	Eastern Siberia	Light-green	—	0.08	—
12 (7)	USSR in Europe	Olive-green	0.02	0.04	—
13	North Milford, U.S.A.		—	0.09	0.0[illegible]
14	Stoneham, Maine, U.S.A.	Light-green	—	0.10	—
15	Tsilaisina, Madagascar	Pink	0.02	0.10	—
			Sodi[illegible]		
16 (13)	China	Pale-blue	—	0.11	0.0[illegible]
17 (14)	China	Greenish-blue	—	0.12	0.0[illegible]
18 (15)	China	Light-green	0.01	0.13	0.0[illegible]
19 (16)	China	Light-green	—	0.15	—
20 (17)	China	Light-yellow	—	0.16	—
21	East Cresciano, Alps	Aquamarine	0.03	0.19	—
22	Willimantic, Connecticut, U.S.A.	Water-clear	0.01	0.13	0.0[illegible]
23 (22)	Central Asia	Yellow	—	0.23	—
24 (23)	Central Asia	Light-green	—	0.25	—
25 (18)	China	Bluish-green	—	0.16	0.1[illegible]
26	Bob Ingersoll, S. Dakota, U.S.A.	Water-clear	0.02	0.20	0.0[illegible]
27	Varutrask, Sweden	Colorless	0.04	0.22	0.0[illegible]
28 (19)	Urals, USSR	Light-green	—	0.21	0.1[illegible]
29	Madagascar	Aquamarine	0.03	0.21	0.1[illegible]
30	Madagascar	Aquamarine	0.03	0.25	0.0[illegible]
31 (20)	Eastern Siberia	Yellowish-pink	0.01	0.21	0.1[illegible]
32	San Diego, California, U.S.A.		0.02	0.13	0.1[illegible]

+Rb	Total	R_2 Fe	Mg	Ca	Total	Be	Al+ Fe^{3+}	O	H_2O	Analyst or source
n greisens and hydrothermal veins										
–	—	—	—	—	—	3.1	2.14	18.3	0.2	V. S. Saltykova
–	—	—	—	—	0.06	3.2	2.23	18.4	0.3	V. S. Saltykova
–	0.08	—	—	0.16	0.16	2.65	2.39	18.0	0.2	V. S. Saltykova
–	0.09	—	0.06	0.05	0.11	2.9	2.0	18.2	0.5	From the collection of M. M. Povilaitis
–	0.08	—	0.1	0.07	0.17	2.9	1.9	18.0	0.5	Zambonini
ls from pegmatites										
–	—	—	—	0.03	0.03	3.15	2.1	18.3	0.19	S. N. Fedorchuk
–	0.03	—	—	0.05	0.05	3.01	2.04	18.1	0.12	A. Ponomarev
–	0.04	0.03	0.02	0.02	0.07	2.99	2.0	18.1	0.05	A. Ponomarev
–	0.06	—	0.03	0.04	0.07	2.72	2.13	18.0	0.11	A. Ponomarev
–	0.03	0.04	—	—	0.04	2.83	1.97	17.9	0.3	From the collection of G. A. Topunova
–	0.08	0.04	—	0.02	0.06	2.97	2.01	18.1	0.6	Yu. N. Knipovich
–	0.06	—	—	0.06	0.06	3.03	1.98	18.1	0.37	S. N. Fedorchuk
–	0.12	—	—	—	—	2.9	1.93	18.0	0.7	C. Doelter (1914-1925)
–	0.10	0.03	—	—	0.03	3.0	1.94	18.0	0.6	C. Doelter (1914-1925)
–	0.12	—	—	—	—	3.0	2.00	18.0	0.6	C. Doelter (1914-1925)
ls from pegmatites										
01	0,13	—	0.02	0.02	0.04	3,04	2.02	18.2	0.2	M. E. Kazakova
05	0.20	—	—	0.02	0.02	2.8	1.97	18.1	0.4	M. E. Kazakova
–	0.20	—	0.03	0.01	0.04	3.05	2.1	18.2	0.6	S. N. Fedorchuk
–	0.15	—	0.03	0.08	0.11	2.99	2.03	18.2	0.6	S. N. Fedorchuk
–	0.16	—	0.02	0.04	0.06	2.95	2.01	18.0	0.6	S. N. Fedorchuk
–	0.22	—	0.04	0.02	0.06	2.86	2.0	18.0	0.5	J. Jakob (1938)
–	0.23	0.02	—	—	0.02	2.87	1.94	18.0	0.6	C. Doelter (1914-1925)
–	0.23	—	0.02	0.02	0.04	2.94	2.02	17.9	0.06	Ibadullaev
–	0.25	—	0.03	0.03	0.06	2.93	1.93	18.0	0.06(?)	Ibadullaev
–	0,26	—	0.02	0.02	0.04	2.86	2.06	18.1	0.7	S. N. Fedorchuk
–	0.27	—	—	—	—	2.85	2.0	18.0	0.6	J. Jakob (1938)
01	0.29	—	—	—	—	2.9	2.0	18.2	0.5	Quensel
–	0.32	—	—	0.04	0.04	3.06	2.01	18.3	0.3	M. E. Kazakova
–	0.35	—	—	—	—	3.1	1.96	18.0	0.5	C. Doelter (1914-1925)
–	0.32	—	—	—	—	3.0	2.06	18.4	0.5	C. Doelter (1914-1925)
–	0.38	—	0.02	—	0.02	2.98	2.29	18.6	0.1	V. S. Saltykova
–	0.32	—	—	—	—	2.97	1.94	18.0	0.6	C. Doelter (1914-1925)

No. of Analysis	Locality	Color of Beryl	R_1	
			K	Na
33 (21)	USSR in Europe	—	—	0.22
34 (27)	China	Smoky	—	0.18
35 (25)	China	Pink	—	0.27
36 (24)	China	Yellowish-green	0.02	0.28
37	Varutrask, Sweden	Milky-white	0.02	0.35
38 (26)	China	White	0.06	0.50
			Sodium-li	
39 (32)	Central Asia	White	—	0.01
40	W. Innitara, Western Australia	Light-green, transparent	0.02	0.16
41 (28)	Central Asia	Yellowish-green	—	0.22
42	Branchville, Connecticut, U. S. A.		—	0.26
43	Eastern Siberia	Light-green, transparent	0.02	0.35
44 (29)	USSR in Europe	Pink	0.02	0.22
45 (30)	USSR in Europe	Light-green	—	0.45
46 (34)	USSR in Europe	Rosterite	—	0.26
47 (31)	China	Water-clear	0.02	0.44
48 (36)	China	White	—	0.26
49	Norway, Maine, U. S. A.	Vorobyevite	0.01	0.21
50	Madagascar	Vorobyevite	—	0.27
51 (37)	Urals	Vorobyevite	—	—
52 (38)	USSR in Europe	Pink	—	0.22
53	Alto do Giz, Brazil	Vorobyevite	0.04	0.18
54	Mina Geraes, Brazil	Cobalt-blue	—	0.24
55	Hebron, Maine, U. S. A.	Rosterite	—	0.21
56	East Kazakhstan	White	—	0.18
57	China	Pink, transparent	—	0.23

[a] Numbers in brackets refer to numbers of analyses in Tables 39-41.

$R_n^{1+}Be_{1\frac{1}{2}n}Al_2[Si_6O_{18}]pH_2O$, where n = 0-1 and p = 0.2-0.8. Taking into account the structural similarity between beryl and milarite, established by N. V. Belov and N. V. Tarkhova (1951), Ginzburg correctly infers that the most probable location of the large alkali atoms in beryl is in the hollow channels, characteristic of the structure of beryl.

It should be especially pointed out that a number of difficulties are encountered in the recalculation of the analyses of alkali beryl; they are caused primarily by the difficulty of accurate determination of each alkali and the complete separation of beryllium from aluminum in the process of the chemical analysis of beryl. The accuracy of the formula is particularly affected by the completeness of analytical separation of beryllium from aluminum, since a slight excess or deficiency of aluminum, compared with the true figure, causes a marked change in the atom number of

		R_2					$Al+$	O	H_2O	Analyst or source
Cs+Rb	Total	Fe	Mg	Ca	Total	Be	Fe^{3+}			
0.01	0.34	—	0.03	0.02	0.05	2.79	1.94	17.9	0.5	E. N. Egorova
0.04	0.35	—	0.02	0.02	0.04	2.87	2.02	18.1	0.2	M. E. Kazakova
0.04	0.46	—	0.04	0.06	0.10	2.8	2.08	18.2	0.3	M. E. Kazakova
—	0.43	—	0.03	0.03	0.06	2.80	2.02	18.1	0.7	S. N. Fedorchuk
0.01	0.51	—	—	—	—	2.94	2.07	18.2	0.6	Quensel
—	0.70	—	0.03	0.06	0.09	2.77	2.0	18.2	0.8	S. N. Fedorchuk
nd lithium-cesium beryls										
0.07	0.32	—	0.07	—	0.07	2.85	1.81	17.8	0.7	A. F. Fioletova (M. F. Strelkin, 1938)
—	0.36	—	0.01	—	0.01	2.9	1.93	18.0	0.8	Norrish
—	0.50	—	—	0.06	0.06	2.65	1.96	18.0	0.06	V. V. Shibaeva
—	0.52	0.03	—	—	0.03	2.20	2.18	17.8	0.8	C. Doelter (1914-1925)
—	0.63	—	0.05	—	0.05	2.73	2.3	18.6	?	V. S. Saltykova
—	0.64	—	—	0.02	0.02	2.52	2.10	18.0	0.8	M. I. Volkova
0.02	0.73	—	0.03	0.05	0.08	2.75	2.0	18.2	0.75	S. N. Fedorchuk
0.02	0.74	—	0.03	0.04	0.07	2.65	2.1	18.4	0.6	E. N. Egorova
0.05	0.80	—	0.01	0.02	0.03	2.66	2.07	18.19	0.75	S. N. Fedorchuk
0.07	0.53	—	0.01	0.03	0.04	2.64	2.03	18.0	0.3	M. E. Kazakova
0.06	0.56	0.01	—	—	0.01	2.72	1.97	18.2	0.7	C. Doelter (1914-1925)
0.07	0.86	—	—	—	—	2.6	2.0	18.3	0.8	C. Doelter (1914-1925)
0.12	0.62	—	0.03	—	0.03	2.6	2.0	18.1	0.6	N. A. Nenadkevich (1911)
0.16	0.78	—	—	0.01	0.01	2.6	2.1	17.8	0.8	E. N. Egorova
0.12	0.71	—	—	—	—	2.51	2.11	18.0	0.6	P. F. Kerr (1946)
0.11	0.72	—	0.03	0.02	0.05	2.62	2.07	17.7	0.7	V. Robling
0.15	0.95	—	—	—	—	2.56	1.99	18.4	0.6	C. Doelter (1914-1925)
0.01	0.38	—	—	—	—	2.72	2.24	18.3	0.4	V. S. Saltykova
0.05	0.60	—	—	—	—	2.90	2.22	18.5	0.4	V. S. Saltykova

oxygen, which deviates from 18 one way or another.

A part of the alkalies determined during the chemical analysis of beryl does not enter into the structure of beryl, but is a component of the gas-liquid inclusions, which are very characteristic of the alkali beryl varieties. It is very difficult to establish the quantitative value of this part in the sum total of alkalies determined analytically. However, if one takes into account that, in the gas-liquid inclusions, the alkali elements occur, as a rule, in the form of halogen compounds, it is hardly correct to take O_{18} as the basis for the recalculation of the formula as, in this case, there must be some (apparently rather small) excess of oxygen, which is equivalent to the amount of alkali metals, present as halogen compounds in the gas-liquid inclusions. Therefore, when recalculating the analyses of beryl, the author gave up the principle of calculating the formula for O_{18}, suggested by A. I. Ginzburg (1955a). When calculating, the constant magnitude he adopted was the number of silicon atoms Si_6, since variations of this quantity are the smallest, regardless of the method of calculation. Similarly, the probability of error in the determination of silica during the chemical analysis of beryl is also slight.

The results of recalculation of 57 analyses of beryl to Si_6, listed in Table 42, show that the excess of oxygen in the formula (compared with O_{18}), varying from 18.1 to 18.6, is most characteristic of the alkali beryl varieties, which usually are richer in gas-liquid inclusions. At the same time, such deviation from the standard in a number of cases points also to an inaccurate analysis; the inaccuracy was, in most cases, due to error in the determination of beryllium or aluminum.

When analyzing, in the light of the data obtained from recalculation, the probable location of the alkali elements in the structure of beryl, one should note that the way in which A. I. Ginzburg treats the essence of this phenomenon evokes one serious criticism. The replacement of one single beryllium atom in tetrahedral coordination by two larger atoms of alkali metals, for which the tetrahedral coordination is absolutely impossible, is very improbable. The statistical relationship observed in this case cannot at all be considered to give the real picture of changes which take place in the beryl structure as a result of the entry of alkali metal atoms.

It seems probable that the solution to the problem of the structural location of alkali atoms in beryl can be found in the structural analogy between beryl and milarite, established by N. V. Belov and T. N. Tarkhova (1951):

Beryl: $Al_2^{(VI)}Be_3^{(IV)}[Si_6O_{18}]$
Milarite: $KCa_2^{(VI)}(Be,Al)_3^{(IV)}[Si_{12}O_{30}]$.

From the crystal-chemical standpoint, it is difficult to find a satisfactory explanation that would justify putting into one group such diverse elements as Be, Li, and Na.

Yet, if one takes into account the structural features of alkali aluminosilicates, it is wholly justifiable to assume that the entry into the beryl molecule of the alkali metals having a low electronegativity will cause the transition of a part of aluminum into tetrahedral coordination. This part of the aluminum can in this instance replace beryllium; then the framework of beryl, built of cation-oxygen tetrahedra

$$(BeAl)_3^{(IV)}Si_6^{(VI)}O_{18}\left(\frac{O}{Be + Al + Si}\right) = 2,$$

will be always preserved.

At the same time, alkali elements, such as lithium, can enter perfectly into the beryl structure in lieu of aluminum, which is in octahedral coordination. Besides, some of the larger atoms of alkali metals (including

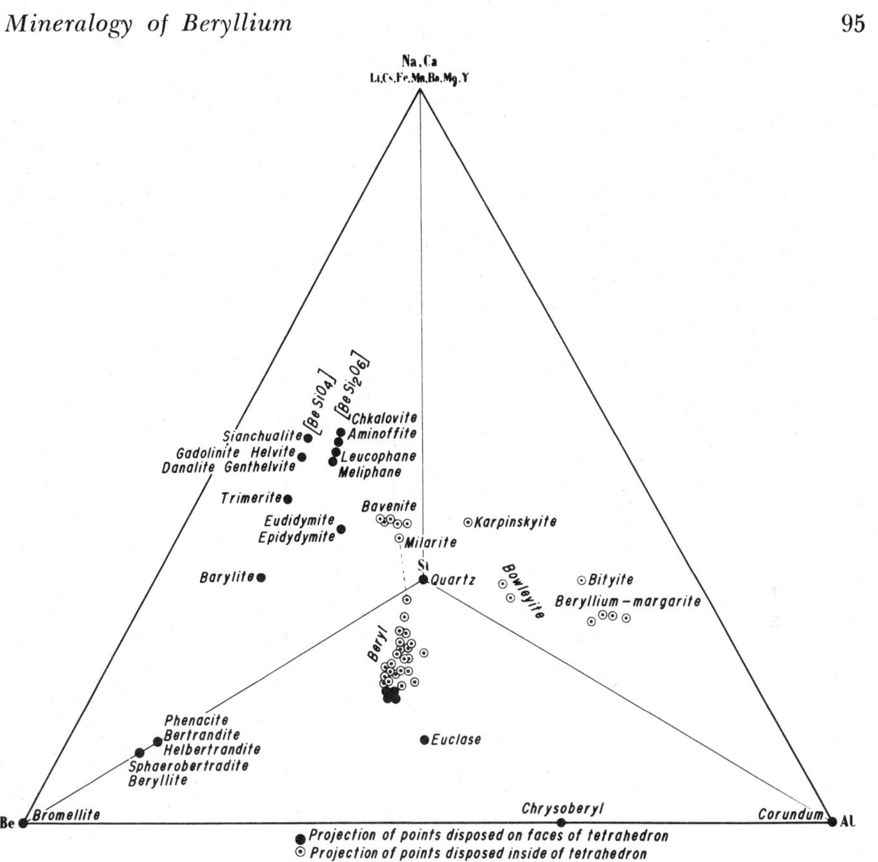

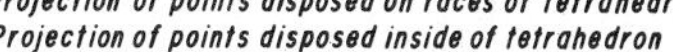

Fig. 16. Diagram of chemical composition of natural beryllium silicates.

cesium) can—by analogy with potassium in milarite—be held in the hollow channels of the hexagonal lattice of beryl.

Such isomorphism can be represented diagrammatically as follows:

$$Al^{(VI)3+} + Be^{(IV)2+} \leftarrow 2R^{1+} + Al^{(IV)3+}.$$

The number of atoms in the cation part of the formula should then increase, as the alkali content increases, because of the alkali metal atoms arranged in the channels; the increase is from 5 to 5.5 (in milarite this number is 6).

It can be seen from the diagram (Fig. 16) that the points representing the composition of beryl shift towards milarite, as the alkali content increases.

The observed isomorphism is fully satisfied by the general beryl formula suggested by A. I. Ginzburg:

$$R_n^{1+}Al_2Be_{3-\frac{1}{2}n}[Si_6O_{18}]pH_2O$$
$$n = 0\text{–}1;\ p = 0.2\text{–}0.8.$$

The expanded crystal-chemical formula of beryl can be represented as follows:

$$R_n^{1+}(Al_{2-n}R_n^{1+})^{(VI)}(Be_{3-n}Al_n)^{(IV)}Si_6O_{18}(0.1\text{-}0.8)H_2O$$

where n varies between 0 and 0.05.

The suggested formula can be illustrated by the most accurate analyses of alkali beryls from various deposits, carried out mostly on transparent crystals without impurities:[11]

55. $(Na,Li,Cs)_{0.50}(Al_{1.55}Li_{0.45})(Be_{2.56}Al_{0.44})[Si_6O_{18}] \cdot 0.6H_2O$.
54. $(Na,Li,Cs)_{0.41}(Al_{1.69}Li_{0.31})(Be_{2.62}Al_{0.38})[Si_6O_{18}] \cdot 0.7H_2O$.
50. $(Na,Li,Cs)_{0.46}(Al_{1.60}Li_{0.40})(Be_{2.60}Al_{0.40})[Si_6O_{18}] \cdot 0.8H_2O$.
46. $(Na,Li,Cs)_{0.49}(Al_{1.75}Li_{0.25})(Be_{2.65}Al_{0.44})[Si_6O_{18}] \cdot 0.6H_2O$.
36. $(Na,K)_{0.25}(Al_{1.82}Li_{0.13}Na_{0.05})(Be_{2.80}Al_{0.20})[Si_6O_{18}] \cdot 0.7H_2O$.

The slight excess of alkalies, which is observed in the recalculation of even the most accurate analyses, is probably related to the presence of free halogen compounds of alkali metals occurring in the gas-liquid inclusions.

In the ideal case, the ratio of the R^{1+} atoms to aluminum, which replaces beryllium in the fourfold coordination, should equal 2 ($R^{1+}/Al^{(IV)3+} = 2$); however, it can be seen from Table 43 that this ratio varies between 1.3 and 3.6, and depends on both the degree of purity of the analyzed material and the accuracy of the analysis itself. The mean ratio of the 24 recalculated analyses listed in Table 43 is 2.02, which confirms the accuracy of the suggested structural formula of beryl.

Another quite controversial problem is the position in the beryl structure of water, which varies usually between 0.8 and 2.8 percent and is most frequently about 2 percent.

V. I. Vernadskii (1908) thought that water occurring in beryl was the water of constitution, and assumed that, in the composition of the orthosilicate H_2BeSiO_4, water takes part in the construction of the lateral chain of the formula, which he represented as follows:

$$nBeSiO_3 \cdot mH_2BeSiO_4 \cdot pBeAl_2Si_4O_{12}.$$

When studying the changes beryl undergoes at high temperatures, N. L. Dilaktorskii (1931) established that the main part of losses on calcination, characteristic of the mineral, is water, which separates mainly in the range 700 to 900°C.

When analyzing the problem of the entry of water into beryl, A. I. Ginzburg (1955a) concluded rightly that water, occurring in beryl, is of zeolitic nature, by assuming that water fills the hollow vertical channels. These conclusions were based on the following data:

1. After the removal of water, the structure of beryl does not change;

[11] Numbers refer to analyses in Table 42.

Table 43 Ratio of alkali cations to the part of aluminum that replaces beryllium in tetrahedral coordination

No. of analysis[a]	Place of sampling	R^{1+}	$Al^{(VI)}$	$Al^{(IV)}$	Be	O	$\frac{R^{1+}}{Al^{(IV)}}$	Sum of cations (less Si)
21	Cresciano, Alps	0.21	1.86	0.14	2.86	18.0	1.5	5.07
22	Willimantic, Connecticut, U. S. A.	0.23	1.81	0.13	2.87	18.0	1.77	5.04
25	China	0.26	1.92	0.14	2.86	18.1	1.86	5,18
26	Bob Ingersoll, South Dakota, U. S. A.	0.27	1.85	0.15	2.85	18.0	1.80	5.12
27	Varutrask, Sweden	0.29	1.90	0.10	2.90	18.2	2.90	5.19
33	USSR in Europe	0.34	1.73	0.21	2.79	17.9	1.62	5.07
34	China	0.35	1.89	0.13	2.87	18.1	2.7	5.24
35	China	0.46	1.88	0.20	2.80	18.2	2,3	5.34
36	China	0.43	1.82	0.20	2.80	18.1	2.1	5.25
38	China	0.70	1.77	0.23	2,77	18,2	3	5.47
40	W. Innitara, Western Australia	0.36	1.83	0.10	2.90	18.0	3,6	5,19
44	USSR in Europe	0.64	1.62	0.48	2.52	18,0	1,33	5.26
45	USSR in Europe	0.73	1.75	0.25	2.75	18,2	2.9	5.48
46	USSR in Europe	0.74	1.75	0.35	2,65	18.4	2,1	5,59
47	China	0.80	1.73	0.33	2.66	18,19	2.4	5.52
48	China	0.53	1.67	0.36	2.64	18.0	1.47	5,20
49	Norway, Maine, U. S. A.	0.56	1.69	0.28	2.72	18,2	2	5.25
50	Madagascar	0.86	1.60	0.40	2.60	18,3	2.1	5.46
51	Urals	0.52	1.60	0.40	2.60	18.1	1.3	5.12
52	USSR in Europe	0.71	1.70	0.40	2.60	17.8	1.77	5.41
53	Alto do Giz, Brazil	0.71	1.62	0.49	2.51	18,0	1.45	5,33
54	Minas Geraes, Brazil	0.72	1.69	0.38	2,62	17,6	1,90	5.41
55	Hebron, Maine, U. S. A.	0.95	1.55	0.44	2.56	18.4	2.16	5.50
56	East Kazakhstan	0.38	1.96	0.28	2.72	18.1	1,36	5.34

Mean: $\frac{R^{1+}}{Al^{(IV)}} = 2.02$

[a] The numbers of the analyses correspond to Table 42.

this fact was confirmed by the X-ray study of various varieties of beryl before and after water had been eliminated by calcination.

2. When beryls are calcined up to 1200°C, water separates out gradually over a considerable temperature range, whereas there are no effects on the differential heating curves.

The structural relation between beryl and milarite, established by N. V. Belov and T. N. Tarkhova (1951), is a useful analogy. In milarite the water molecules and the potassium atoms are arranged in the vertical channels of the hexagonal lattice of the mineral.

The dehydration curves of beryls (Fig. 17) show that two types of water are present in beryl crystals.

The relatively low-temperature water, which usually amounts to not

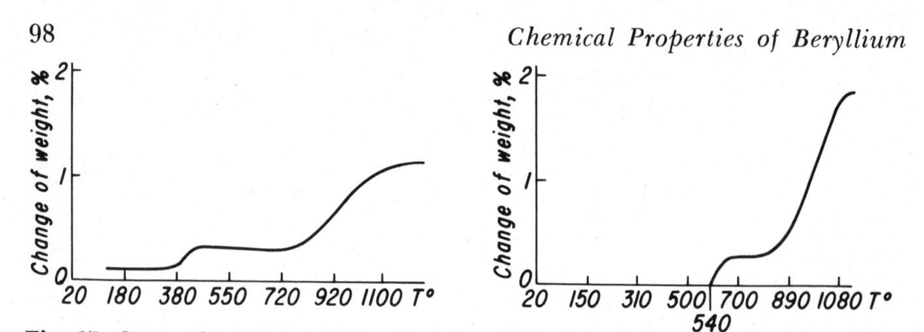

Fig. 17. Curves for loss-in-weight when beryl is calcined (according to A. I. Ginzburg). Left, curve for aquamarine (from a hydrothermal-pneumatolytic deposit). Right, curve for alkali beryl (from lithium pegmatites).

more than 0.2 to 0.3 percent, separates in the range 350 to 600°C and is associated with the content of gas-liquid inclusions, which break up at about 400°C and higher.

The "zeolitic" water proper separates from beryl at temperatures within 600 to 1200°C; the high temperature of water separation distinguishes it substantially from the usual zeolitic water occurring in other silicates. A. I. Ginzburg (1955a) believes that this high temperature of water separation in beryls is caused by the development of capillary phenomena related to the position of water in the narrow and long vertical channels which, in the mineral structure, play the part of micro-capillary vessels that retain water energetically. Most of the water in beryl (0.2 to 1.0 percent) separates at temperatures above 1000°C. Of a particularly high-temperature nature is the water in alkali beryl, which is apparently associated with the channels in the beryl structure that are partly sealed by the large cations of alkali metals and thereby prevent the separation of water. The maximum amount of water is usually in the alkali varieties, although in some alkali-free beryl the water content exceeds 2 percent. (Table 39, analysis 1).

Mean data relating to the number of water molecules in various beryl varieties, calculated for Si_6,[12] are listed in Table 44.

Table 44 Water content in various beryl modifications (number of molecules per Si_6)

Nature of beryl	Number of analyses	Water content	
		Variation limits	mean value
Alkali-free beryls from pneumatolytic-hydrothermal deposits	5	0.2—0.5	0.32
Alkali-free beryls from pegmatite deposits	9	0.1 — 0.7	0.40
Sodium beryls	21	0.1 — 0.8	0.50
Sodium-lithium beryls	17	0.3—0.8	0.65

In general, other elements play a small part in the composition of beryls. An exception is iron, which, as already mentioned, is one of the main chromophores. In all analyses calcium is present (usually 0.1 to 0.5 percent), while magnesium and manganese are much less abundant. Individual analyses show the presence of very small quantities of Ba, Sr, Ni, Ti, Cr, Co, and V (Gavrusevich, 1946). The last four cations mentioned are also chromophores, and they determine the occurrence of the emerald-green (Cr, V) or bright-blue (Co, less Ti) color. The rare elements occurring in beryl as impurities include gallium (up to 0.01 percent) (Borovik and Sosedko, 1937), and in some alkali-free beryl, scandium (up to 0.075 percent), which probably (along with iron) replaces aluminum.

Finally, in our consideration of the chemical composition of beryl, it is necessary to mention briefly the occurrence in the mineral of the admixtures of the gases–He, A, and CO_2, and some anions–Cl^{1-}, F^{1-}, HCO_3^{1-}, CO_3^{2-}, and SO_4^{2-}.

Table 45 Dependence of the helium content of beryl on the age of the deposit

Age of pegmatite	Amount of helium per 1g of beryl, mm^3/g	
	According to Rayleigh (1933)	According to V. G. Khlopin and A. A. Abishev for USSR (1941)
Precambrian	6.98 — 77.6	2.611 — 3.836
Paleozoic	1.47 — 16.8	0.033 — 6.430
Mesozoic	0.157 — 2.27	0.026 — 0.045
Cenozoic	0.0758 — 0.384	

Helium content, according to numerous analyses of beryls from various deposits, varies from 0.02 to 17.20 mm^3/g. Its occurrence in beryl has been studied in detail by a number of Soviet authors (Burkser, Kapustin, and Kondoguri, 1937; Khlopin, 1949; Cherdyntsev and Kozak, 1949).

The origin of the excess helium in beryl is explained by the occlusion of helium from the mineral-forming solutions during the process of crystallization of the beryl (Khlopin, 1949; Cherdyntsev and Kosak, 1949). However, because radioactive minerals are the regular associates of beryl in beryl-bearing pegmatites, it is highly probable that helium is formed in the reaction $Be^9 + \gamma \rightarrow Be^8 + n_0 \rightarrow 2He^4$.

The possibility of such transformation is sufficiently substantiated in the papers of H. R. Crane and C. Lauritsen (1935) and of E. S. Burkser (1937), and is confirmed by the fact that the highest helium contents are associated with beryl from the oldest pegmatites (Table 45).

[12] The individual analyses in which the proportion of water was below 0.5 percent were not taken into account, because it is probable that in the given case a considerable part of water, which separates from beryl above 700 to 800°C, was not determined.

Table 46 Helium content of various generations of beryl (on the basis of the analysis of 40 specimens by V.V. Cherdyntsev and L.V. Kozak)

Nature of beryl	Helium content, mm^3/g
High-temperature beryl from pegmatites	0.13–5.35
Medium-temperature beryl from pegmatites	0.65–1.7
Low-temperature sodium-lithium beryl from albitized pegmatites	0.05–0.74
Rosterite and vorobyevite	0.02–0.64
Beryl from pneumatolytes	0.61–1.5

Very noteworthy also is the association between the highest helium concentrations and the early alkali-free beryl varieties from pegmatites (Table 46). This relationship can be explained by the fact that the helium-containing channels in the structure of beryl are filled, in the case of alkali beryls, with alkali atoms and water, whereas in the alkali-free varieties, these channels are to a large extent hollow (Ginzburg, 1955a).

A number of beryls have an excess argon content; because of it, these beryls cannot be used in the determination of the absolute age by the K/A method (Gerling and Polkanov, 1958).

The occurrence of CO_2, Cl^{1-}, F^{1-}, HCO_3^{1-}, and CO_3^{2-}, and SO_4^{2-} in beryl is related to gas-liquid inclusions. Thus far the peculiarities of distribution of these impurities have not been studied systematically.

Carbon dioxide is a fairly common component of gas-liquid inclusions in certain varieties of beryl (especially in alkali-free beryls which crystallize in cavities). On the strength of single determinations, the CO_2 content is measured by hundredths of 1 percent. Chlorine (Cl^{1-}) occurring in inclusions as chlorides was also recorded in quantities equal to hundredths of 1 percent; data relating to its occurrence are obviously insufficient. Finally, fragmentary information relating to the occurrence of sulfates and fluorides in the gas-liquid inclusions in beryl are not borne out by any quantitative data.

ORIGIN AND PARAGENESIS. Beryl is highly segregated within deposits and is encountered in genetically highly diverse formations, from pegmatites to low-temperature carbonate veins. The detailed analysis of various types of deposits is given in a separate chapter. Here we think it expedient to indicate the most characteristic associations which accompany definite generations of beryl in various types of deposits.

It has been noted already that a highly characteristic feature of beryl is the definite dependence of its crystal habit on the conditions of mineral formation (Fig. 10).

PEGMATITE DEPOSITS

1. Alkali-free beryl—massive block quartz.
2. Alkali-free beryl (aquamarine, beryl, heliodor) in cavities—quartz, microcline (orthoclase), muscovite, zinnwaldite, and rarely topaz.
3. Alkali-free beryl (more rarely sodium beryl)—massive block quartz, muscovite, and microcline-perthite.
4. Alkali-free or sodium beryl—muscovite and quartz.
5. Sodium beryl—granular albite, muscovite, and quartz.
6. Sodium-lithium beryl—granular albite (or cleavelandite), muscovite, and quartz.
7. Sodium-lithium-cesium beryl—cleavelandite, quartz, and spodumene.
8. Sodium-lithium-cesium beryl—albite (cleavelandite), lepidolite, and quartz.

PNEUMATOLYTIC-HYDROTHERMAL AND HYDROTHERMAL DEPOSITS

1. Alkali-free beryl—quartz, potassium feldspar, and wolframite.
2. Alkali-free beryl—quartz and wolframite (or molybdenite).
3. Alkali-free beryl—quartz, muscovite (in greisens) (or siderophyllite), and topaz.
4. Alkali-free beryl—potassium feldspar (or albite), and fluorite.
5. Alkali-free beryl—calcite.
6. Alkali-free beryl—calcite and parasite.

Milarite: $KCa_2(Be_2Al)[Si_{12}O_{30}]0.5H_2O$

Milarite is a very rare beryllium mineral, discovered at only two places in the world, namely Graubunden, Switzerland, and Thuringia, Henneberg, Germany.

The original chemical analysis of milarite from the Swiss Alps did not disclose beryllium, which was determined erroneously as aluminum. The second analysis of milarite, carried out in 1931 by C. Palache (1931), established in the mineral 5.24 percent beryllium; this discovery enabled Palache to relate this mineral to the group of the alkali silicates of beryllium and aluminum.

The physical properties of milarite are listed in Table 47. The mineral has a low specific gravity, low refractive indices, and a very weak birefringence—the lowest among beryllium silicates.

Recalculation of the chemical analysis of milarite results in the empirical formula $KCa_2Be_2AlSi_{12}O_{30} \cdot O.5H_2O$ (Table 48).

Table 47 Physical properties of milarite

Properties	Characteristic
System	Hexagonal
Dimensions of unit cell, Å	a_0=10.54; c_0=13.96
Crystal habit	Prismatic
Color	Colorless and pale-green
Cleavage	None
Luster	Glassy
Hardness	5.5–6
Specific gravity	2.55–2.59
Refractive indices	
ω	1.532
ε	1.529
Birefringence (ω-ε)	0.003
Optical sign	(-)
2V	Abnormally biaxial crystals with a very small 2V were observed. On being calcined to 750°C, such crystals become uniaxial.

The crystal structure of milarite was determined by N. V. Belov and co-workers (Belov and Tarkhova, 1949; Pasheva and Tarkhova, 1953). The structural pattern is determined by the occurrence of four binary rings of silicon-oxygen tetrahedra with a radius of 3.13 Å (very close to the radius of the silicon-oxygen ring in beryl), which surround the sixfold axis of the crystal (Fig. 18). At the contacts of the rings are the beryllium-oxygen and alumino-oxygen tetrahedra (on binary axes) and the atoms of calcium, surrounded by eight oxygen atoms (on threefold axes). In the horizontal projection, the structure of milarite is very close to that of beryl. The place of aluminum in beryl is occupied by calcium in milarite, whereas the aluminum of milarite (in fourfold coordination) occupies, along with beryllium, the position corresponding to that of the Be tetrahedra in beryl. The potassium atoms in milarite are arranged between the silicon-oxygen rings, apparently analogously to the arrangement of the alkali atoms in alkali beryl.

The formula of the silicon-oxygen radical in milarite is determined by binary sixfold rings (Si_{12}) connected by six common oxygen atoms (O_{30}).

The occurrence of silicon-oxygen rings connected by a framework of beryllium-oxygen and alumino-oxygen tetrahedra enables the structure of milarite to be analyzed as a tectocyclic structure; this particularly follows because the ratio (Al + Be + Si):O is 1 to 2.

From this aspect it is interesting to follow the analysis of milarite structure given by T. Ito (1952), who explained it as a framework of binary sixfold rings of the composition $[(Be_{0.10}Si_{0.90})_{12}O_{30}]$, connected by tetra-

Table 48 Recalculation of the chemical analysis of milarite

Components	%	Atomic quantities of		Number of atoms per Be + Al + Si = 15
		Cations	Oxygen	
SiO_2	71.66	1193	2386	12
Al_2O_3	4.68	092	138	0.92
BeO	5.24	209	209	2.1
CaO	11.70	209	209	2.1
K_2O	4.91	104	52	1
Na_2O	0.46	014	007	—
H_2O+	1.02	—	057	—
H_2O-	0.05	—	—	—
Total	99.72	—	3001 Less H_2O	

hedral groups $[Be_{0.27}Al_{0.33}Si_{0.40}]$ and by Ca atoms. The potassium atoms and water molecules are arranged in channels formed by the binary beryllium-silicon-oxygen rings. The potassium atom that connects the binary rings is surrounded by twelve oxygen atoms, six of which belong to one of the binary rings, and six to the other. If one takes into account the composition of the unit cell of the mineral, the structural formula of milarite can be represented in accordance with Ito's data as $2KCa_2[(Be_{0.27}Al_{0.33}Si_{0.40}) \cdot (Be_{0.10}Si_{0.90})_{12}O_{30}] \cdot 0.5H_2O$.

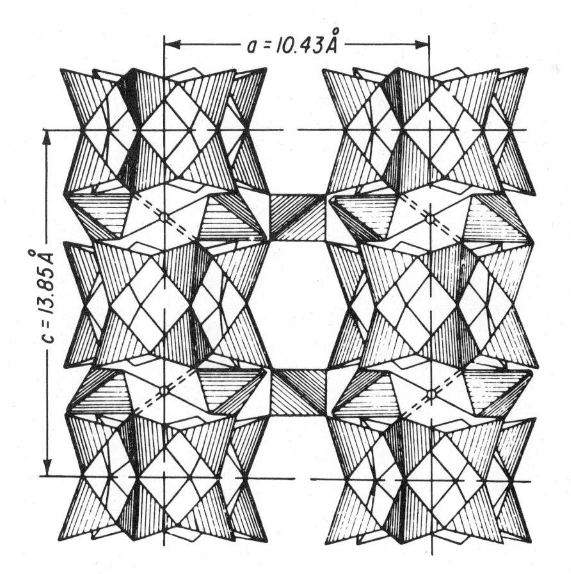

Fig. 18. Vertical projection of the structure of milarite (according to N. V. Belov). The silicon-oxygen tetrahedra are shaded.

It can be seen that Ito arrived, in general, at the same structural pattern as N. V. Belov. They differ in their approach to the appraisal of the part played by beryllium in the tectocyclic structure of milarite. N. V. Belov distinguishes clearly between the function of the silicon-oxygen tetrahedra, which form the double rings, and that of the beryllium-oxygen tetrahedra, which connect these rings.

According to Ito it is possible to use more freedom when interpreting the function of beryllium and silicon in the structure of the mineral, and he stresses the possibility of substituting beryllium for some of the silicon atoms in the double rings.

The crystal structure of milarite determines its beryl-like crystal habit, the absence of cleavage, the low specific gravity, the low refractive index, and the very low birefringence (Table 47).

ORIGIN AND PARAGENESIS. Milarite is a typical hydrothermal mineral. It is found in low-temperature hydrothermal veins composed of calcite in association with adularia, barite, fluorite, and chalcopyrite (Palache, 1931; Heide, 1915). Apparently, for the mineral to form, it is necessary to have a substantially alkaline medium and the occurrence of both berylliums and aluminum with a considerable preponderance of silicon: (Be + Al):Si = 1:4.

Orthosilicates

Phenacite: $Be_2[SiO_4]$

Phenacite is one of the few beryllium minerals that have a relatively wide occurrence.

The physical properties of phenacite are listed in Table 49. The mineral is particularly characterized by a high hardness, refractoriness, and resistance to acids. The crystals of phenacite have a variable habit which depends on the conditions of formation of the mineral (Pough, 1936); commonly they have numerous faces.

In regard to chemical composition, phenacite is the orthosilicate of beryllium $Be_2[SiO_4]$; it usually contains only very small proportions of impurities (Table 50).

The structure of phenacite has been studied in detail (Bragg, 1937). Its rhombohedral cell contains $6Be_2SiO_4$ and has a fairly complicated spatial arrangement of atoms. Each oxygen atom in the unit cell is connected with one silicon atom and two beryllium atoms, and belongs simultaneously to three tetrahedral groups (one silicon-oxygen and two beryllium-oxygen groups). Thus the structure of phenacite is formed by the repetition of the regular group SiBeBe, which surrounds one atom of oxygen. It is analogous to the structure of the orthosilicate of zinc, willemite $Zn_2[SiO_4]$ (Fig. 19).

Table 49 Physical properties of phenacite

Properties	Characteristic
System	Trigonal, rhombohedral symmetry
Dimensions of unit cell, Å	a_{rh}=7.684; α=108°01'
Nature of segregation and crystal habit	Separate crystals, on the walls of drusy cavities and fissures, radiating growths. Crystal habit rhombohedral, prismatic, acicular, usually depends on the conditions of mineral formation. Twins along (1010) are often observed.
Color	Colorless or white, more rarely yellow or pinkish (becomes in time colorless when exposed to light)
Luster	Glassy
Cleavage	Imperfect on (1120)
Hardness	7.5
Specific weight	2.9–3.0
Refractive indices:	
ε	1.670
ω	1.654
Optical nature	Uniaxial, positive

ORIGIN AND PARAGENESIS. Phenacite is formed in a wide range of natural conditions–from pegmatitic to late hydrothermal, and perhaps even supergene conditions.

However, most phenacite is related to the hydrothermal process. It is possible to mark two most important factors which determine the possibility of occurrence in natural processes of the beryllium orthosilicate, phenacite, instead of the much more usual beryllium and aluminum metasilicate, beryl:

Table 50 Chemical composition of phenacite

Components	%	Atomic quantities of		Number of atoms per O_4
		cations	oxygen	
SiO_2	54.73	911	1822	1.02
Al_2O_3	0.14	002	003	—
BeO	43.86	175	1750	1.96
FeO	0.24	004	006	—
MgO	0.15	004	014	—
CaO	0.63	011	011	—
H_2O^-	0.20	—	—	—
P. p. p.	0.37	—	—	—
Total	100.35			

1. Scarcity of silicon—this determines the formation of the orthosilicate not completely saturated with silica, with the ratio Be:Si = 2:1 (it is known that in beryl this ratio is reversed, that is Be:Si = 1:2).

2. Scarcity of aluminum—this makes it impossible for beryl to be formed even when an excess of silica is available.

The formation of phenacite, related to the general scarcity of silicon and associated with the local sudden preponderance of silicon with respect to aluminum in the process of mineral formation, is observed when beryllium-containing emanations or solutions react with rocks depleted in SiO_2, such as limestones, ultrabasic rock. Thus, for example, phenacite is a highly characteristic mineral of beryllium-bearing skarns, where it is

Fig. 19. Rhombohedral structure of phenacite-willemite. Si tetrahedra ruled; Be(Zn) tetrahedra light (according to N. V. Belov).

encountered in close association with fluorite and magnetite, and of peculiar fluorite-rich metasomatic deposits in limestones. Phenacite concentrations in such formations are associated in many places with abundant beryllium.

There also exists a regular relation of phenacite with the "crossing-line" pegmatites, in which the phenacite, formed in the reaction zones of mica-plagioclase veins (mainly in the chlorite zone), is associated as an accessory mineral with chlorite, phlogopite, fluorite, and chrysoberyl (Urals).

The phenomena of the formation of phenacite is related to a scarcity of aluminum at any stage of mineral formation and occurs fairly commonly, but the scale of this process is usually small. The scarcity of aluminum can be explained both by its lack of ability to migrate in the late hydrothermal solutions and by the capture of aluminum by some minerals formed in association with phenacite. These factors determine the usual paragenesis of phenacite related to the final stages of the formation of pegmatites, and more rarely to hydrothermal vein formations.

In pegmatites: (*a*) Fine prismatic and slender-prismatic crystals and crystal druses on the walls of late fissures and leached out cavities, and on the faces of crystals of quartz and feldspar in cavities; phenacite is the latest accessory mineral (Sin'-tszyan, Transbaikalia).

(*b*) Rhombohedral and short-prismatic crystals and crystal druses in cavities in association with topaz, which, in this case, is the collector of aluminum (Ilmen Mountains, Urals; El Paso County, Colorado, etc.)

(*c*) A product of the late-hydrothermal alteration of the earlier beryllium minerals—danalite[13] or beryl (the alteration of the beryl proceeds along with the formation of a micaceous mineral that captures aluminum).

In hydrothermal veins: (*a*) Fine prismatic and short-prismatic crystals in cassiterite-quartz veins containing sulfides, topaz, fluorite, and beryl (forming later than topaz and beryl) (Cornwall, U.K.; Ehrenfriedersdorf, Germany; etc.).

(*b*) Short-prismatic crystals in calcite veins with magnetite, hematite, and sulfides (Fremont, France).

(*c*) Short-prismatic crystals in Alpine veins with adularia, hematite roses, and chlorite (Reckingen, Switzerland, etc.).

Artificial phenacite can be obtained by passing a current of gaseous SiF_4 above beryllium oxide. When attempting the synthesis from pure SiO_2 and BeO in equivalent proportions, P. P. Budnikov and A. M. Cherepanov (1950) found that no phenacite was formed when these oxides were roasted up to 1600°C.

The synthesis of phenacite from BeO and SiO_2 is carried out most easily in the presence of fluoroberyllates (Sobolev and Novoselova, 1959). In these conditions large crystals of phenacite form at lower temperatures (650 to 900°C).

Euclase: $AlBe(OH)[SiO_4]$

Euclase is an extremely rare beryllium mineral. It is found from time to time in various parts of the world, mostly in placers. It was first described in 1799 by Haüy from specimens sent from Peru, and was analyzed by Vauquelin.

The physical properties of euclase are very characteristic (Table 51). The mineral has a high hardness and strong birefringence. Its crystals are usually well formed and display many faces. The transparent colored varieties of euclase supply excellent material for jewelry.

Euclase is an orthosilicate of beryllium and aluminum with the empirical formula $AlBeSiO_4(OH)$. The few chemical analyses of euclase (Table 52) fit well into this formula and sometimes show a small excess of water.

The structure of euclase was first studied by J. Biscoe and B. E. Warren (1933), who showed that the structure contains isolated SiO_4 groups. The aluminum atoms in the structure of the mineral are in octahedral coordination, and are surrounded by five oxygen atoms and one hydroxyl. The beryllium atoms are surrounded by three atoms of oxygen and one hydroxyl. Thus the structural formula of euclase can be represented as

[13] A. I. Ginzburg, who studied such phenacite formations from pegmatites of Imalka, eastern Transbaikalia, considers them to be supergene.

Table 51 Physical properties of euclase

Properties	Characteristic
System	Monoclinic
Dimensions of unit cell, Å	a_0=4.62; b_0=14.24; c_0=4.75; β=79°44'
Form of segregation and crystal habit	Prismatic, abounding in faces
Color	Colorless to pale-green and blue
Cleavage	Perfect on (010) and imperfect on (110) and (001)
Hardness	7.5
Specific gravity	3.05–3.10
Refractive indices:	
γ	1.671
β	1.655
α	1.651
Optic sign	(-)
2V	50°
Optical orientation	Plane of optic axes (010)

$AlBe(OH)[SiO_4]$. The unit cell of euclase contains $4AlBe(OH)[SiO_4]$.

N. V. Belov (1950) notes that the basic structural motif of this mineral is the densest cubic packing anions, analogous to the packing characteristic of pyroxenes. Another common feature of euclase with pyroxenes is the presence in its structure of $[Be(O,OH)_3]$chains, analogous to the $[SiO_3]$ chains in pyroxenes (Fig. 20). Thus, in view of the isolated $[SiO_4]$ tetrahedra, euclase is an orthosilicate of neso structure. At the same time, the endless chains of $[Be(O,OH)_3]$ tetrahedra make it possible to analyze euclase as the "model structure" of metasilicates (Belov, 1950).

Table 52 Chemical composition of euclase

Components	%	Minas Geraes, Brazil (C. Doelter, 1914-1925)		
		Atomic quantities of		Number of atoms per Si = 1
		cations	oxygen	
SiO_2	41.63	693	1386	1
Al_2O_3	34.07	668	1002	0.9
BeO	16.97	679	679	0.98
FeO	1.03	014	014	—
CaO	0.14	003	003	—
SnO_2	0.34	—	—	—
H_2O	6.04	668	334	1 (H₂O + F)
F	0.38	—	020	
Total	100.60			

ORIGIN AND PARAGENESIS. Euclase is a typical hydrothermal mineral, mostly in the low-temperature vein formations of Alpine type (Swiss Alps, Brazil). The well formed euclase crystals are found in the cavities of Alpine veins among metamorphic schists, where they grow on the segregations of feldspar, crystals of quartz, fluorite, etc. In these types of formations euclase is associated with late apatite, rutile, hematite, herderite, carbonates, and gilbertite. Of similar nature are the segregations of euclase in the cavities of the miarolitic granites and some pegmatites. Euclase, in association with bertrandite and potassium mica, was recorded as a secondary mineral product of the late-hydrothermal transformation of beryl (Strand, 1953).

Fig. 20. Axonometric view of the structure of euclase (according to N. V. Belov).

Diorthosilicates

The subclass of diorthosilicates comprises five beryllium minerals in whose structure are found (or assumed from the recalculations of chemical analyses) binary radicals $[Si_2O_7]$.

In recent years, in addition to the generally known representatives of this subclass (barylite and bertrandite), there have been added three secondary beryllium hydrosilicates from the pegmatites of the Lovozero rock mass, most probably close to bertrandite—helbertrandite, spherobertrandite, and beryllite.

Helbertrandite is considered a hydrated bertrandite with the formula $Be_4[Si_2O_7](OH)_2 \cdot nH_2O$, whereas spherobertrandite and beryllite differ from bertrandite by a greater Be/Si ratio and by a correspondingly greater content of the hydroxyl group (OH).

If we assume that the bertrandite core of minerals of this group is $Be_3[Si_2O_7]$, their formulae will be as follows:

Bertrandite:	$Be(OH)_2 \cdot Be_3[Si_2O_7]$;
Helbertrandite:	$Be(OH)_2 \cdot Be_3[Si_2O_7] \cdot nH_2O$;
Spherobertrandite:	$Be_2(H)_4 \cdot Be_3[Si_2O_7]$;
Beryllite:	$Be_2(OH)_4 \cdot Be_3[Si_2O_7] \cdot H_2O$.

Such representation, which illustrates the common chemical nature of these minerals, is conventional, as the structure of minerals of this group does not contain any $Be(OH)_2$. However, when taking into account that in the structure of minerals OH is connected only with Be atoms, we find that the suggested formulae are rational.

Barylite: $BaBe_2[Si_2O_7]$

An extremely rare beryllium mineral established only in two genetically similar contact-metasomatic deposits in the world—Långban, Sweden, and Franklin, New Jersey, U.S.A. Originally it was described by mistake as an aluminum barium silicate. The true nature of the mineral was established thirty years after its discovery, as a result of the repeated analysis carried out by G. Aminoff in 1923.

The physical properties of barylite are listed in Table 53. The mineral has the high hardness (7) characteristic of beryllium diorthosilicates, and a high specific gravity related to the features of its chemical composition.

Its chemical composition is a barium beryllium diorthosilicate, with the empirical formula $BaBe_2Si_2O_7$ (Table 54).

Table 53 Physical properties of barylite

Properties	Characteristis
System	Orthorhombic
Dimensions of unit cell, Å	a_o=9.79; b_o=11.61; c_o=4.63
Form of segregation and crystal habit	Separate crystals of prismatic or tabular habit
Cleavage	Good on (001) and (100) and less clear on (010)
Color	Milky white
Luster	Glassy
Hardness	7
Specific weight	4.7
Refractive indices:	
γ	1.703–1.695
β	1.696–1.685
α	1.691–1.681
Optic sign	(+)
2V	65°–70° (81°)
Optical orientation	Plane of optic axes parallel to (100)

Table 54 Chemical composition of barylite

Components	Långban, Sweden				Franklin, New Jersey, U. S. A.			
	%	Atomic quantities of		Number of atoms per SiO_2	%	Atomic quantities of		Number of atoms per SiO_2
		cations	oxygen			cations	oxygen	
SiO_2	35.51	592	1184	2	36.42	604	1208	2
BeO	16.01	640	640	2.2	15.77	628	628	2
BaO	47.43	310	310	1.09	46.49	302	302	1
CaO	0.42	007	007	—	—	—	—	—
MgO	0.21	005	005	—	—	—	—	—
PbO	—	—	—	—	0.29	—	—	—
FeO	—	—	—	—	0.11	—	—	—
Fe_2O_3	0.04	—	—	—	—	—	—	—
Al_2O_3	0.05	—	—	—	—	—	—	—
H_2O	0.57	—	—	—	0.40	—	—	—
Total	100.24		2146	5.29	99.67		2138	5
Analyst	Alstrom (Aminoff, 1923)				Bauer (Palache and Bauer, 1930)			

The X-ray investigation of the mineral (Yggberg, 1941; Smith, 1956) confirmed the presence, in the structure of barylite, of binary tetrahedra Si_2O_7, which are disposed in a long axis parallel to (100) of the unit cell. Like silicon, beryllium is also arranged inside the tetrahedral oxygen groups. In the structure of barylite the barium atoms are surrounded by ten oxygen atoms.

ORIGIN AND PARAGENESIS. Barylite was found in the contact-metasomatic formations of the deposits at Långban, Sweden and Franklin, New Jersey, U.S.A. in paragenesis with barite, calcite, hedyphane, garnet, and willemite. In the Långban deposit, well-formed barylite crystals in association with hedyphane and garnet were detected in accumulations of barite, enclosed in granular hematitic skarn. In the Franklin deposit, barylite, in intergrowth with hedyphane and willemite, was encountered in central portions of streaky veins consisting mainly of calcite.

Bertrandite: $Be_4[Si_2O_7](OH)_2$

Bertrandite is one of the few relatively widely occurring beryllium minerals.

The physical properties of the mineral and its optical features are given in Table 55.

Bertrandite is a basic diorthosilicate of beryllium with the formula $BE(OH)_2Be_3Si_2O_7$; the percentages of its components vary as follows:

Table 55 Physical properties of bertrandite

Properties	Characteristic
System	Orthorhombic
Dimensions of unit cell, Å	a_0=8.67; b_0=15.19; c_0=4.53
Form of segregation and crystal habit	Fine lamellar along (001), tabular or prismatic, usually twins
Cleavage	Perfect on (001), medium on (110), (010) and (100)
Color	Colorless or pale-yellow
Luster	Glassy (pearly on 001)
Hardness	6
Specific gravity	2.59–2.60
Optical sign	(-)
Refractive indices:	
γ	1.611–1.614
β	1.603–1.605
α	1.584–1.591
2V	73–75°
Optical orientation	Plane of optic axes (010)

BeO: 39.6 to 42.02;
SiO_2: 49.26 to 51.80;
H_2O: 6.90 to 8.87

The structural pattern of bertrandite is determined by the presence of isolated binary tetrahedra [Si_2O_7], connected by beryllium-oxygen tetrahedra that are also paired to form binary groups by the common $(OH)^{1-}$ ion (Ito and West, 1932). The structure of bertrandite is similar to that of calamine $Zn_4[Si_2O_7](OH)_2 \cdot H_2O$. There is, however, no complete analogy here, as can be seen in the marked difference between the parameters of the unit cells of the minerals, and also in many crystallographic features.

ORIGIN AND PARAGENESIS. Bertrandite occurs in most deposits of beryllium minerals, but large accumulations are not known. It forms in the final stages of the pegmatitic or greisenic process, growing in the form of fine tabular crystals on the walls of fissures or on earlier minerals (quartz, feldspar, beryl, and tourmaline) in the miarole cavities of pegmatites and geisens. In many places, bertrandite also forms as the product of the late-hydrothermal alteration of helvite, danalite, and beryl. In the pseudomorphs of bertrandite after beryl in association with bertrandite, there is usually bavenite or euclase, which combines with the aluminum from the beryl.

Table 56 Physical properties of helbertrandite

Properties	Characteristic
System	?
Form of segregation	Vitreous irregular segregations, size up to 5 mm. (Under high magnification—finest spherolites)
Color	Pale-violet
Luster	Glassy
Fracture	Conchoidal
Hardness	About 4
Specific gravity	2.176
Refractive index: N	1.525 (varying from 1.511 to 1.530), crypto-crystalline
Birefringence: $\gamma-\alpha$	Small (under high magnification gray interference colors are observed)

Helbertrandite: $Be_4[Si_2O_7](OH)_2 \cdot nH_2O$

Helbertrandite is an aqueous crypto-crystalline beryllium silicate, apparently akin to bertrandite in structure. It was discovered and described by E. I. Semenov (1957a) during the investigation of secondary minerals from the pegmatites of nepheline syenites.

The physical properties of the mineral are listed in Table 56.

The chemical composition of helbertrandite corresponds to the empirical formula $Be_4Si_2O_7(OH)_2 \cdot 3H_2O$ (Table 57).

Table 57 Chemical composition of helbertrandite

Components	%	Atom quantities of		Number of atoms per Si_2	Formula
		cations	oxygen		
SiO_2	38.70	645	1290	2	
Al_2O_3	1.20	023	034	—	
BeO	34.16	1366	1366	4.04	$Be_4[Si_2O_7](OH)_2 \cdot 3H_2O$
CaO	1.93	034	034	—	or
H_2O^+	15.62	1740	870	7.93	$Be(OH)_2 \cdot Be_3[Si_2O_7] \cdot 3H_2O$
H_2O^-	8.17	908	454		
Total	99.78		2724 without H_2O		

Based on the variable water content, the general formula of helbertrandite is $Be_4[Si_2O_7](OH)_2 \cdot nH_2O$.

The interplanar spacings of helbertrandite, as measured by powder pattern, correspond to those of bertrandite, so that this mineral can be considered a hydrated crypto-crystalline bertrandite.

ORIGIN AND PARAGENESIS. Helbertrandite is one of the latest products of the epithermal and, possibly, of the supergene alterations of epididymite $Na[BeSi_3O_7(OH)]$. This mineral forms in the leached-out cavities of epididymite usually in close paragenesis with other products of its alteration—spherobertrandite and beryllite. In many places the latter envelops the segregation of helbertrandite in the form of a thin radiating crust.

Spherobertrandite: $Be_5[Si_2O_7](OH)_4$

Spherobertrandite is a rare beryllium silicate, most probably akin to bertrandite. It is found only in the alkalic pegmatites of the Lovozero rock mass (Semenov, 1957a).

The physical properties of spherobertrandite are listed in Table 58.

The chemical composition of spherobertrandite fits the empirical formula $Be_5Si_2O_7(OH)_4$ (Table 59).

Water separates from spherobertrandite in the narrow temperature range of 600 to 800°C, so that it can be assumed to be the water of constitution. The ratio Si:O = 2:7 points to the possible presence of binary tetrahedra Si_2O_7 in the structure of the mineral. Thus the structural formula of spherobertrandite can be represented as $Be_2(OH)_4Be_3[Si_2O_7]$. The

Table 58 Physical properties of spherobertrandite

Properties	Characteristic
System	Unknown
Form of segregation	Spherolites, diameter up to 2 mm, chains of spherolites up to 1 cm long
Color	Yellow to colorless
Luster	Glassy
Hardness	5
Specific gravity	About 2.5
Refractive indices:	
γ	1.612
α	1.595
Optic sign	(−)
2V	About 70°

Table 59 Chemical composition of spherobertrandite

Components	%	Atom quantities of		Number of atoms
		Cations	Oxygen	
SiO_2	41.03	684	1368	2
Al_2O_3	1.40	27	40	-
Fe_2O_3	0.07	-	-	-
BeO	45.20	1808	1808	5
H_2O^+	11.70	1300	650	4
Total	99.40		3216 without H_2O	

higher content of water of constitution, compared with bertrandite, probably determines the lower hardness and weaker birefringence, which are characteristic of spherobertrandite.

ORIGIN AND PARAGENESIS. Spherobertrandite is the late hydrothermal alteration mineral of albitized epididymite contained in alkalic pegmatites of the Lovozero rock mass. The spherolites of spherobertrandite are observed in the leached cavities of epididymite along with other products of the alteration of epidiymite—helbertrandite and beryllite. The formation of pseudomorphs of spherobertrandite and epididymite after chkalovite was also noted (Semenov, 1957a).

Beryllite: $Be_5[Si_2O_7](OH)_4 \cdot H_2O$

Beryllite, the secondary beryllium mineral of alkalic pegmatites, described in 1954 by M. V. Kuz'menko (1954), is the third beryllium mineral that can probably be related to the subclass of silicates with binary tetrahedra.

The physical properties of beryllite are given in Table 60.

The chemical composition of beryllite was represented by M. V. Kuz'menko with the aid of the formula $Be_3SiO_4(OH)_2 \cdot H_2O$. However, the chemical analysis of beryllite (Table 61) enables its formula also to be calculated as $Be_5[Si_2O_7] \cdot (OH)_2 \cdot H_2O$. The latter formula designates beryllite as hydrated spherobertrandite (Semenov, 1957a).

The structure of beryllite, like that of spherobertrandite, requires more accurate determinations. The dual nature of water in the mineral is confirmed by the results of the thermal investigation of beryllite. (See heating and dehydration curves, Figs. 21, 22).

Table 60 Physical properties of beryllite

Properties	Characteristic
System	Unknown
Form of segregation	Fine spherolites, diam. 2–3 mm, scaly formations, thin fibrous crusts in leached cavities
Color	White
Luster	Silky
Hardness	Soft
Specific gravity	2.196
Refractive indices:	
γ	1.555–1.560
β	1.549–1.553
α	1.539–1.541
Optic sign	(-)
2V	Small

ORIGIN AND PARAGENESIS. Beryllite is, like spherobertrandite and helbertrandite, a secondary beryllium mineral of the natrolite-albite alkalic epididymite-containing pegmatites. The mineral forms of the leached cavities in albite and epididymite in the form of crusts of spherolites and kaolin-like accumulations of crypto-fibrous structure.

Table 61 Chemical composition of beryllite

Components	%	Atom quantities of		Number of atoms per Si + Al = 2
		cations	oxygen	
SiO_2	34.10	568	1136	2
TiO_2	traces	—	—	
Al_2O_3	1.63	032	048	
Fe_2O_3	0.12	002	003	
MgO	traces	—	—	
BeO	40.00	1600	1600	5
CaO	0.50	009	009	
Na_2O	2.42	078	039	
H_2O^+	18.95	2104	1058	
H_2O^-	3.25	360	180	8
Total	100.47		2835 without H_2O	

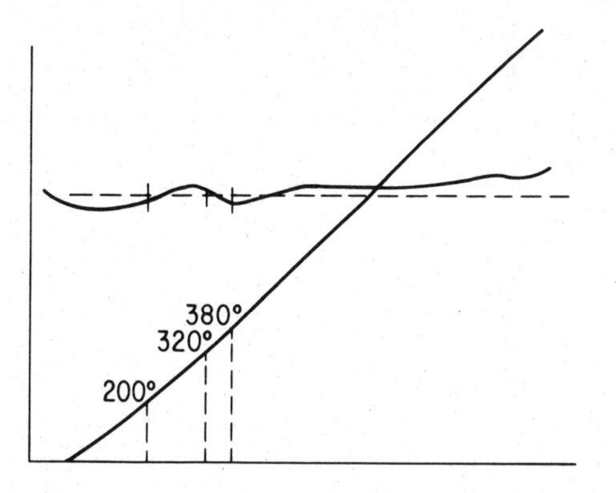

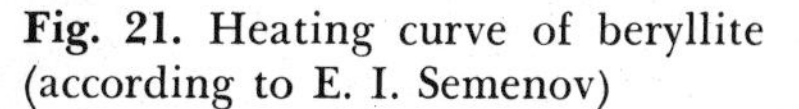

Fig. 21. Heating curve of beryllite (according to E. I. Semenov)

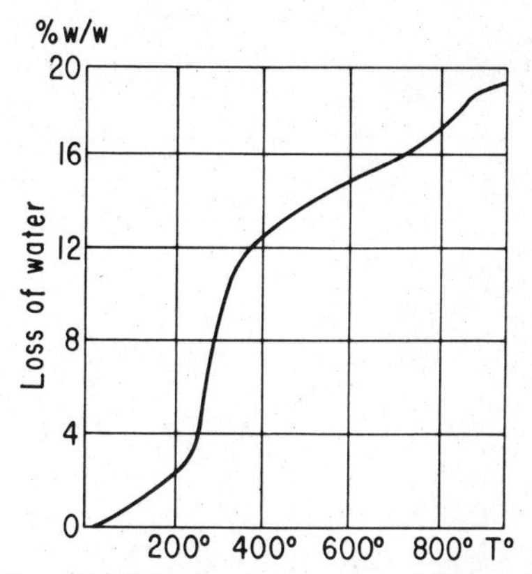

Fig. 22. Dehydration curve of beryllite (according to M. V. Muz'menko).

BORATES

Two beryllium borates—hambergite and rhodizite—are known in nature. Both are extremely rare.

Hambergite: $Be_2(OH)[BO_3]$

Hambergite is a very rare basic beryllium borate, discovered *in situ* only in two places in the world—Langesund Fjord, Norway and Imalo and Maharitra, Madagascar. Hambergite also has been found in the gem-bearing placers of Kashmir (Dana *et al.*, 1944–1951).

The physical properties and optical characteristics of this mineral are listed in Table 62.

The chemical composition of hambergite is fairly constant (Table 63) and fits well into the formula $Be_2BO_3(OH)$.

ORIGIN AND PARAGENESIS. Like helvite, hambergite is one of the two beryllium minerals encountered in both syenitic and granitic pegmatites. In the syenitic pegmatites, (Langesund Fjord) hambergite was discovered together with barkevikite, biotite, sodalite, fluorite, analcite, and zircon. In granitic pegmatites (Madagascar), it is found in replaced spodumene-albite pegmatites that contain beryl and danburite.

Rhodizite: $(K,Na)_{1\text{-}2}(Li,Al_{1.5\text{-}4}(O,OH)_4 \cdot Al_4[(BeB)_3B_4O_{12}]_2$

Rhodizite is a very rare and little studied alkali beryllium and aluminum

Table 62 Physical properties of hambergite

Properties	Characteristic
System	Orthorhombic
Dimension of unit cell, Å	a_0=9.73; b_0=12.18; c_0=4.42
Form of segregation and crystal habit	Prismatic, vertically striated, often flattened on (100)
Color	Grayish-white, white
Cleavage	Perfect on (010) and medium on (100)
Hardness	7.5
Specific gravity	2.359
Refractive indices:	
γ	1.628–1.631
β	1.587–1.590
α	1.553–1.559
Optic sign	(+)
2V	87°
Optical orientation	γ=c; β=b; α=a

borate, known only from a few pegmatitic deposits in the Urals (Murzinka) and in Madagascar (Manjaka and Antandrocomby).

The physical properties of rhodizite are given in Table 64. The mineral has a high hardness.

Of the three analyses of rhodizite available in the literature, only two can be used for the derivation of the formula, because in the early analysis of rhodizite from Murzinka, beryllium was determined as aluminum and the accuracy of the analysis is doubtful.

It can be seen from the chemical analyses of rhodizite (Table 65) that its composition is subjected to considerable variations, owing to which the usually quoted formulae $KNaLi_4Al_4Be_3B_{10}O_{27}$ (Betekhtin, 1950) and

Table 63 Chemical composition of hambergite (in percent)

Components	Langesund Fjord, Norway	Imalo, Madagascar
BeO	53.25	54.80
B_2O_3	36.72	35.10
H_2O	10.03	10.95
Total	100.00	100.85
Analyst	Bekström (Brögger, 1890)	Pisani (Lacroix, 1910)

Table 64 Physical properties of rhodizite

Properties	Characteristic
System	Cubic
Dimension of unit cell, Å	a_0=7.303
Form of segregation and crystal habit	Fine, in dodecahedral form
Color	Colorless to white and yellowish
Luster	Glassy to adamantine
Cleavage	Indistinct on (111)
Hardness	8
Specific gravity	3.30–3.38
Refractive index:	
N	1.693 (Na)
	Characterized by a weak anomalous double refraction

$NaLiBe_7Al_6B_{14}O_{38}$ (Winchell and Winchell, 1951) do not correspond to the actual composition of the mineral.

The empirical formulae are:

1. $$(Rb,Na)_{1.86}Li_4Al_{4.87}(Be,B,Si)_{12.97}O_{28}$$

or

$$(Rb,Na)_2Li_4Al_5(Be,B)_{13}O_{28};$$

Table 65 Chemical composition of rhodizite

Components	1				2			
	%	Atomic quantities of cations	Atomic quantities of oxygen	Number of atoms	%	Atomic quantities of cations	Atomic quantities of oxygen	Number of atoms
Li_2O	7.30	488	244	3.97	0.68	046	023	0.37
Na_2O	3.30	106	053	0.86	1.78	058	029	0.47
K_2O	—	—	—	—	1.41	030	015	0.24
Rb_2O	5.90	126	063	1	2.29	024	012	0.19
Cs_2O	—	—	—	—	3.47	026	013	0.21
Al_2O_3	30.50	598	897	4.87	27.40	538	807	4.34
MgO	—	—	—	—	0.11	003	003	—
BeO	10.10	404	404	3.28	14.93	598	598	4.83
SiO_2	1.36	023	046	0.19	3.18	053	106	0.43
B_2O_3	40.60	1168	1752	9.5	43.33	1244	1866	10
P. p. p.	0.45	050	025	—	1.42	158	079	1.2
Total	99.51		3455 less H_2O		100.00		3471 less H_2O	

2. $(K,Na,Rb,Cs)_{1.1}Li_{0.37}Al_{4.34}Be_{4.83}Si_{0.43}B_{10}O_{28}\cdot 0.6H_2O$

or

$$(K,Na,Rb,Cs)\ (Li_{0.4}Al_{1.2})\ (Be,Al)_8Be_{10}O_{27}\ (OH).$$

If the analyses available in the literature relate indeed to one and the same mineral, then the variable composition of rhodizite can be explained only by the presence, in the structure of the mineral, of free cavities, occupied to a certain extent by the atoms of alkali metals depending on the variable charge of the beryllium-boron-oxygen framework. The possibility of relating rhodizite to borates of tecto structure was considered by A. S. Povarennykh (1955b) who, by analogy with the structure of the tectoborate, boracite, suggested the following structural formula of rhodizite:

$$(K,Na)_2(Li,Al)_8(O,OH)_4[(Be,B)_{14}O_{24}]$$

or

$$(K,Na)\ (Li,Al)_4\ (O,OH)_2[\ (Be,B)_3B_4O_{12}].$$

The recalculation of the available analyses of rhodizite on the basis of the structure of the boron-oxygen radical of the tectoborates results in the following formulae:

1st analysis: $(K,Na)_2Li_4Al_4O_4[\ (Al_1Be_{3.3}B_{9.5})O_{24}]$

or

$$(K,Na)_2Li_4Al_4O_4[\ (Al,Be,B)_3B_4O_{12}]_2;$$

2nd analysis: $(K,Na)\ (Li_{0.4}Al_{1.2})\ (Al,Be)_4\ (O_3OH)[\ (Be_4B_{10})O_{24}]$

or

$$(K,Na)\ (Li_{0.4}Al_{1.2})\ (Al,Be)_4\ (O_3OH)[\ (Be,B)_3B_4O_{12}]_2.$$

It can be seen that the possibility of the isomorphous substitution of beryllium for boron, which results in the change of the charge of the radical, brings about substantial variations in the cationic part of the formula. The most typical is apparently the first analysis. In the second analysis, the obviously insufficient amount of alkalies is compensated by the statistical substitution of aluminum for a considerable proportion of lithium (according to the scheme $3Li^{1+}$ for $1Al^{3+}$), and by the substitution of the OH group for a certain part of the additional O ions.

In general the formula of rhodizite can be expressed as follows:

$$(K,Na)_{2-x}(Li_{4-y}Al_{y/3})(O_{4-x}OH_x)Al_4[(Be,B)_3B_4O_{12}]_2.$$

After simplification the formula becomes this:

$$(K,Na)_{1-2}\ (Li,Al)_{1.5-4}\ (O,OH)_4Al_4[\ (Be,B)_3B_4O_{12}]_2.$$

ORIGIN AND PARAGENESIS. Rhodizite is related to the final stages of formation of granitic pegmatites enriched in boron. In the miarolitic pegmatites of the Murzinka district, Urals, it occurs as fine crystals that grow on rubellite and quartz in cavities. Larger dodecahedral and tetrahedral crystals (up to 2 cm) are described from the rubellite-enriched spodumene-albite pegmatites of the Antandrocomby district, Madagascar.

ANTIMONATES

Swedenborgite, the beryllium and sodium antimonate, is the only known mineral of this class and is found in only one deposit in the world.

Swedenborgite: $NaBe_4SbO_7$

Swedenborgite was discovered in the Långban deposit, Sweden by Aminoff, who described it in 1924 as an aluminum sodium antimonate because, in the original analysis of the mineral, beryllium was erroneously determined as aluminum (Aminoff, 1924).

Swedenborgite crystallizes in the hexagonal system and forms separate transparent prismatic crystals whose crystal habit reminds one of corundum crystals. The physical properties of the mineral are quoted in Table 66. The characteristic features are the high hardness and resistance to acid.

The chemical composition of swedenborgite corresponds to the formula of beryllium sodium antimonate $NaBe_4SbO_7$ (Table 67).

The unit cell contains $2NaBe_4SbO_7$.

The structure of the mineral is determined basically by the densest packing and can be represented as consisting of two kinds of cube-octahedra formed around sodium and around oxygen (Belov, 1947). Inside every

Table 66 Physical properties of swedenborgite

Properties	Characteristic
System	Hexagonal
Dimensions of unit cell, Å	a_0=5.47; b_0=8.92
Form of segregation and crystal habit	Separate, short-prismatic habit
Color	Colorless to yellow, transparent. Under the microscope, colorless
Cleavage	Distinct on (0001)
Hardness	8
Specific gravity	4.29
Optical sign and axiality	Optically negative, uniaxial
Refractive indices:	
ω	1.772
ε	1.770

Table 67 Chemical composition of swedenborgite

Components	1				2			
	%	Atomic quantities of		No. of atoms per Sb + P = 1	%	Atomic quantities of		No. of atoms per Sb + P = 1
		cations	oxygen			cations	oxygen	
Na_2O	8.50	274	137		8.49	274	137	
K_2O	0.21	004	002		—	—	—	
CaO	0.94	017	017	0.91	0.90	016	016	0.9
MgO	0.52	012	012		0.65	016	016	
BeO	34.72	1375	1375	4.06	34.92	1395	1395	4
Sb_2O_5	54.17	334	835	1	54.41	336	840	1
P_2O_5	0.23	004	002		0.63	008	020	
H_2O	0.39							
Total	99.68		2382	7.1	100.00		2424	7
Analyst	G. Aminoff, 1924				G. Aminoff, 1933			

Corrected analysis (Dana et al., 1949–1954)

cube-octahedron with oxygen in the center there are arranged four beryllium-oxygen tetrahedra which converge in the center at the common oxygen atom.

Each Sb ion is in the octahedral environment of six oxygen ions, whereas the sodium ions are surrounded by twelve oxygen ions (Pauling *et al.*, 1935).

ORIGIN AND PARAGENESIS. Swedenborgite was found in calcite streaks and lenses in the skarns of the Långban deposit, Sweden, in association with bromellite, richterite, and manganophyllite. The paragenetic relationships between swedenborgite and the associated minerals have not yet been studied.

PHOSPHATES

The phosphate class comprises seven beryllium minerals, four of which (hurlbutite, moraesite, väyrynenite, and faheyite) were discovered during the past few years. With the exception of moraesite and kolbeckite, all minerals are normal or basic orthophosphates of beryllium and of mono- or divalent metals, of the type $M^{1+}Be[PO_4]$; $M^{2+}Be_2[PO_4]_2$, $M^{2+}Be[PO_4]$ (OH,F) etc. Moraesite is a basic aqueous beryllium phosphate, while kolbeckite can be related to the group of normal aqueous phosphates in which some phosphorus has been replaced by silicon silicophosphates. We list below the possible grouping of the known natural beryllium phosphates, based on the features of chemical composition:

type $M^{1+}Be[PO_4]$	beryllonite $NaBe[PO_4]$;
type $M^{2+}Be[PO_4](OH, F)$	herderite $CaBe[PO_4](OH,F)$,
	väyrynenite $MnBe[PO_4](OH)$;
type $M^{2+}Be_2[PO_4]_2$	hurlbutite $CaBe_2[PO_4]_2$;
type $M^{2+}M_2^{3+}Be_2[PO_4]_4$	faheyite $(Mn, Mg)Fe_2^{3+}Be_2[PO_4]_4 \cdot 6H_2O$;
type $Be_{3-m}[PO_4](OH)_m$	moraesite $Be_2[PO_4](OH) \cdot 4H_2O$;
silicophosphates	kolbeckite $(Al, Be)_5[(P, Si)O_4]_4 \cdot 8H_2O$.

The relatively small number of known natural beryllium phosphates probably fail to give the real picture of their abundances. This is caused by the rarity of minerals of this group and their difficult diagnosis. As a result of the intensified mineralogical and geochemical research in the field of beryllium deposits in pegmatites, new beryllium phosphates will surely be discovered in the future. In particular, it is highly probable that a ferrous analogue of väyrynenite, a lithium analogue of beryllonite, etc. exist.

Except the early-forming hurlbutite and kolbeckite (for which information pertaining to its origin is rather incomplete), all known natural beryllium phosphates are late minerals of beryl-containing pegmatites, related to a variable extent to the phenomena of dissolution of the primary beryllium minerals (mainly beryl) and of the redeposition of beryllium in a new form as phosphate.

Beryllonite: $NaBe[PO_4]$

Beryllonite, a double phosphate of sodium and beryllium, is an extremely rare mineral, found only in three pegmatitic deposits in the world (Stoneham and Newry, Maine, U.S.A.; Viitaniemi, Finland).

It is found usually in the form of well developed, multifaced crystals of short-prismatic and thick-tabular habit. Outwardly it resembles quartz, alkali beryl (rosterite), and topaz. The physical properties of beryllonite are given in Table 68.

The chemical composition of this mineral is fairly constant (Table 69) and corresponds to the formula $NaBe[PO_4]$. The unit cell of beryllonite contains $12NaBe\ [PO_4]$.

The structure of beryllonate is similar to that of trimerite (Gossner and Besslein, 1934; Wehrenberg, 1954).

ORIGIN AND PARAGENESIS. Beryllonite occurs in the albitic replacement complex in albitized beryl-bearing pegmatites where it formed by the dissolution of early beryl. Multifaced crystals of beryllonite, in association with apatite, green tourmaline, and smoky quartz crystals, coat or fill small cavities in albite. Other minerals associated with beryllonite are

Table 68 Physical properties of beryllium phosphates

Properties	Beryllonite	Herderite and hydroxyl-herederite	Väyrynenite	Hurlbutite	Faheyite	Moraesite	Kolbeckite
System	Monoclinic	Monoclinic	Monoclinic	Orthorhombic	Hexagonal	Monoclinic	Monoclinic (?)
Dimensions of unit cell, Å	$a_0 - 8.16$; $b_0 - 7.79$; $c_0 - 14.08$; $\beta = 90°00$	$a_0 - 4.80$; $b_0 - 7.68$; $c_0 - 9.80$; $\beta = 90°06$	$a_0 - 10.47$; $b_0 - 2\times 7.20$; $c_0 - 4.75$; $\beta = 102°49$	$a_0 - 8.29$; $b_0 - 8.80$; $c_0 - 7.81$	$a_0 - 9.43$; $c_0 - 16.00$	$a_0 - 8.55$; $b_0 - 36.90$ $c_0 - 7.13$; $\beta = 97°4$	
Color	Colorless, white, yellowish	Colorless, yellowish, greenish	Pink, red	Colorless to yellowish-whitish and bright-green	White, bluish, brownish	White	Blue to blue-gray
Optical sign	(—)	(—)	(—)	(—)	(+)	(—)	?
Refractive indices γ	1.560—1.563	1.621—1.627	1.667	1.604	1.652	1.490	?
β	1.555—1.560	1.612 -1.616	1.662	1.601	1.631	1.482	?
α	1.549—1.554	1.592—1.604	1.640	1.595		1.462	?
Optical orientation	$x = b$; $y = a$; $z = c$	$c = z \sim 3°$; $c = x \sim 87°$ $y = b$		$x = b$; $y = c$		$c = y = 11°$	
2V	67—68°	67—75°	46°	70°		65°	?
Cleavage	Perfect on (010), medium on (100), imperfect on (001).	Poor on (110).	Perfect on (001). Poor on (010).	Not found	Perfect, parallel to axis c.	Perfect along two directions parallel to axes b and c.	Perfect on (010).
Hardness	5.5—6	5—5.5	5	6	(?)	?	3.5—4
Specific gravity	2.806—2.845 2.831 (theoretical)	2.85—3.01	3.183	2.877	2.660 (experimental) 2.670 (theoretical)	1.805	2.39

Table 69 Chemical composition of beryllonite (in percent)

Components	Stoneham, Maine, U.S.A.	Newry, Maine, U.S.A.	Viitaniemi,[a] Finland
Na_2O	23.64	23.28	20.87%
K_2O	—	0.92	0.36
CaO	—	0.40	3.85
Li_2O	—	0.07	—
Al_2O_3	—	0.21	—
Fe_2O_3	—	0.07	—
BeO	19.84	19.12	18.24
P_2O_5	55.86	55.40	53.09
SiO_2	—	—	1.77
Insoluble residue	—	0.16	0.75
P.p.p.	0.08	0.52	0.80
H_2O^+	—	—	0.64
H_2O^-	—	—	0.16
Total	99.42	100.15	99.82
Analyst	Wells (Doelter, 1914–1925)	Shannon (Palache and Shannon, 1928)	Volborth (Volborth, 1954a,b,c)

[a] Apparently with a small admixture of hydroxyl-herderite.

cassiterite, triplite, hurlbutite, väyrynenite, and herderite. The relationships between beryllonite and the calcium-beryllium phosphates—hurlbutite and herderite—are of some interest. Both the formation of beryllonite after hurlbutite (Volborth, 1954b), and the replacement of beryllonite by fibrous hydroxyl-herderite have been recorded (Palache and Shannon, 1928).

Herderite: $CaBe[PO_4](F,OH)$

Herderite, the only beryllium phosphate to be discovered in the USSR, is a rare accessory mineral of the beryl-bearing pegmatites that are characterized by an abundance of replacement phenomena.

It is in short-prismatic (sometimes dipyramidal) crystals, usually with a hexagonal habit. The crystals commonly are twinned, with numerous faces, and they closely resemble the crystals of datolite. Herderite may also be in radiating fibrous aggregates. Its physical properties are given in Table 68.

Herderite is a double basic orthophosphate of calcium and beryllium in which the hydroxyl group is partly or almost completely replaced by fluorine. Depending on the fluorine content, we distinguish between the herderites proper (fluorine predominates as compared with OH) and

Table 70 Chemical composition of herderite

Components	Paris, Maine, U.S.A.	Newry, Maine, U.S.A.	Stoneham, Maine, U.S.A.	Eastern Transbaikalia
CaO	34.04	32.24	33.21	34.54
MgO	—	0.76	—	—
MnO	—	0.16	—	—
Al_2O_3	—	0.50	—	—
BeO	16.13	16.50	15.76	15.55
P_2O_5	44.05	39.74	44.31	43.25
H_2O	5.85	7.97	—	—
F	tr	0.87	11.32	2.06
Insoluble residue	0.44	2.02	—	—
P. p. p.	—	—	—	5.46
Total	—	100.76	104.60	100.86
Correction for fluoride to oxide equivalent		0.37	4.77	0.86
	100.51	100.39	99.83	100.00
Analyst	Wells (Doelter, 1914-1925)	Shannon (Palache and Shannon, 1928)	Mackintosh (Hidden and Mackintosh, 1884)	S.N. Fedorchuk (From the collection of A.I. Ginzburg)

hydroxyl-herderite (with a small fluorine content). As the fluorine content decreases, the refractive indices of the mineral increase (Table 68),[14] and its specific gravity decreases slightly (from 3.01 to 2.85).

The results of the chemical analyses of herderite (Table 70) fit well into the formula $CaBe\ PO_4\ (F,OH)$.

Herderite is a structural analogue of datolite $CaBSiO_4(OH)$ (Strunz, 1936); this is reflected in the resemblance in the crystal forms of both minerals and in the similarity of unit cell dimensions as given below (in Å):

	Herderite	Datolite
a_0	9.64	9.80
b_0	7.62	7.68
c_0	4.82	4.80

ORIGIN AND PARAGENESIS. Herderite, like beryllonite, is typically a late mineral in the albitic replacement complex of the beryl-containing pegmatites where the alternation of beryl takes place during albitization. The crystals of herderite are characteristic of the small leached cavities in the albitized zone, where they coat the surface of the earlier minerals—quartz, albite (cleavelandite), and apatite. Late tabular apatite occurs in many places with the herderite in these cavities.

[14] In Table 68 the lowest value of refractive indices given for herderite is 9 percent fluorine; the highest value, for hydroxyl-herderite, is 0.87 percent fluorine.

There are descriptions of aggregates of fibrous hydroxyl-herderite after beryllonite that are pseudomorphs (Palache and Shannon, 1928), and also of symplectic intergrowth of herderite and hurlbutite (Volborth, 1954a, 1954b, 1954c).

Cookeite is also associated with herderite; in the pegmatites of Madagascar it forms, with herderite, peculiar pseudomorphs after tourmaline.

Väyrynenite: (Mn,Fe)Be[PO_4](OH)

The manganese analogue of herderite is väyrynenite, which was found in 1954 in the pegmatites of Viitaniemi, Finland; it is one of the recently discovered beryllium phosphates.

This mineral is in pink and red irregular segregations and solid masses. Faceted crystals have not yet been found (Volborth 1954a, 1954b, 1954c). The physical properties of väyrynenite and its optical constants are given in Table 68.

The chemical composition of väyrynenite (Table 71) fits well into the formula (Mn,Fe)Be[PO_4] (OH), considering that the analyzed mineral apparently contained about 10 percent beryllonite.

The unit cell of väyrynenite contains 8 MnBe(PO_4)(OH). The chemical analysis of väyrynenite showed dominant manganese and 4.59 percent ferrous iron, which points to the occurrence of isomorphism between Mn^{2+} and Fe^{2+}, characteristic of the phosphate class, and allows one to assume that the ferrous analogue of väyrynenite FeBe[PO_4] (OH) occurs in nature.

Table 71 Chemical composition of vayrynenite

Components	%	Atomic quantities of		Number of atoms	Formula
		cations	oxygen		
Na_2O	1.42	046	023		
K_2O	1.18	026	013	Na, K—0.1	
CaO	1.82	032	032		(Mn, Fe) Be [PO_4] (OH) — 90%
BeO	12.10	484	484		NaBe [PO_4] — 10%
Al_2O_3	2.45	050	075	Be, Al—0.94	
MnO	30.57	428	428	Mn, Fe—0.87	
FeO	4.59	064	064	P — 1	
P_2O_5	40.36	566	1415		
H_2O^+	5.00	454	227	OH — 0.8	
H_2O^-	0.08				
	0.78				
Total	100.35				
Analyst	A. Volborth, 1954				

Table 72 Chemical composition of hurlbutite

Components	%	Without insoluble residue	Atom quantities of		Number of atoms per O_4
			Cations	Oxygen	
CaO	21.84	21.99	392	392	0.485~0.5
BeO	21.30	21.44	857	857	1.06 ~ 1
P_2O_5	56.19	56.57	797	1991	0.984~1
Insoluble residue	0.76	–	–	–	–
Total	100.09	100.00		3240	4

ORIGIN AND PARAGENESIS. In albitized beryl-bearing pegmatites, väyrynenite occurs in paragenesis with gilbertite and morinite, and is formed by the replacement of the earlier beryllium phosphates (hurlbutite and herderite) by manganese-containing solutions.

Hurlbutite: $CaBe_2[PO_4]_2$

The double phosphate of beryllium and calcium of the formula $CaBe_2[PO_4]_2$, named hurlbutite by M. E. Mrose (1952), was first discovered in an albitized pegmatite containing beryl and triphylite in Newport, New Hampshire, U.S.A. Later hurlbutite was also found in the beryl-bearing pegmatites of Viitaniemi, Finland, which contained various phosphates including beryllium phosphates (Volborth, 1954a, 1954b, 1954c).

Crystals of hurlbutite have a prismatic habit with a predominant development of the *c* (001) and *m* (110) faces, and are usually included in massive quartz or feldspar. The physical properties of hurlbutite and its optical characteristics are given in Table 68.

The chemical composition of hurlbutite fits well into the formula $CaBe_2[PO_4]_2$ (Table 72).

The unit cell of hurlbutite contains 4 $CaBe_2[PO_4]_2$.

A possible structural analogue of hurlbutite in the group of calcium borosilicates is danburite $CaB_2Si_2O_8$, which is related to the subclass of diorthosilicates with additional oxygen anions–$CaB_2[Si_2O_7]O$:[15]

	Hurlbutite	Danburite
a_o	8.29 Å	8.75 Å
b_o	8.80 Å	8.01 Å
c_o	7.81 Å	7.72 Å

[15] The artificiality of such a classification should be noted, because from the point of view of the crystal-chemical part played by boron in silicates, the formula of danburite should be assumed more correctly to be $Ca[B_2Si_2O_8]$.

ORIGIN AND PARAGENESIS. Hurlbutite is an early mineral in beryl-bearing pegmatites rich in phosphates; here, it is in close paragenesis with muscovite, albite, and triphylite. In a number of places, well developed hurlbutite crystals were found in the massive block quartz. Replacement of hurlbutite by albite, beryllonite, amblygonite, and other phosphates, and symplectic intergrowths of hurlbutite in herderite have been observed.

Faheyite: $(Mn, Mg)Fe_2^{3+}Be_2[PO_4] \cdot 6H_2O$

Faheyite, a hydrated phosphate of beryllium, ferric iron, and manganese, was discovered by M. L. Lindberg (1953).

This mineral is found in the secondary cavities of the albitized pegmatites of Sapucai, Minas Geraes, Brazil, in the form of fibrous aggregates. Individual acicular crystals of faheyite, 0.08 x 0.01 mm in size, are usually grouped into fibrous clusters and rosette-shaped formations which coat other minerals.

The physical properties of faheyite are listed in Table 68.

Ferric iron has a substantial role in the chemical composition of faheyite and is accompanied by manganese and magnesium (Table 73).

For this mineral Lindberg deduces the formula $(Mn,Mg,Na)Fe_2 \cdot Be_2PO_4 \cdot 6H_2O$, and explains the admixture of sodium, shown by the analysis, as the result of the isomorphous substitution of sodium for the divalent manganese.

In view of the unlikeliness of such an isomorphism, the occurrence of

Table 73 Chemical composition of faheyite

Components	%	Recalculation without insoluble residue	Atom quantities of		Number of atoms per O_4
			cations	oxygen	
Na_2O	0.84	0.93	0300	0150	0.050
K_2O	trace	trace	—	—	
MgO	1.14	1.26	0313	0313	0.208
MnO	5.99	6.61	0932	0932	
FeO	nil	—	—	—	
Fe_2O_3	21.42	23.65	2962	4443	0.499
Al_2O_3	0.10	0.11	0021	0032	
Mn_2O_3	nil	—	—	—	
BeO	7.26	8.02	3205	3205	0.536
P_2O_5	38.11	42.08	5928	14821	0.992
F	trace	—	—	—	
H_2O	14.90	16.45	—	—	
Insoluble residue	9.44	—	—	9131	
Total	99.20	99.11		23896	
Analyst	Lindberg, 1953				

sodium can be explained with greater probability by a mechanical admixture of any sodium-containing phosphate (perhaps beryllonite). This assumption is partly corroberated by a certain beryllium excess observed in the recalculation for O_4 (Tables 73, 74).

It is quite possible that a manganese analogue of faheyite, manganese-faheyite, occurs in nature.

The unit cell of faheyite contains 3 $(Mn,Mg)Fe_2Be_2 \cdot (PO_4)_4 \cdot 6H_2O$.

ORIGIN AND PARAGENESIS. The formation of faheyite is related to the late hydrothermal stage at the end of the formation of the phosphate-enriched Sapucai pegmatite, because fibrous masses of faheyite coat quartz crystals, and flat rosettes cover the surface of muscovite plates.

In association with faheyite are the following late phosphates, formed mostly by the alteration of triphylite: vivianite, childrenite, variscite, hureaulite, and moraesite.

Table 74 Recalculation of the analysis of faheyite for faheyite and beryllonite

Cations	Faheyite	Beryllonite	Faheyite. Recalculation for P = I	Formula
Na	–	0.050	–	
Mn, Mg	0.208	–	0.22	Faheyite (93.5%)
Fe, Al	0.499	–	0.53	
Be	0.486	0.050	0.51	Beryllonite (6.5%)
P	0.942	0.050	I	

Moraesite: $Be_2[PO_4](OH) \cdot 4H_2O$

Moraesite, structurally the simplest natural beryllium phosphate, was discovered by Lindberg in 1953 (Lindberg *et al.*, 1953) during the detailed mineralogical study of one of the beryl-bearing pegmatites of the Mines Geraes region, Brazil, which is characterized by abundant phophatic minerals.

Moraesite forms radiating spherolites and thick fibrous crusts on the associated minerals, and also is present as aggregates of thin acicular, brittle, long-prismatic crystals. The physical properties of moraesite and its optical characteristics are listed in Table 68.

The chemical composition of moraesite relates it to the basic, water-rich beryllium phosphates of the type $Be_{3-m}[PO_4](OH)_m \cdot {}^nH_2O$ (Table 75).

The unit cell of moraesite contains 12 $Be_2(PO_4)(OH) \cdot 4H_2O$.

ORIGIN AND PARAGENESIS. Moraesite forms in the final stages of pegmatite formation by dissolution and replacement of beryl by phosphorus-containing solutions.

The radiating formations and fibrous crusts of moraesite crystallize in leached out cavities in beryl, and coat the surface of the earlier minerals—albite, quartz, and muscovite—that accompany beryl. In paragenesis with moraesite are various phosphates—frondelite, hureaulite, childrenite, roscherite, vivianite, and variscite—that are the products of the transformation of triphylite, the primary phosphatic mineral in these pegmatites.

The nature of its paragenesis with the accompanying phosphates suggests a late segregation of moraesite, whose crystals usually grow on

Table 75 Chemical composition of moraesite

Components	%	Atom quantities of		Number of atoms per P = 1
		Cations	Oxygen	
BeO	25.28	1012	1012	2
Al_2O_3	none	—	—	
Fe_2O_3	0.11	—	—	
P_2O_5	34.76	491	1226	1
H_2O	39.80	—	2212	4.5
Insoluble residue	0.30	—	—	
Total	100.25		2238 without H_2O	

frondelite and other secondary phosphates; most probably the crystallization of moraesite resulted from residual beryllium and phosphorus-containing solutions after the separation of the main mass of the secondary phosphates that formed compounds with iron, manganese, calcium, and aluminum.

Kolbeckite: $Ca_{0.4}(Al,Be)_5[(P,Si)O_4]_4 \cdot 8H_2O$

Kolbeckite is the least studied mineral in the beryllium phosphate group; the information available is extremely scarce (Thurnwald and Benedetti-Pichler, 1932).

This mineral was discovered in the Schmiedeberge district, Saxony, in the form of fine blue crystals in a wolframite-bearing quartz vein, an association that distinguishes it from other beryllium phosphates, which, as a rule, are found in pegmatites.

The physical properties of kolbeckite are listed in Table 68.

The chemical composition of kolbeckite differs from that of other beryllium phosphates by the presence of silicon, which replaces part of the

Table 76 Chemical composition of kolbeckite

Components	%	Atom quantities of		Number of atoms per P + Si = 1	Calculated formula
		cations	oxygen		
Al_2O_3	21.35	418	627	0.66	P + Si = 630
Fe_2O_3	0.29	004	006		$O = \frac{2538}{630} = 4$
CaO	3.22	057	057	0.09	
BeO	8.74	350	350	0.55	$Ca_{0.09}Al_{0.66}Be_{0.55}[(P_{0.76}Si_{0.24})O_4]_4 \cdot 2H_2O$
SiO_2	9.25	154	308	0.24	
P_2O_5	33.80	476	1190	0.76	$Ca_{0.4}(Al, Be)_5[(P, Si)O_4]_4 \cdot 8H_2O$
H_2O	23.45		1300		
Total	100.10		2538 less H_2O		

phosphorus (Table 76). The derived formula can be simplified if it is assumed that calcium, which, compared with other cations, occurs in a very small proportion, is an occasional impurity. Then the formula of kolbeckite can be represented in the general form as $(Al,Be)_5[(P,Si)_4]_4 \cdot 8H_2O$.

The composition of kolbeckite apparently can serve as an example that illustrates the possibility of the compensational heterovalent isomorphism $P^{5+} + Al^{3+}$ for $Si^{4+} + 2Be^{2+}$.

Table 77 Chemical analysis of beryllium-tengerite

Components	%	Atom quantities of		Number of atoms
		cations	oxygen	
$(Y)_2O_3$	40.8	362	443	1.04
$(Ce)_2O_3$	7.0	043	064	
BeO	9.7	388	388	1
Fe_2O_3	4.0	050	075	—
CO_2	19.6	425	850	1.1
SiO_2	0.4	—	—	—
H_2O^+	14.1	1390	695	—
H_2O^-	3.2		178	
Total	100.0		1745 without Fe_2O_3 and H_2O	
Analyst	W. E. Hidden, 1905			

CARBONATES

Beryllium-tengerite: (Y,Ce)Be[Co_3]$(OH)_3 \cdot H_2O$

To distinguish beryllium-tengerite from tengerite, the name beryllium-tengerite is given to the double basic carbonate of yttrium and beryllium, which is an alteration product of gadolinite. It was found in the Baringer Hill deposit, Texas, U.S.A., (Hidden, 1905).

This mineral, found as crusts of radiating spherolites, has been investigated only slightly, and its physical properties are not well known.

The chemical composition of this mineral (Table 77) fits well into the formula (Y,CE)Be $CO_3(OH)_3 \cdot H_2O$[16] this is to be expected in view of the special origin of beryllium-tengerite.

[16] The admixture of iron carbonate was excluded in recalculation.

CHAPTER 3

Peculiarities of the Isomorphous Entry of Beryllium into Crystal Structures of Minerals

Beryllium is one of the elements widely distributed as isomorphous admixtures in various minerals. It is detected by means of accurate analytical methods in ten-thousandths and, less commonly, in thousandths of 1 percent in an overwhelming majority of endogenous and exogenous rocks and minerals. Yet the isomorphous admixture of beryllium, measured by hundredths, and still less by tenths of 1 percent or by a few percent is rarely found and is only known for a limited number of minerals. The isomorphous entry of beryllium into the crystal lattice of minerals, determined by the dimensions, charge, and polarizing properties of its ion, is extremely common and is an excellent illustration of the close relationship between the atomic structure of an element and its behavior in natural processes. Of more than 100 elements of Mendeleev's periodic system, only three ions, Si^{4+}, P^{5+}, and V^{5+}, have dimensions close to those of the bivalent positive ion of beryllium. The coordination number of Be^{2+} with respect to oxygen is always 4, as it is for silicon and zinc. However, beryllium differs from zinc in the dimensions of the ion:

$$Be^{2+} = 0.34 \text{ Å}, \; Zn^{2+} = 0.80 \text{ Å}.$$

Pentavalent phosphorus and pentavalent vanadium, whose ionic radii are close to that of beryllium, are characterized by a distinctly different electronegativity.

It should be noted that, notwithstanding the difference of the ionic radii, the dimensions of the cation-oxygen tetrahedra of beryllium and zinc are probably close, owing to the high polarization capacity of the latter. This determines the structural similarity found in a number of the natural compounds of these elements. A certain similarity of the crystal-chemical properties of beryllium and zinc also can be explained by the closeness of the ionization potentials and excitation potentials of their valency electrons (Chapter 1).

The only positively charged ion, whose radius and electronegativity are close to those of beryllium, is silicon. This similarity is expressed very clearly in the oxygenic tetrahedral complexes of both elements, which are of virtually equal size. It should be also noted that, unlike silicon compounds, there is the possibility of substituting hydroxyl for a part of the oxygen (Belov, 1950) in the beryllium-oxygen tetrahedra.

A very interesting crystal-chemical feature of beryllium is the structural analogy between the polymorphous varieties of beryllium fluoride BeF_2 and the various modifications of SiO_2; this was first established by Brandenberger (Brandenberger, 1932). The analogy between the structures of the tetrahedral complexes $[BeF_4]^{2-}$ and $[SiO_4]^{4-}$ is also noted by Warren and Hill (Warren and Hill, 1934), who studied in detail the structure of the vitreous beryllium fluoride.

At present there are three polymorphous varieties of BeF_2 known. Two of them (αBeF_2 and γBeF_2) are structural analogues of cristobalite, while one modification, obtained by the crystallization of BeF_2 in the presence of NaF in the range of 425 to 528°C, displays a clear structural similarity to α-quartz.

The quartz-like polymorphous variety of BeF_2 crystallizes, like quartz, in the hexagonal system and has very close parameters of crystal lattice:

α-quartz	$a_0 = 4.90$ Å; $c_0 = 5.39$ Å; $c_0/a_0 = 1.10$
BeF_2	$a_0 = 4.72$ Å; $c_0 = 5.18$ Å; $c_0/a_0 = 1.10$

Because of the identical coordination number of silicon and beryllium with respect to oxygen, the very close ionic radii of Be^{2+} and Si^{4+}, and the radii of the complexes $[BeO_4]^{6-}$, $[BeF_4]^{2-}$, and $[SiO_4]^{4-}$, it can be seen that beryllium enters the structure of some silicates by replacing the silicon-oxygen tetrahedral complexes with beryllium-oxygen and beryllium-fluoride (and the analogous beryllium-hydroxyl complexes. At the same time the occurrence of numerous beryllium minerals, some of which are fairly widespread and form considerable accumulations in a number of places, suggests that the heterovalent isomorphism between beryllium and silicon can occur under certain limited conditions, which are determined by the physico-chemical features of the mineral forming process. Otherwise, a complete dissemination of beryllium as a result of the capture of Be^{2+} ions by the very common silicates would be expected, and this does not take place. Obviously, the main factor against the isomorphous capture of beryllium by silicates is the difference between the charges of beryllium and silicon. To effect the isomorphous substitution of Be^{2+} for Si^{4+}, another cation with a high charge, which compensates the disturbance of the electrostatic equilibrium of the lattice, must enter simultaneously into the lattice.

Thus the possibility of the isomorphous substitution of $[BeO_4]^{6-}$ for $[SiO_4]^{4-}$ is determined to a certain extent by the presence or absence, during the mineral-forming process, of free high-valency cations which can compensate in the lattice of any silicate mineral for the disturbance of electrostatic equilibrium by the substitution of Be^{2+} for Si^{4+}. However, the substitution, in the oxygenic tetrahedral complex, of the less electronegative beryllium for silicon does not result in a more energetically stable crystal, because such substitution weakens the degree of covalency and consequently the bond strength in the silicon-oxygen framework of the crystal structure of the mineral. The existence of a number of internal and external causes which oppose the silicon-beryllium isomorphism with a parallel entry of high-valency cations into the mineral structure is responsible for the fact that such isomorphism rarely occurs on a widespread scale in nature.

There is apparently a greater possibility of isomorphism between silicon and beryllium with the parallel replacement of oxygen by fluorine or hydroxyl. However, in the latter case the entry into the mineral structure of a beryllium-fluoride complex instead of the silicon-oxygen complex, which is twice as strong, is energetically disadvantageous for the crystal lattice as a whole, and this should substantially reduce the extent of such isomorphism.

When analyzing the features of the heterovalent isomorphism of beryllium with cations of kindred properties, one should bear in mind that there exists a possibility of an isomorphous substitution of beryllium not only for silicon, but also for aluminum. Aluminum, when in fourfold coordination, also replaces silicon with the formation, in aluminosilicates, of tetrahedral complexes whose dimensions are similar to those of silicon-oxygen complexes. In nature, the isomorphism of beryllium and aluminum is only observed in aluminosilicates in which aluminum in tetrahedral coordination plays the structural role of silicon. In comparison with silicon, the smaller difference in valencies and the close electronegativity of beryllium and aluminum determine the wider limits of their isomorphism, which, in some cases, are expressed by a few percent.[1]

As a result of a detailed analysis of the available material dealing with the detection of beryllium in various minerals, it is possible to draw up the following types of beryllium isomorphism:

I. Heterovalent silicon-beryllium isomorphism with the participation of high valency cations:

1. Feldspars, nepheline garnet, aegirine, steenstrupine, allanite	$(K,Na)^{+} + [SiO_4]^{4-} \leftarrow (Tr)^{3+} + [BeO_4]^{6-}$
2. Allanite	$2Ca^{2+} + [SiO_4]^{4-} \leftarrow 2\,(Tr)^{3+} + [BeO_4]^{6-}$
3. Thortveitite	$2Sc^{3+} + [SiO_4]^{4-} \leftarrow 2Zr^{4+} + [BeO_4]^{6-}$
4. Clinohumite, pyroxenes, amphiboles	$Mg^{2+} + [SiO_4]^{4-} \leftarrow Ti^{4+} + [BeO_4]^{6-}$

II. Heterovalent silicon-beryllium isomorphism with the participation of fluorine and hydroxyl:

Vesuvianite, epidote, allanite	$[SiO_4]^{4-} \leftarrow [BeO_2(F,OH)_2]^{4-}$

III. Heterovalent silicon-beryllium isomorphism with the participations of hydroxyl:

Bavenite, micas, beryllium-margarite, margarite, muscovite, lepidolite, etc.	$[AlO_4]^{5-} \leftarrow [BeO_3(OH)]^{5-}$

IV. Isostructural isomorphous series of beryllium compounds:

1. Phenacite-willemite	$Be_2[SiO_4]$ — $Zn_2[SiO_4]$
2. Bertrandite-calamine	$Be_4[Si_2O_7](OH)_2$ — $Zn_4[Si_2O_7](OH)_2 \cdot H_2O$
3. Beryl-cordierite	$Al_2Be_3[Si_6O_{18}]$ — $(Mg,Fe)_2Al_3[Si_5AlO_{18}]$
4. Chrysoberyl-olivine	Al_2BeO_4 — $Mg_2[SiO_4]$
5. Gadolinite-homilite	$Y_2Fe^{2+}Be_2Si_2O_{10}$ — $Ca_2Fe^{2+}B_2Si_2O_{10}$
6. Calcium fluoroberyllate-cyrtolite-thorite (orangite)	Ca, $Be(F,OH)_4$ — $Zr[SiO_4]$ — $Th[SiO_4]$

[1] In one of the earlier papers of the author (Beus, 1953b) it was shown that the possibility of an isomorphous substitution of beryllium for aluminum has not been proved. Owing to data obtained later, it is possible to change this opinion.

7. Sodium lithium fluoroberyllate-diopside (possible series) — $Na, LiBe_2(F,OH)_6 - Ca, Mg[Si_2O_6]$
8. Herderite-datolite (possible series) — $Ca\ Be[PO_4](OH,F) - CaB[SiO_4](OH)$

V. Minerals containing an admixture of beryllium, whose location in the mineral structure is not clear:

1. Wavellite
2. Metamict tantalo-niobates.

The specific examples given below show the occurrence in nature of the various forms of beryllium entry into minerals.

Heterovalent Silicon-Beryllium Isomorphism with the Participation of Rare Earths, Titanium, and Zirconium

The isomorphous substitution of beryllium for silicon with the compensation of the disturbed electrostatic equilibrium by the parallel substitution of rare-earth elements for the monovalent or bivalent cations, is apparently widespread, although such substitution does not result in an increase in energy (Beus, 1953a). In an overwhelming majority of cases, the limits of simultaneous isomorphous entry of beryllium and rare earths into the silicates are very narrow and are expressed in thousandths of 1 percent. Only rarely, in some rare-earth minerals proper, is there an appreciable beryllium content (tenths of 1 percent, and even a few percent). An interesting regularity was found during an investigation of the distribution of isomorphous beryllium admixture in feldspars of the normal granitic pegmatites. A comparison of many chemical determinations of beryllium in the minerals of this group disclosed that its highest contents (thousandths of 1 percent) are found in the feldspars of some pegmatites enriched in rare-earth minerals. In particular, relatively increased beryllium concentrations were found in oligoclase and microcline-perthite from the block zone of Karelian pegmatites, which contain appreciable proportions of the yttrium-earth tantalo-niobates (in oligoclase 0.003 to 0.004 percent; in microcline 0.002 to 0.003 percent) (Beus and Fedorchuk, 1955).

The analysis of feldspars for rare earths (semiquantitative determination) confirmed the presence of yttrium in oligoclase, and of lanthanum in microcline, in proportions from 0.001 to 0.01 percent. No beryllium-bearing minerals are found in these pegmatites.

Higher beryllium concentrations were noted in some minor minerals of the rare-earth granitic pegmatites, such as garnet, biotite, and musco-

Table 78 Recalculation of the analysis of garnet

Components	%	Atom quantities of		Number of atoms per 12 atoms of oxygen
		cations	oxygen	
SiO_2	34.93	583	1166	2.93
Al_2O_3	14.80	290	435	1.45
B_2O_3	0.15	008	012	—
Fe_2O_3	16.60	208	312	1.05
Y_2O_3	2.45	022	033	0.11
MnO	22.28	314	314	1.58
CaO	4.52	080	080	0.4
BeO	0.39	015	015	0.07
Na_2O	1.67	059	027	0.27
K_2O	0.16	004	002	
H_2O	0.45	—	—	—
CO_2	0.41	—	—	—
Total	98.81		2396	

vite. The presence of rare earths was always established qualitatively.

T. Iimori (1938), when analyzing garnet from the Iisaka Region pegmatite, Fukushima prefecture, Japan, enriched in rare-earth minerals, found in it 0.39 percent BeO and 2.45 percent rare earths of the yttrium group. The recalculation of the analysis given in Table 78, fits well into the crystal-chemical garnet formula: $(Mn_{1.58}Fe_{0.50}Ca_{0.28}Na_{0.28}Y_{0.11})(Al_{1.45}Fe_{0.55})\cdot[(Si_{2.93}Be_{0.07})O_{12}]$.

In a number of places beryllium is found in much higher proportions in some rare-earth minerals, whose complex composition makes it possible to effect many mutually compensating isomorphous substitutions in both the cationic and anionic parts of the minerals, such as allanite, steenstrupine, and chevkinite.

The peculiar features of the isomorphous entry of beryllium into allanite will be analyzed below, during the discussion of the isomorphism between $[SiO_4]^{4-}$ and $[BeO_2(OH,F)_2]^{4-}$; we quote here, as an example, the recalculation of an analysis of beryllium-containing steenstrupine, carried out by Blomstrand (Doelter, 1914-1925). Although the analyzed specimen was a partly altered steenstrupine, it is convenient for recalculation, because the analysis gives separate figures for beryllium, aluminum, and the yttrium and cerium rare earths.

As a basis for recalculation, the formula of steenstrupine was used as given by Betekhtin (1950), $(Ca,Na)_4Mn^{2+}(Ce,La,Al,Fe^{3+})_6Si_9O_{27}(OH)_7\cdot 3H_2O$; it had the ratio 20:27 for the sum of cation atoms to oxygen atoms (Table 79).

As a result of recalculation, a formula of beryllium steenstrupine is obtained, which differs from that referred to before by a smaller (Ca + Na) value (3 as against 4) and by a correspondingly higher value of the sum of high-valency cations (8 compared with 7). The increased hydroxyl content in the formula is probably due to the incipient oxidation of the mineral (in particular, by the higher degree of oxidation of manganese).

The analysis of the beryllium-containing chevkinite from Nelson, Virginia, U.S.A., can also be easily recalculated if the grouping of beryllium with silicon is assumed. It should be noted that the formula of chevkinite has not yet been formally established. A. G. Betekhtin (1950) indicated that chevkinite was a rare-earth metamict analogue of sphene with the formula $(Ca,Ce)Ti[SiO_4]O$. However, the recalculation of analyses of chevkinite for $Si = 1$ results in fairly diverse formulae: $(La,Th,Ca)(Ti,Fe)[SiO_4]O$, $(La,Ca)(Ti,Fe)\cdot[SiO_4]_2(O,OH)_4$, etc.

As a result of the recalculation of the analysis of beryllium-containing chevkinite for $Si + Be = 2$ (Table 80), the formula $(Ca,Ce)(Ti,Fe)_2[(BeSi)O_4]_2(OH,O)$ was obtained; it differs from that given by A. G. Betekhtin in that the number of the calcium group cations is smaller by the factor of two and that the numbers of oxygen atoms and the hydroxyl groups in the side chain are correspondingly reduced.

The isomorphous substitution of beryllium for silicon with the parallel entry of a tetravalent cation into the mineral structure can be illustrated by the example of titanoclinohumite and thortveitite.

Table 79 Recalculation of the analysis of beryllium steenstrupine

Components	%	Recalculation for the cation total = 20			
		Atom quantities of		Number of atoms	Sum of cationic valencies
		cations	oxygen		
SiO_2	20.61	343	686	6.75	×4 = 27.00
BeO	1.22	049	049	0.96	×2 = 1.92
P_2O_5	4.53	064	160	1.26	×5 = 6.30
Na_2O	2.53	080	040	1.57	×1 = 1.57
CaO	4.22	075	075	1.47	×2 = 2.94
$(Y)_2O_3$	2.19	017	025	0.33	×3 = 0.99
$(La,Dy)_2O_3$	15.52	108	162	2.12	×3 = 6.36
Ce_2O_3	17.03	104	156	2.04	×3 = 6.12
ThO_2	3.84	014	028	0.24	×4 = 0.96
PbO	1.02	004	004	0.08	×2 = 0.16
Nb_2O_5	1.58	012	030	0.23	×5 = 1.15
Al_2O_3	0.40	008	012	0.16	×3 = 0.48
Mn_2O_3	5.79	074	111	1.45	×3 = 4.35
Fe_2O_3	5.18	066	099	1.30	×3 = 3.90
$H_2O^{\pm}$	12.73	—	—	—	—
Total	98.39	1018	1637	19.96	64.20

Formula:

$$(Na, Ca)_{3.04}(Y, La, Ce)_{4.81}(Mn^{3+}, Fe^{3+}, Al)_3(Si, P, Be)_{8.97}O_{27}(OH)_{10},$$

$$(Na, Ca)_3(Y, La, Ce)_5(Mn^{3+}F^{3+})_3(Si, P, Be)_9O_{27}(OH)_{10}.$$

Table 80 Recalculation of beryllium-bearing chevkinite for Be + Si = 2

Components	%	Atom quantities of cations	Atom quantities of oxygen	Numbers of atoms per Be + Si = 2	
SiO_2	23.28	387	775	1.64	2
BeO	2.15	086	086	0.36	
TiO_2	21.16	265	530	1.12	1.89
ZrO_2	2.29	019	038	0.08	
MgO	0.64	016	016	0.06	
FeO	5.56	078	078	0.33	
Fe_2O_3	5.65	070	105	0.30	
CaO	5.48	098	098	0.41	1.22
Ce_2O_3	11.89	072	108	0.30	
Dy_2O_3	15.38	082	123	0.35	
La_2O_3	4.98	030	045	0.13	
Na_2O	0.32	010	005	0.04	
H_2O	1.90	212	106		
Total	100.68		2114	$O=\frac{2114}{236}=8.957$	

Analyst C. Hintze, 1897

The characteristic crystal-chemical feature of the humite group minerals is the possibility of substitution of Ti^{4+} for Mg^{2+} with the parallel compensational substitution of O_2 for a part of (OH) (Borneman-Starynkevich and Myasnikov, 1950). Under suitable geochemical conditions, the compensation can also take place by substituting Be^{2+} for Si^{4+}; this is known in some contact-metasomatic deposits in which beryllium-containing clinohumite is found. The only complete analysis of beryllium clinohumite, carried out by Zambonini (Zambonini, 1919), can be used to study the location of beryllium in the structure of the mineral in accordance with the considerations referred to above (Table 81).

The substitution of beryllium for silicon with the parallel substitution of zirconium for scandium, which probably takes place in thortveitite, unfortunately cannot be illustrated by a similar recalculation, owing to the incompleteness of chemical analyses given in the literature. However, the sole fact of beryllium and zirconium being simultaneously present in the analysis of thortveitite already suggests the possibility of such isomorphism.

Heterovalent Silicon-Beryllium Isomorphism with the Participation of Fluorine and Hydroxyl

The heterovalent isomorphous substitution of beryllium for silicon, with the simultaneous substitution of fluorine or hydroxyl for oxygen, is widespread, as shown by analytical data, although the limits of such isomorphism are, as mentioned before, narrow and usually do not exceed tenths of 1 percent for either of the pair of isomorphous ions.

The most clearly analyzed form of isomorphism is found in minerals of the vesuvianite group, whose individual representatives are characterized by abnormally high beryllium concentrations, in excess of 1 percent.

The occurrence of high beryllium concentrations in some vesuvianite specimens was first indicated by C. Palache and H. Bauer (1930), who investigated the vesuvianite of the Franklin deposit, New Jersey, U.S.A. The unusually high beryllium content (9.2 percent) in the analyzed specimen prompted some investigators (Washington, 1931) to express the opinion that beryllium was the normal component of vesuvianite and that it had not been previously shown by chemical analysis, owing to its similarity to aluminum. However, accurate analyses of a great number of specimens from various deposits, which were carried out later, showed that beryllium is found only in vesuvianite from deposits of a certain type (skarn formations at the contact between beryllium-bearing granites with limestones), the beryllium content of the minerals usually varying within the limits of hundredths and tenths of 1 percent, rarely attaining 1 percent.

The nature of isomorphous entry of beryllium into vesuvianite has remained obscure until quite recently, especially as the only complete analysis of beryllium vesuvianite, before 1955, given in the paper by Palache and Bauer (1930), cannot be recalculated into a formula that would bear any resemblance to the formula of vesuvianite; this places the analysis under a shadow of doubt. More recent analyses of beryllium-rich

Table 81 Recalculation of beryllium titano-humite to O_{16}

Components	%	Atom quantities of		Numbers of atoms per O_{16}
		cations	oxygen	
SiO_2	36.83	613	1226	3.89
BeO	1.30	052	052	0.33
MgO	51.53	1278	1278	8.11
CaO	0.03	—	—	—
FeO	4.90	068	068	0.43
MnO	0.28	004	004	0.03
NiO	0.07	001	001	
PbO	0.14	—	—	—
Fe_2O_3	0.42	006	009	0.05
Al_2O_3	0.07	002	003	
TiO_2	1.92	024	048	0.15
K_2O	0.09	002	001	0.01
Na_2O	0.03	—	—	—
H_2O^+	2.99	332	166	2.1
F	0.03	—	—	—
Total	100.68		2686	

Formula:

$$(M^{2+}_{8.57}Ti_{0.15}M^{3+}_{0.05})\,[(Si_{0.97}Be_{0.08})\,O_4]_4\,(OH)_2.$$

vesuvianite from the same deposit (Franklin, New Jersey, U.S.A.), quoted in the paper by C. S. Hurlbut (1955), give cation ratios completely different from those in the first analysis. Moreover, these analyses disclose fluorine, which is completely absent in Palache's analysis.

On examining the complete analyses of beryllium-bearing vesuvianite, one notices a close, direct relation between the amount of beryllium and the content of fluorine and hydroxyl in the mineral (Table 82). Taking into account the structural analogy of the tetrahedra complexes $[SiO_4]$ and $[BeF_4]$ as well as the fact that beryllium fluoride is the most probable form of beryllium transfer under conditions of a high fluorine concentration, one may assume the possibility of beryllium being substituted in vesuvianite for silicon, with the parallel substitution of fluorine and hydroxyl for a part of the oxygen ions in the beryllium-oxygen tetrahedra.

The recalculation of analyses of beryllium-bearing vesuvianite to the structural formula, derived by F. Machatschki (1953), showed that all of the fluorine and hydroxyl must be introduced into the radical in order to compensate for the entry of beryllium instead of silicon in the vesuvianite structure. A recalculation based on the sum $O + F + OH = 34$ yielded atom ratios which fit fairly well into the formula $Ca_8(Al,Fe,Mg)_6[(Si,Be)_9(O,F,OH)_{34}]$[2] (Table 83).

Thus beryllium vesuvianite can be considered to be the structural analogue of anhydrous vesuvianite without the OH group in the side chain (Beus, 1957).

Beryllium allanite (Table 84) is also an excellent example for illustrating the complex nature of compensation during the isomorphous substitution of beryllium for silicon.

The occurrence of an isomorphous admixture of beryllium in some allanite, mainly from granitic pegmatites, was noticed more than once by a number of investigators (Chernik, 1907; Iimori, 1939). When investigating the crystal-chemical features of the epidote-group minerals, F. Machatschki (1938) pointed for the first time to the possibility of substituting beryllium and phosphorus in beryllium-bearing allanite for silicon, and expressed the assumption that allanite belonged to silicates with a chain structure having this general formula:

$$(Ca,Ce^{3+})_2(Al,Fe,Mg^{2+})_2[(Si,Al,Be)O_3]_4(OH,F).$$

The recalculation of analyses of beryllium-bearing allanite (allowing for the possible partial isomorphism between bivalent iron and the yttrium rare earths), fits very well into the structural scheme suggested by Machatschki (Table 85), and yields the following formulae:

1. Beryllium allanite from Saxony

$$(Y,Ce,Ca)_2(Fe,Y,Al)_2[(Si,Be)_4O_{12}].$$

[2] Almost the same figures are obtained in recalculation from $Si + Be = 9$.

Table 82 Recalculation of chemical analyses of beryllium vesuvianite

Components	Franklin, New Jersey, U. S. A.									Kazakh, USSR		
	1			2			3			4		
	%	Atom quantities of		%	Atom quantities of		%	Atom quantities of		%	Atom quantities of	
		cations	oxygen		cations	oxygen		cations	oxygen		cations	oxygen
SiO_2	34.25	568	1136	34.83	574	1148	36.61	609	1218	39.10	651	1302
BeO	9.20	367	367	3.95	158	158	1 56	062	062	0.77	031	031
Al_2O_3	9.70	190	285	12.98	254	381	16.67	328	492	16.40	322	483
Fe_2O_3 } FeO	trace	—	—	5.69	072	108	3.31	042	063	6.32	080	120
MgO	3.17	079	079	2.91	072	072	2.87	071	071	2.79	069	069
MnO	4.84	068	068	0.24	003	003	3.28	046	046	1.69	024	024
ZnO	4.86	060	060	—	—	—	0.14	002	002	—	—	—
CaO	33.15	591	591	33.84	603	603	33.64	600	600	32.29	576	576
Na_2O	—	—	—	0.86	028	014	0.17	006	003	—	—	—
K_2O	—	—	—	0.08			0.26	006	003	—	—	—
H_2O	1.31	146	073	0.86	096	048	0.68	076	038	—	—	—
F	?		?	3.07		162	0.91	—	047	1.24	—	065
Total	100.48		2659	99.31		2535	100.10		2598	100.60		2605
Correction for fluoride to oxide equivalent				1.29			0.38			0.52		
				98.03			99.72			100.08		
Analyst or source	C. Palache, H. Bauer, 1930			C. S. Hurlbut, 1955						From the collection of A. M. Zasedatelev		

2. Beryllium allanite from Norway

$$(Ca,Fe,Y,Ce,Na)_2(Al,Fe,^{2+},Fe^{3+})_2[(Si,Be,Al)_4O_{11}(OH)]\cdot nH_2O$$

3. Beryllium allanite from Japan

$$(Ce,Fe^{2+},Y,Ca)_2(Al,Fe^{2+},Fe^{3+})_2[(Si,Be,Al)_4O_{12}](OH).$$

4. Beryllium allanite from Sweden

$$(Ce,K,Y,Ca,Fe^{2+})_2\cdot(Al,Fe^{3+},Mg,Fe^{2+})_2[(Si,Be,Al,P)_4O_{11}(OH,F)](OH).$$

Heterovalent Aluminum-Beryllium Isomorphism with the Participation of Hydroxyl

The heterovalent isomorphism of aluminum and beryllium in tetrahedral coordination can be illustrated by the example of bavenite, margarite, and some other micas. Although the structure of bavenite had not

Table 83 Recalculation of analyses of beryllium-bearing vesuvianite to $O+F+OH=34$

	2[a]		3[a]		4[a]	
Na	0.36	8.16	—	8.33	—	7.75
Ca	7.8		7.74		7.44	
Mn	—		0.60		0.31	
$Fe^{2+}+Fe^{3+}$	0.94	5.18	0.54	5.69	1	6.06
Mg	0.94		0.9		0.9	
Al	3.3		4.25		4.16	
Si	7.4	9.4	7.9	8.7	8.5	8.9
Be	2.0		0.8		0.4	
OH	1.25	34	1	34	—	34
F	2.10		0.6		0.3	
O	30.65		32.4		33.7	

[a] The figures correspond to the numbers of analyses in Table 82

been determined until now, the recalculation of analyses results in the formula $Ca_4(Be,Al)_4Si_9O_{26-n}(OH)_{2+n}$. At the same time, the ratio of amounts of the isomorphous aluminum and beryllium atoms in bavenite varies according to analyses between $Al_{1.76}Be_{2.44}$ and $Al_{1.20}Be_{2.86}$.

Another interesting example of an analogous isomorphism is found in the minerals of the bityite–beryllium-margarite–bowleyite group. It is known that a very characteristic feature of brittle micas of the margarite type is the occurrence of a number of isomorphous admixtures which complicate to a large extent the composition of minerals of this group. The simplified structural formula of margarite is usually represented as

Table 84 Chemical analyses of beryllium allanite (muromontite)

Components	Saxony			Nesgrube, Norway			Iisaka, Japan			Skuleboda, Sweden		
	%	Atom quantities of		%	Atom quantities of		%	Atom quantities of		%	Atom quantities of	
		cations	oxygen		cations	oxygen		cations	oxygen		cations	oxygen
SiO_2	31.09	505	1010	31.03	516	1032	30.58	509	1018	23.93	399	798
BeO	5.52	225	225	3.71	148	148	2.49	100	100	3.83	153	153
P_2O_5	—	—	—	—	—	—	—	—	—	0.23	003	008
Al_2O_3	2.24	044	066	9.29	182	273	12.71	250	375	10.84	213	319
Fe_2O_3	—	—	—	—	—	—	5.74	72	108	7.68	096	144
FeO	11.23	156	156	20.68	290	290	10.82	150	150	3.00	042	042
MgO	0.42	010	010	2.06	051	051	—	—	—	0.95	024	024
TiO_2	—	—	—	—	—	—	—	—	—	0.26	003	003
ZrO_2	—	—	—	—	—	—	0.57	004	008	—	—	—
MgO	0.90	013	013	0.07	001	001	2.05	029	029	0.12	002	002
CaO	0.71	013	013	6.68	120	120	8.20	146	146	2.43	043	043
SrO	—	—	—	—	—	—	—	—	—	0.05	001	001
ThO_2	—	—	—	—	—	—	0.26	001	002	1.03	004	008
$(Y)_2O_3$	37.14	328	492	1.02	010	015	23.94[a]	150	225	6.10	054	081
$(Ce)_2O_3$	9.08	084	136	11.09	069	103				17.50	103	155
Na_2O	0.65	022	011	0.56	018	009				0.59	018	009
K_2O	0.17	004	002	0.90	020	010	3.33	370	185	1.98	042	021
H_2O^+	0.85 (±)	094	047	} 12.24						7.98	886	442
F	—						—			1.92		
H_2O^-	—						—			0.19		
CO_2	—						—			8.84		
C	—						—			0.83		
Total	100.00	1404	2134	99.33	1425	2052	100.69	1411	2161	100.31	1200	1811
Analyst or source	Kerndt (1848) from G. P. Chernik, 1907			Ferbes from G. P. Chernik, 1907			T. Iimori, 1939			P. Quensel, 1944		

[a] The recalculation is based on the molecular weight = 320

Table 85 Recalculation of the chemical analysis of beryllium-bearing allanite (muromontite) for the cation sum = 8

Cations	Saxony		Nesgrube, Norway		Iisaka, Japan		Skuleboda, Sweden	
	Number of atoms	Sum of cationic valencies	Number of atoms	Sum of cationic valencies	Number of atoms	Sum of cationic valencies	Number of cations	Sum of cationic valencies
Si	2.89	×4 = 11.56	2.90	×4 = 11.60	2.87	×4 = 11.48	2.66	×4 = 10.64
Be	1.28	×2 = 2.56	0.83	×2 = 1.66	0.56	×2 = 1.12	1.00	×2 = 2.00
P	—	—	—	—	—	—	0.02	×5 = 0.10
Al	0.25	×3 = 0.75	0.27	} ×3 = 3.06	0.57	} ×3 = 4.23	0.32	} ×3 = 4.26
			0.75		0.84		1.12	
Fe^{3+}	—	—	—	—	0.46	×3 = 1.38	0.64	×3 = 1.92
Ti, Zr	—	—	—	—	0.02	×4 = 0.08	0.02	×4 = 0.08
Mg	0.06	×2 = 0.12	0.28	×2 = 0.56	—	—	0.16	×2 = 0.32
Fe^{2+}	0.89	×2 = 1.78	1.01	} ×2 = 3.32	0.71	} ×2 = 1.70	0.08	} ×2 = 0.56
			0.65		0.14		0.20	
	0.63 }							
(Y)	1.24 }	×3 = 5.16	} 0.44	×3 = 1.32	0.85	×3 = 2.55	0.36	×3 = 1.08
(Ce)	0.48	×3 = 1.44					0.69	×3 = 2.07
Th	—	--	—	—	—	—	0.03	×4 = 0.12
Ca	0.07	×2 = 0.14	} 0.68	×2 = 1.36	0.82	×2 = 1.64	0.31	×2 = 0.62
Mn	0.07	×2 = 0.14			0.16	×2 = 0.32		
(Na, K)	0.14	×1 = 0.14	0.23	×1 = 0.23	—	—	0.40	×1 = 0.40
Total	8.00	24.24	8.04	23.11	8.00	24.50	7.98	24.17

$CaAl_2[Al_2Si_2O_{10}](OH)_2$; however, along with the main elements occurring in the structure of the mineral, the analyses usually detect a number of admixtures, the most common being sodium, lithium, magnesium, iron, manganese, chromium, fluorine, and, as already mentioned, beryllium.

When turning our attention to the features of the entry of beryllium into the margarite structure, we may assume, on the basis of the crystal-chemical features of beryllium referred to above, that it can enter into only the aluminum-silicon-oxygen radical, where beryllium can be substituted for aluminum or silicon in tetrahedral coordination.

On the basis of the recalculation of analyses (Chapter 2), the compensation of the disturbed electrostatic equilibrium of the lattice is effected according to the scheme $[AlO_4]^{5-} \leftarrow [BeO_3(OH,F)]^{5-}$. Detailed recalculations show that the previously assumed (Beus, 1956c) silicon-beryllium isomorphism scheme for the margarite-group minerals is less probable.

Considerably smaller limits of the isomorphous entry of beryllium were found in other micas. Muscovites from beryllium-bearing pegmatites have a beryllium content of 0.003 to 0.014 percent (mean value of 25 analyses of muscovite from various deposits amounts to 0.006 percent), which is more than ten times the mean beryllium content of the lithosphere, and thrice the content of beryllium derived from the granitic pegmatites (Beus and Fedorchuk, 1955). Like muscovite from the rare-earth pegmatites, beryllium is present everywhere (roughly in the same proportions) in the muscovites of greisens, especially in those with a higher fluorine content.

A higher beryllium content was also noted in phlogopite (up to 0.06 percent) and biotite (up to 0.003 percent) from the pegmatite deposits of the "crossing line," which contain an abundance of fluorine.

Isostructural Isomorphism of Beryllium Compounds with Zinc, Zirconium, Thorium, and Other Silicates

The resemblance between the crystal structures of a number of zinc silicates and some beryllium minerals indicate that, given suitable conditions, isomorphous mixtures are likely to occur between analogous beryllium and zinc minerals (Beus, 1953b). Phenacite and willemite offer a specific example of such structural similarity:

Phenacite:	triginal system	$Be_2[SiO_4]$, a_{rh} —8.69 Å; α =107°46′
Willemite:	trigonal system	$Zn_2[SiO_4]$, a_{rh} — 7.68 Å; α = 108°01′.

Indeed, when these two geochemically different elements occasionally meet in the process of mineral formation, beryllium is captured by the zinc silicates, as shown by examples of beryllium-containing willemites of the peculiar contact deposits in the Franklin region, New Jersey, U.S.A.

Another beryllium mineral that has an analogue among zinc silicates is bertrandite $Be_4[Si_2O_7](OH)_2$, whose structure is substantially similar to that of calamine $Zn_4[Si_2O_7]\cdot(OH_2)\cdot H_2O$. Thus far no clear phenomena of isomorphism have been found between these minerals, although a slight beryllium content is detected in the calamine of a number of deposits (Badalov, 1955).

A marked similarity of crystal structure is found in beryl $Al_2Be_3[Si_6O_{18}]$, the most widespread beryllium mineral, and cordierite $(Mg,Fe)_2Al_3[Si_6AlO_{18}]$. The beryllium ions are replaced in the ring structure of cordierite by aluminum ions that are arranged between the ring radicals, in which aluminum is substituted for one silicon ion.

It is quite probable that, given suitable geochemical conditions, beryllium can enter the cordierite lattice so that the structure of cordierite remains unaltered. This is borne out by the increased beryllium content of cordierite from some beryl-containing pegmatites.

While considering the occurrence of structural analogues of a number of beryllium minerals in the large silicate class, one should note the analogy between the structure of chrysoberyl Al_2BeO_4 and forsterite $Mg_2[SiO_4]$. E. S. Fedorov previously recognized this analogy from the similarity between the crystal forms of both minerals.

An appreciable content of beryllium in forsterite from various deposits has not been found. This is doubtless due to the general scarcity of beryllium in deposits from which the forsterite specimens studied were obtained. At the same time the complete analyses of chrysoberyl from various deposits show in many specimens an admixture of equivalent quantities of magnesium (or iron) and silicon; this finds an explanation in the fact that chrysoberyl contains an isomorphous admixture of forsterite (Chapter 2).

A very interesting crystal-chemical feature is found in the fluoroberyllates of the alkali and alkaline-earth metals, which have a series of complete structural analogues among the silicates. This allows the use of fluoroberyllates as structural models of the corresponding silicates, which facilitates the experimental investigation of some refractory silicate systems (Toropov and Bondar, 1955). The observed structural similarity is of importance in geochemistry, namely, in the possible isostructural isomorphism of compounds of the types $M^{1-2}[BeF_4]$ and $M^{2-4}[SiO_4]$. In particular, the common admixture of beryllium in cyrtolite and thorite (orangite), which attains tenths of 1 percent, is explained by the similarity between the structure of zircon (also thorite) and that of calcium fluoroberyllate:

$$CaBeF_4 \qquad a_o = 6.64\ \text{Å};\ c_o = 6.22\ \text{Å}$$
$$ZrSiO_4 \qquad a_o = 6.60\ \text{Å};\ c_o = 5.88\ \text{Å}.$$

It is reasonable to assume the possibility of isostructural isomorphism even without the participation of fluorine, according to the scheme $(Zr,Th)SiO_4 \leftarrow CaBe(OH)_4$, which apparently is present in nature.

We must expect in the future the discovery of new examples of isomorphism between beryllium and silicon, based on the similar structures of a number of silicates (diopside, monticellite, etc.) and of the corresponding fluoroberyllates of alkali metals. Other structural analogues of beryllium minerals include homilite ($Ca_2Fe^{2+}Be_2Si_2O_{10}$)–gadolinite ($YFe^{2+}Be_2Si_2O_{10}$) and datolite ($CaBSiO_4(OH)$)–herderite ($CaBePO_4(OH)$).

The structural similarity of beryllium and boron is marked in certain compounds in which boron is surrounded by oxygen-ion tetrahedra.

An example of such an isomorphism can be found in the little-studied mineral, erdmannite, detected in 1853 by Esmark in the nepheline-syenite pegmatites of southern Norway (analysis by Engstrom in the paper by Brögger, 1906). The recalculation of the analysis of erdmannite to Si + B + Be = 4 (Table 86) fits satisfactorily into the typical gadolinite-homilite formula. Another example of isomorphism between beryllium and boron may be hyalotekite. Unfortunately, the formula of this little investigated mineral has not yet been established.

The recalculation of the analysis of beryllium-containing hyalotekite from Långban, Sweden, based on the grouping–(Pb,Ba,Ca) = A; cation in tetrahedral coordination (Be,B,Si) = B; (O,+OH,+F) = O (Table 87) –results in the formula $A_2B_4O_{10}$ or $(Ca,Ba,Pb)_2(Be,B,Si)_4(O,OH)_{10}$. The

Table 86 Recalculation of the chemical analysis of erdmannite

Components	%	Atom quantities of		Number of atoms per Si + B + Be = 4
		cations	oxygen	
SiO_2	25.15	419	838	2.15 } 4
B_2O_3	8.18	235	352	1.20 } 4
BeO	3.16	126	126	0.65 } 4
CaO	18.78	335	335	1.72
FeO	3.16	044	044	0.23
Fe_2O_3	3.01	038	057	0.19
Ce_2O_3	9.00	054	081	0.28
$(Dy, La)_2O_3$	8.66	052	078	0.27
Y_2O_3	1.64	006	009	0.03
Er_2O_3	0.50	003	004	0.01
ThO_2	9.93	037	074	0.19
ZrO_2	2.14	017	034	0.09
Na_2O	1.02	032	016	0.16
K_2O	0.42	008	004	0.04
H_2O	5.25		291	
Total	100.00			

Formula:

$$(Ca, Na)_{1.88}(Th, Zr)_{0.28}(Ce, Y)_{0.59}Fe_{0.42}(Be, B, Si)_4O_{10}(OH)$$

$$(Ca, Ce, Th, Fe)_3(Be, B, Si)_4O_{10}(OH).$$

Table 87 Recalculation of the chemical analysis of hyalotekite

Components	%	Atom quantities of		Number of atoms per Si+B+Be = 4
		cations	oxygen	
SiO_2	39.47	657	1314	3.30
B_2O_3	3.73	106	159	0.53
BeO	0.75	030	030	0.15
PbO	25.11	112	112	0.56
BaO	20.08	130	130	0.65
CaO	7.82	139	139	0.70
MnO	0.29	004	004	0.02
MgO	0.09	003	003	0.01
Al_2O_3	0.18	004	006	0.02
Fe_2O_3	0.06	002	003	0.01
K_2O	0.89	020	010	0.10
Na_2O	0.17	006	003	0.03
F	0.06	—	003	
P. p. p. (H_2O)	0.59	066	033	
Total	99.29		1949	
Analyst	G. Lindstrom, 1888-1889			

derived formula is similar to that of calcium borosilicate, datolite ($Ca_2B_2Si_2O_8(OH)_2$). On the basis of this analogy, the formula of hyalotekite in general form can be represented as $(Ca,Ba,Pb)_2$ $(Be,B,Si)_4 \cdot O_8(O,OH)_2$.

Wavellite and a number of representatives of the group of rare-earth tantalo-niobates belong to the minerals in which the form of occurrence of beryllium admixture (up to 1 percent in wavellite) (Preiss and Gliszezynski, 1950) can depend both on the occurrence of intergrowths of any beryllium phosphate and on the possible substitution of beryllium for a part of aluminum. So far we have no data for an absolute solution of this problem. Also, we have no certain explanation of the usual admixture of beryllium (tenths of 1 percent) in the metamict tantalo-niobates, which can be caused both by the presence of micro-inclusions of gadolinite and by the sharply manifested ability of beryllium ions to be adsorbed in colloidal systems.

PART II

Genetic Types of Beryllium Deposits

Genetic Classification of Beryllium Deposits

All known beryllium deposits are postmagmatic formations genetically related to the late stages of the pegmatitic process or to the various stages of hydrothermal-pneumatolytic and hydrothermal processes.

The overwhelming majority of these deposits, including all industrial deposits, are related to acid intrusive rocks and are the products of the pneumatolytic and hydrothermal separations of the granitic magma. Notwithstanding the higher content of disseminated beryllium in many places, only a small number of beryllium mineral deposits are associated with basic rocks. Moreover, in all deposits of this kind, the range of beryllium accumulation is greatly limited. In the present work, a possible classification of beryllium deposits, based on their genetic and paragenetic features, is proposed (Table 88).

Until recently, the industrial utilization of beryllium deposits was limited to the beryl-bearing granitic pegmatites, from which large crystals of beryl were handpicked. Small sizes and the relative rarity of pegmatite deposits of industrial beryl greatly limited the possibility of obtaining a considerable amount of beryllium, and permitted the mineral to be utilized in only the most suitable branches of industry. However, as the fields of beryllium utilization continued to widen, it became necessary to pay serious attention to other types of beryllium mineral deposits, which had not been utilized previously, owing to the complex nature of the dressing of beryllium ores.

Already, the beryllium deposits in greisens are used in industry, and in the near future there will be exploitation of other, more complex types of beryllium deposits, many of which contain considerable beryllium concentrations. When estimating the likely paths of the further utilization

Table 88 Genetic types of beryllium deposits

TYPES OF DEPOSITS	ENCLOSING ROCKS	BERYLLIUM MINERALS		CHARACTERISTIC PARAGENESIS		EXAMPLES OF FOREIGN DEPOSITS	INDUSTRIAL IMPORTANCE ABROAD
		MAIN	MINOR	MAIN MINERALS	ACCOMPANYING RARE-METAL MINERALS		
				PEGMATITIC DEPOSITS			
Miarolitic, streaky (syngenetic) granite pegmatites.	Granites, gneissic granites.	Beryl.	Phenacite.	Microcline, quartz, albite.	—	Brazil (Minas-Geraes), etc.	Precious stones.
Block and fully differentiated biotite-microcline granite pegmatites.	Granites, gneissic granites, gabbro, amphibolites.	Gadolinite or beryl.	—	Microcline (ordinary or amazonite), quartz, biotite.	Fergusonite and other tantalo-niobates of rare earths; allanite, xenotime, monazite.	U.S.A., Texas (Baringer Hill), South Norway (Iveland, Setersdalen, etc.)	Very rare sub-type; can be used as source of yttrium and rare earths of its group.
Block and fully differentiated muscovite-microcline granite pegmatites.	Granites of the endo-contact part of intrusions; various magmatic and metamorphic rocks of the roof of intrusions.	Beryl.	Phenacite, chrysoberyl, bertrandite, herderite, beryllonite, etc.	Microcline, quartz, muscovite, albite, black tourmaline, iron and manganese phosphates.	Triphylite, columbite-tantalite.	North-east Brazil (Rio Grande do Norte, Paraiba), India (Rajputana, etc.), Argentina, Madagascar, etc.	Widespread sub-type. Commercially important.
Replaced muscovite-albite granite pegmatites.	Do.	1. Beryl (sodium and sodium-lithium variety).	Bertrandite, beryllonite, herderite, etc.	Albite, quartz, muscovite, spessartite.	Lithiophilite, tourmaline, columbite-tantalite.	Australia (Wodgina), China, U.S.A. (Conn. etc.), north-east Brazil, etc.	Do.
		2. Helvite.	Phenacite.	Albite, quartz.	Columbite-tantalite.		Rare type.
Replaced spodumene-albite and lepidolite-albite granite pegmatites.	Do.	Beryl (rosterite and vorobyevite).	Beryllonite, bertrandite, phenacite, etc.	Albite, quartz, muscovite, polychromic tourmalines, spessartite.	Lithiophilite, amblygonite, columbite-tantalite, microlite, spodumene, pollucite, lepidolite, petalite.	U.S.A. (New Mexico—Harding deposit—etc.), South-West Africa.	Important commercial type, exploited for the rare elements.

Granite pegmatites of the crossing line (mica-plagioclase veins).	Ultra-basic rocks, serpentinites.	Beryl.	Emerald, phenacite, chrysoberyl, bavenite.	Oligoclase, albite, phlogopite, quartz, margarite.	—	Africa (Transvaal—Somerset mine deposit—etc.), Australia (Poona etc.)	Fairly rare valuable commercial type.
Replaced hackmanite-natrolite, albite-natrolite and ussingite pegmatites of nepheline syenites.	Poikilitic nepheline syenites, lujavrites.	Epididymite.	Eudidymite, chkalovite.	Albite, natrolite, hackmanite, aegirine or eudialyte, ussingite.	—	Greenland.	No commercial value.
HYDROTHERMAL-PNEUMATOLYTIC DEPOSITS							
Quartz-muscovite, quartz-topaz, quartz-beryl greisens.	Granite.	Beryl, helvite.	Bertrandite, phenacite, bavenite.	Quartz, muscovite, topaz, fluorite.	Cassiterite, wolframite.	U.S.A. (Nevada, South Dakota).	Are studied in connection with work on the development of methods for the beneficiation of disseminated beryl.
Feldspar-quartz, quartz, mica-quartz, and other veins.	Granites and granite-enclosing metamorphic rocks.	Beryl.	Bertrandite, phenacite, helvite.	Quartz, fluorite, muscovite.	Wolframite, cassiterite, molybdenite.	U.S.A. (New Mexico, Luna Co.; Colorado, Chaffee Co., etc.); Argentina (San Louis province), etc.	Are studied in connection with work on the development of methods for the beneficiation of disseminated beryl.
Quartz, quartz-hematite veins.	Granites, limestones.	Helvite, danalite.	Beryl, bertrandite, phenacite.	Quartz, muscovite, hematite, sulfides.	Wolframite, cassiterite, molybdenite.		None as yet.
Fluorite pneumatolytes and hydrothermalites in limestones.	Limestones.	Phenacite, chrysoberyl.	Euclase.	Fluorite, muscovite.	Cassiterite.	U.S.A. (Alaska, Seward peninsula, Cape Mountain and Lost River deposits).	None as yet.
Skarns (fluorite-mica-magnetite).	Do.	Helvite, danalite, chrysoberyl.	Phenacite, beryl.	Fluorite, vesuvianite, magnetite, mica.		U.S.A. (New Mexico, Iron Mountain and other deposits).	Are studied in connection with the development of the technological flowsheet.
HYDROTHERMAL DEPOSITS							
Carbonate veins.	Limestones.	Beryl (emerald), helvite.	—	Calcite.	Parisite.	Columbia (Muso district).	No information.
Alpine veins.	Metamorphozed rocks.	Euclase.	Phenacite, milarite, bavenite.	Quartz, orthoclase, zeolites.	—	Switzerland, Germany.	None.

of various types of beryllium deposits in view of the continuing development of the technology of ore dressing and processing, it can be said with confidence that in the near future it will be the disseminated beryllium deposits, containing the largest beryllium reserves, that will become of main importance in industry.

The known genetic types of deposits are described in the next three chapters in accordance with the suggested classification.

CHAPTER 4

Pegmatitic Beryllium Deposits

The value of granitic pegmatites as a source of accumulations of beryllium minerals (mainly of precious beryl and emerald) was known as early as the Middle Ages. Even today granitic pegmatites are the main industrial source of beryl ores. The maximum world production in 1956 (except the USSR) amounted to 12,700 metric tons of beryl (over 450 metric tons of beryllium).

On the basis of the historical concept that granitic pegmatites are the only industrial source of beryl, V. M. Goldschmidt and C. Peters (1932) and later K. Rankama and T. Sahama (1950) arrived at unfounded geochemical conclusions, namely that pegmatites are the only geological formations in which the beryllium concentration is great enough to be of industrial importance.

It is shown below that the industrial role of granitic pegmatites as a source of beryllium is determined not so much by its overall concentration—which, on the average, is not very high for pegmatites—as by the specific conditions of pegmatite formation, which sometimes result in a considerable accumulation of beryllium in the late stages of formation.

Brief Geologic Features of Beryllium-Bearing Granitic Pegmatites

The beryllium-bearing pegmatite districts are usually related spatially to the exo- and endocontact zones of the granitic intrusions that form at moderate depths and occur most commonly in the cores of large anticlinal structures, whose limbs or axial parts are disturbed, to varying degrees, by regional fractures. At the same time, the age of the intrusive complexes, to which the beryllium-bearing pegmatites are related, indicates that the formation of the rare-earth pegmatite districts, with their higher beryllium concentrations, formed during all epochs—from the Archean to the Tertiary. Thus with respect to beryllium, it is impossible to speak about the metallogenic distinctness of any orogenic cycle for the earth as a whole.

The calculation of the quantitative ratio of the rare-metal pegmatite districts of various ages, carried out by A. I. Ginzburg on the basis of published data, showed that 53 percent of the rare-metal pegmatite districts are of preCambrian age, 37 percent of Paleozoic, 7 percent of Mesozoic, and 3 percent of Cenozoic. A more detailed calculation would apparently change this ratio even more towards the preCambrian districts because in the calculation Ginzburg did not take into account the gadolinite-bearing pegmatites which are usually related to preCambrian intrusive complexes. This great predominance of the preCambrian districts is due mainly to the special geological features of the North American and African continents, which have an abundance of preCambrian intrusive complexes and related rare-metal pegmatite districts. These features are not found on the continent of Europe, where there are more beryl-bearing pegmatite districts related to the intrusive complexes of the Hercynian or even younger geosynclinal zones. For example, in the Soviet Union, rare-metal pegmatite districts of preCambrian age are concentrated in the region of the Baltic shield, whereas the young beryl-bearing pegmatite districts, related mainly to the Hercynian orogenic zones, are more widespread.

When dealing with the composition of granites to which the beryl-bearing pegmatite districts are related, we must point to the occurrence of two different granitic groups, each of which is related to particular types of pegmatites with beryllium minerals.

As a rule, the beryl-bearing pegmatites are related to the normal biotite or binary microcline granites (uniformly granular, or porphyritic), some of which pass into the more basic varieties of granitoids, such as granodiorites, adamellites, and quartz monzonites. On the basis of numerous analyses, the composition of these granitoids is close to the mean composition of biotite granites according to Daly. The increase in the basic character is usually combined with a wide development of the phenomena of hybridism. This is very characteristic of all acid intrusive complexes to which the beryl-bearing pegmatite districts are related. It should be stressed here that in the pegmatite-bearing intrusions of this group muscovite granites as a rule are absent or else are quite subordinate to the biotite varieties, which are the main components of the intrusive complex.

The alkalic granites, a much rarer group to which, in individual cases, the gadolinite-bearing amazonite pegmatites are related, contain 5 to 20 percent of alkalic amphibole and aegirine. Typical examples in the USSR are the alkalic granites of West Kievy, Kola Peninsula.

The structure of the beryl-bearing pegmatite districts usually is controlled by the features of the disjunctive tectonics of the roof of the granitic intrusion, and by the nature of the relief of its apical part. The role of these factors depends on the level of the erosional exposure of the granitic intrusion.

The disjunctive tectonics of the roof are the determining factors of the structure of pegmatite districts related to the granitic intrusions slightly exposed by erosion. The size and shape of this type of pegmatite district is usually controlled by a large-scale fracture zone and extends for tens of kilometers parallel to the disturbed zone.

The role of regional faulting is of much less importance in the beryl-bearing pegmatite districts related to intrusions whose apical part has been deeply eroded. Here, the relief of the apical part of the intrusion is the factor that determines the structure of the district. The pegmatites in this group are concentrated in the depressions of the apical part of the intrusion, which contain pendents of the roof rocks; they also form accumulation within the exo- and endocontact zones of the granitic rock mass.

From the morphogenetic aspect, there are two main groups of pegmatites whose formations have fairly divergent features. The first group presents schlieren-type, stock-shaped, irregular, or vein-like bodies which show a gradual transition into the enclosing parental granites. These are the so-called syngenetic (Ginzburg, 1952b) or facies (Vlasov, 1951) pegmatites, which have crystallized *in situ,* without any distinct evidence of displacement within the parent intrusion.

The second, much more widespread group of pegmatites in general is present in vein-like deposits intruded into fissures and weakened zones of various origin, into the upper parts of granitic intrusions, and into the enclosing rocks of the roof.[1]

There are some transitions between the pegmatites of the first and second group; this is indicated by the occurrence, in the schlieren-type pegmatites, of transgressing apophoses, which cut the parent granites and have a sharp intrusive contact with them. In general there is a certain antipathy between these two groups of pegmatites. The vein-like intrusive pegmatites are never associated with intrusions in which schlieren-like syngenetic pegmatites are widely developed, and conversely, the schlieren-like pegmatites are almost never contained in the granite intrusions with which the intrusive pegmatites are associated.

In all pegmatite areas the pegmatites within a large-sized pegmatite district are irregularly distributed. Areas with abundant pegmatites alternate with areas that have almost no pegmatites; thus it is possible to define the

[1] For the relationship between the forms of beryl-hearing pegmatites and the features of jointing of the enclosing rocks, see A. A. Beus, 1956a.

smaller pegmatite districts as the "second order"; in some places, this is an individual pegmatite deposit. The structure of each of these deposits is determined by the specific geological conditions of the area. The main factor which determines the structure of the discordant pegmatites is the nature of the jointing followed by the pegmatite melt-solution. The main factors that determine the structure of the ore section in concordant pegmatites are the composition and nature of the enclosing schistose rocks.

The detailed analysis of problems related to the features of geological structure of the rare-metal (including beryl-bearing) pegmatite districts can be found in the published papers of the author (Beus, 1948, 1956a), Ginzburg (1948, 1952a, 1952b, 1955a, 1955b), Zalashkova (1957), and some other investigators.

Internal Structure of Beryllium-Bearing Granitic Pegmatites

One of the main features of beryllium-bearing granitic pegmatites is the clear regularity of their internal structure, which objectively reflects each stage of the complex process of their formation.

The importance of the knowledge of irregularities of the internal structure in the understanding of the pegmatite genesis was first established by A. E. Fersman, who, in his classical work,[2] noted the probable relation between the zonal structure of pegmatites and the change of the physicochemical conditions of the pegmatite-forming melt.

When further developing the ideas of A. E. Fersman, K. A. Vlasov (1946) was the first to develop the texture-paragenetic classification of granitic pegmatites, in which he succeeded in proving clearly the evolution of textures of pegmatites as a function of the development of the pegmatitic process.

In his texture-paragenetic classification, Vlasov, on the basis of the analysis of the mutual relationship of two rock-forming minerals of pegmatites (feldspar and quartz), distinguishes four pegmatite types, each succeeding pegmatite being the natural genetic continuation of the preceding one.

The detailed merits of this classification have been considered elsewhere (Beus, 1948, 1951; A. I. Ginzburg, 1952). Here, we need only note that his sketch of the general line of development of internal structure (texture, Ed.) of granitic pegmatites has since been borne out by all available data from all of the pegmatite districts in the world. At the same time, it is quite obvious that such a general scheme cannot account for all of the variations in the pegmatitic process, whose trend and manifestation depend on the distinctive combination of geological and geochemical factors that determine pegmatite formation in a given geological situation.

[2] "Pegmatites", Vol. 1, 1940, p. 82.

The detailed investigation of beryl-bearing pegmatite districts in the USSR and in some regions of China and East Germany, carried out by the author between 1944 and 1956, has enabled him to differentiate twelve paragenetic complexes or zones in the rare-metal pegmatites; the regular spatial combination of all (or a part) of them illustrates the wide variety of the internal structure and the paragenesis of pegmatite formations (Beus, 1948, 1951, 1953a, 1954).

The term "zone" is defined here as the spatial segregation of a specific association of minerals in the pegmatite that is the derivative of a certain stage of the pegmatitic process (paragenetic complex). Each zone has its own qualitative mineralogical composition, structure, and quantitative relations between minerals, and consequently its own chemical composition. Thus a zone, studied as evidence of a certain stage of the pegmatitic process, should reflect by its structure and chemical-mineralogical composition the nature of this process—that is, the physico-chemical conditions of its formation.

Not all zones are alike; they vary from the rudimentary nest-like segregations formed in the early stages of the pegmatitic process to extensive bands in the pegmatite body (ideal zone). In the later stages of pegmatitic development a zone can be changed either completely or partly; traces of its existence remain as relics in the replacement zones that develop at this time.

In all types of granitic pegmatites, without exception, there is a clear relationship between the rare-metal (including beryllium) minerals and certain paragenetic complexes or zones. This makes it possible to analyze objectively the conditions of formation of beryllium minerals in pegmatites, starting with the peculiarities of the formation of a specific paragenetic association having a definite chemical composition and completely defined structure.

The classification of zones in granitic pegmatites (Table 89) and the characteristics of the observed regularities of the zoning of pegmatites in time and space have been dealt with in a number of earlier papers (Beus, 1948, 1951, 1953a, 1954). The nature of the development of zones and the paragenetic features of the main and accessory minerals were used for distinguishing six main paragenetic types of beryllium-bearing granitic pegmatites. Among the observed types one finds natural transitions, but each type is quite distinct, as shown in Table 90, and this explains the peculiar features of the development of zones in various types of beryllium-bearing pegmatites.

The detailed investigation of zoning in pegmatite formations is of great practical value. The prospecting and exploratory work carried out during the past decade in pegmatite deposits especially underlines the value of the investigation of the internal horizontal and vertical zoning of pegmatites for the appraisal and exploration of pegmatite deposits. Unless we take into account the characteristic regularities expressed in the zonal

Table 89 Classification of zones of beryl-bearing pegmatites

Zones and replacement complexes	Location and nature of development in the pegmatite	Structure and size of segregations of rock-forming minerals	Rock-forming minerals
(a) Zone of pegmatoid granite.	Outer zone of some streaky pegmatites. Sometimes the main or entire mass of intruded veins in the roots of pegmatite injections.	Granitic. From 0.5 to 10–15 cm feldspar phenocrysts.	Quartz, microcline and quartz, plagioclase.
(b) Zone of aplite-like pegmatite.	Thin fringe, developed continuously or in sections in the endo-contact of the pegmatite where there is no zone (a). Particularly characteristic of intruded pegmatites.	Fine-granular (aplitic, grano-blastic).	Quartz, oligoclase, microcline.
(c) Zone of graphic pegmatite.	Continuous zone or sections among medium-grained pegmatite in the outer part of pegmatites. Sometimes the whole mass of pegmatite.	Graphic. Quartz from 0.3 to 2 cm along the c-axis.	Quartz (22–30%), microcline (70–75%), or quartz (28–39%), oligoclase (57–71%).
(d) Zone of medium-grained and coarse-grained pegmatite.	In essentially graphic pegmatites—in central portions of pegmatites. In block pegmatites—in the outer part.	Apographic, pegmatoid. From 1 to 10 cm.	Quartz-microcline-perthite, or quartz-oligoclase, or quartz-oligoclase-microcline. In many pegmatites granular albite is substituted for the microcline of the zone.
(e) Zone of small-block pegmatite.	In the central part of pegmatites of block structure, or around the central core of veins; composed of block quartz.	Block. From 0.1 to 1 m.	Quartz-microcline-perthite (orthoclase-perthite) or quartz-oligoclase.
(f) Zone of block microcline (block plagioclase).	Large blocks, rarely a solid belt round segregations of block quartz in the center of the vein. Less frequently thick blocks in quartz in the central part of the pegmatite.	Block, giant-crystalline. From 1 to 10 m and more.	Microcline-perthite (orthoclase-perthite). In the group of plagioclase pegmatites—oligoclase to andesine.

CHARACTERISTIC TYPOMORPHIC MINERALS	RELATIONSHIP TO OTHER ZONES	RARE-EARTH MINERALS	IMPORTANCE FOR RARE METALS
Biotite, magnetite.	Gradual transitions into porphyritic granite and the zone of graphic pegmatite are known.	Monazite, allanite (as accessory minerals).	Absent in pegmatites interesting from commercial viewpoint. In prospecting the presence of pegmatites of this type only indicates the absence of rare metals.
Biotite, magnetite, black tourmaline, garnet, muscovite, cordierite.	Usually has a sharp contact with inner zones of the pegmatite. In replaced modifications often albitized. Differs from the outwardly similar fine-grained albite replacement complex in the composition of accessory minerals and of the rock-forming feldspar.	Minerals characteristic of inner zones can occur as single grains.	The product of reaction between the pegmatitic melt and the enclosing rocks in the early stages of crystallization. A strong development of the aplitic-pegmatite zone showing no trace of replacement is, in general, an unfavorable prospecting feature as regards rare metals.
Biotite, magnetite, garnet, muscovite after biotite.	Passes gradually into the zone of medium-grained pegmatite of apographic structure. On albitization commonly preserves the relict graphic structure.	As a rule, does not contain rare-earth minerals. The latter may be introduced in the process of albitization of the zone.	Strong development of graphic zone showing no trace of replacement processes is an unfavorable prospecting feature as regards rare metals.
Muscovite, black tourmaline. In the oligoclase modifications—magnetite, ilmenite.	Related by gradual transitions to the zone of graphic pegmatite. Passes also gradually into small-block pegmatite. On incomplete albitization usually preserves the relict apographic structure.	Sometimes contains beryl (more frequently in negligible quantities). The proportion of beryl increases in the albitized sections of the zone.	The presence of the medium-grained pegmatite zone containing traces of the albitization processes and very small proportions of rare-metal minerals points to the possibility of finding higher concentrations of these minerals in the block zones, especially in bulges and domes of pegmatites.
Do.	Connected by gradual transition with the preceding and two following zones.	Beryl, columbite-tantalite—in pocket-like accumulations. In plagioclase modifications—ilmenite.	Pegmatites with a central part of the zone of block pegmatite (without full differentiation into the zones of block quartz and microcline) are characterized in a number of cases by a commercial content of beryl, but, as a rule, are small-scale deposits.
As a rule, monomineralic. Sometimes small inclusions of quartz, usually regularly oriented.	Connected with zone (d) through small block pegmatite. An abrupt boundary with block quartz; idiomorphism of block microcline is usually observed with regard to block quartz.	At the boundary between block microcline and block quartz—agglomerates of beryl, tantalite-columbite, samarskite etc. In oligoclase and oligoclase-microcline modifications—gadolinite.	Wide development of block microcline in the pegmatite is a positive exploration feature enabling it to be isolated for a more detailed study.

Table 89 Classification of zones of beryl-bearing pegmatites

ZONES AND REPLACEMENT COMPLEXES	LOCATION AND NATURE OF DEVELOPMENT IN THE PEGMATITE	STRUCTURE AND SIZE OF SEGREGATIONS OF ROCK-FORMING MINERALS	ROCK-FORMING MINERALS
(g) Zone of block quartz.	Large blocks, lenses, solid core in the central part of bodies. Sometimes occurs in fractures which intersect earlier zones, especially the zone of block microcline.	Block (massive). From 1 to 10 m and more.	Mainly monomineralic. Sometimes includes large idiomorphic crystals and blocks of microcline.
(h) Quartz-spodumene zone.	Lenses or solid core in the central part of pegmatites. Sometimes around a central core composed of block quartz.	Giant-crystalline. Spodumene from 0.1 to 10 m along the long axis.	Quartz, spodumene. Usually albite as secondary replacement mineral.
(i) Muscovite replacement complex: (1) quartz-muscovite complex (zone). (2) albite-muscovite complex (zone).	At the boundary between the quartz blocks (or quartz core) and the zones (c), (d), (f); also near the contacts, along fractures and pockets in zones (d) and (f). Rarely between the zone of block microcline and zone (d).	Granular-lamellar, medium-lamellar, to coarse-lamellar (1–20 cm), massive-lamellar.	Muscovite, quartz (with a small proportion of albite and relics of microcline) in weakly albitized modifications. Muscovite, albite (in albitized modifications).
(j) Albite replacement complex: (1) cleavelandite complex (zone). (2) fine granular albite complex (zone of saccharoidal or fine-lamellar albite).	Around the quartz-spodumene zone or the zone of block quartz; sometimes segregates in the vein parts adjacent to the contacts; develops as solid zone or in sections. Commonly related to fractures.	1. Lamellar, radial-lamellar (0.5–3 cm). 2. Fine-lamellar (0.1–0.5 cm). Fine-granular (up to 0.1 cm). Under the microscope granular-prismatic, prismatic, fluid-prismatic, bostonitic, fluid-bostonitic.	1. Cleavelandite, quartz. 2. Saccharoidal or fine-lamellar albite with or without quartz. Relics of microcline common.
(k) Lepidolite replacement complex: (1) quartz-lepidolite complex (zone). (2) albite-lepidolite complex (zone).	Central portions of pegmatites. Commonly in apical loci.	From fine to medium-lamellar.	Lepidolite, albite, quartz.
(l) Greisen replacement complex.	In various parts of the bodies. Near the quartz core or at the selvages. Sometimes related to fracturing.	Do.	Muscovite, albite, quartz.

CHARACTERISTIC TYPOMORPHIC MINERALS	RELATIONSHIP TO OTHER ZONES	RARE-EARTH MINERALS	IMPORTANCE FOR RARE METALS
As a rule, monomineralic. Sometimes near the boundary with block microcline, crystals of triphylite, apatite and rare-metal minerals.	Has sharp boundaries with zone (f). Sometimes connected by gradual transition with small-block pegmatite.	At the boundary with block microcline are quartz-crystals and pockets of beryl, columbite-tantalite, samarskite, etc.	Thick zone of block quartz, segregated in the shape of a core or axis in the pegmatite, is a positive exploration feature, especially when a thick zone of block microcline is present.
	Commonly a gradual transition to the zone of block quartz.	Alkali beryl (rosterite, vorobyevite), columbite-tantalite, microlite.	An ore zone for spodumene and a very positive exploration feature for the presence of rare-metal minerals in other zones.
Phosphates of iron and manganese, sulphides.	Replaces the feldspars of the zones (d), (e), (f).	Green and bluish-green beryl, columbite-tantalite.	In a number of places contains commercial concentrations of beryl, less often columbite-tantalite. Sections of the zone at the boundary between block quartz and block microcline, are commonly an economic ore-zone of beryl.
1. Greenish muscovite, green tourmaline, lithiophilite and secondary phosphates of iron and manganese, spessartite. 2. (a) Greenish muscovite, phosphates of iron and manganese. (b) Fine crystals of almandine-spessartite or fine needle-shaped crystals of black tourmaline.	On albitization of the zone of graphic or medium-grained pegmatite in a number of places the relict graphic or apographic structure is preserved due to the unreplaced quartz ingrowths. On replacement of the quartz-spodumene zone there forms a quartz-spodumene complex with the relict structure of the quartz-spodumene zone. The zone of block microcline is replaced completely in some places. Block quartz is usually replaced along fractures.	1. Alkali beryl (rosterite, vorobyevite) of white or rose color, columbite-tantalite, microlite. 2. Yellowish fine-crystalline beryl, columbite-tantalite.	Wide development of albitization is a very favorable feature in exploration and evaluation of pegmatites for the content of rare metals.
Rubellite, achroite.	Forms after zones (g) and (j), and especially after the quartz-spodumene zone.	Rosterite, vorobyevite, columbite-tantalite, microlite, pollucite.	The presence of the lepidolite zone points to a wide development of the replacement processes and is a very positive feature in prospecting for rare metals.
	Forms in the replacement of the albite complex of block microcline and quartz.	Columbite-tantalite.	Manifestation of greisenization in pegmatites is a positive feature when prospecting for tantalite-columbite.

structure of beryl-bearing pegmatites, it is impossible to appraise a deposit and to determine the correct direction of geological exploration.

Features of Individual Pegmatite Types

Miarolitic Schlieren-Type Pegmatites

The beryl-bearing miarolitic schlieren-type pegmatites usually occur in the endocontact part of the pegmatite-bearing granitic intrusions; most of them are small, irregular, and without distinct contacts with the enclosing parent granites.

The outer part of the pegmatites of this group usually consists of graphic pegmatite that passes into coarse-grained pegmatite of pegmatoid structure in the central part of the pegmatite body. In the coarse-grained pegmatites (less frequently in graphic pegmatites) there are cavities—miaroles—which

Table 90 Nature of change of zonality in various groups of beryl-bearing granitic pegmatites

GROUPS	ZONE OF GRAPHIC PEGMATITE	ZONE OF MEDIUM- AND COARSE-GRAINED PEGMATITE	ZONE OF BLOCK PEGMATITE	ZONE OF BLOCK MICROCLINE	ZONE OF BLOCK QUARTZ
Graphic and cognate medium-grained biotite-microcline pegmatites (including syngenetic miarolitic pegmatites).	Predominant development.	Rudimentary development.	Absent.	Absent.	Absent.
Block biotite-microcline and biotite-plagioclase-microcline pegmatites.	Weak or normal development.	Weak or normal development.	Normal or predominant development.	Weak or normal development.	Normal development.
Block and fully-differentiated muscovite-microcline pegmatites.	Weak development. Commonly absent. May be albitized with preservation of structure.	Normal development.	Development from normal to weak.	Predominant development.	
Replaced muscovite-albite pegmatite.	Are replaced partly or completely, or are absent.		Partly or completely replaced.		Normal development.
Replaced spodumene-albite pegmatites.	Are replaced partly or completely, or are absent.		Predominant or normal development, partly (less often completely) replaced.		
Replaced lepidolite-albite pegmatites.	Do.		Normal development; usually strongly or completely replaced.		

contain druses and well-developed crystals of feldspars, quartz, topaz, accessory beryl, tourmaline, and some other minerals. The miarolitic pegmatites are of practical value only as a source of gems and piezo-quartz. Industrial accumulations of beryl in pegmatites of this group are unknown.

The largest pegmatites of this type in some places are differentiated to a high degree. In them is a zone of block pegmatite and also a zone of block quartz. The individual blocks of microcline-perthite and quartz are more than 1 m in width. Cavities attain gigantic sizes—10 m or more in the largest dimension.[3]

In some miarolitic pegmatites, replacements are developed which are always associated with, and surround, miarolitic cavities. The most intense replacement is observed in connection with cavities which form in the apical parts of pegmatites. With depth the number of replacement complexes decreases until none are present. In some pegmatites, the upper horizons may contain cavities around which strong albitization or even lepidolitization has taken place, whereas in deep levels, the evidence of replacement around the cavities is absent (Beus, 1951).

There are also differences in the manner in which the replacement

QUARTZ-SPODUMENE ZONE	MUSCOVITE REPLACEMENT COMPLEX (ZONE)	ALBITE REPLACEMENT COMPLEX (ZONE)	LEPIDOLITE REPLACEMENT COMPLEX (ZONE)	GREISEN REPLACEMENT COMPLEX (ZONE)
Absent; may be present in rudimentary form in the druses of miarolitic pegmatites.				Absent.
Absent.	Absent, or rudimentary development.		Absent.	Do.
Absent.	Wide development.	Weak development, though individual sections can be substantially albitized.	Do.	
Absent or rudimentary development.	Do.	Predominant development.		Develops here and there in the apical portions of pegmatitic bodies.
Strong development (to predominant).		Wide development to predominant.	Rudimentary to weak development.	Do.
Weak development; usually replaced.	Weak development; usually replaced.	Do.	Normal development.	Absent.

[3] Pegmatites of this type were recently studied in Volhynia (UkrSSR), and are described under the apt name of "chamber" pegmatites by N. P. Ermakov (1955) and L. P. Chernyshkova (1957).

processes manifest themselves. In addition to the usual albitization, the miarolitic pegmatites may contain zinnwaldite, muscovite, and lepidolite replacement complexes. In the largest chambers there is also evidence of late-hydrothermal kaolinization and the replacement of feldspars by loose hydromica aggregates, resulting in the deposition of a thick layer of monomineralic clays on the floor of the chamber. The replacement complexes referred to above are usually not very well developed, but the paragenesis of the minerals that fill the miarolitic cavities and the manner in which the replacement processes manifest themselves allow the separation, in the miarolitic pegmatites, of a continuous series which virtually corresponds to the paragenetic types of the intruded (vein-like) pegmatites (Table 91).

The principal differences between these two groups of pegmatites differing in geological position are the following.

1. Presence of miarolitic cavities in the syngenetic (facies) miarolitic pegmatites (this being one of the most characteristic features of pegmatites of this group); the rare occurrence of miarolitic cavities in the normal vein-like (intruded) pegmatites.

Table 91 Features of paragenesis of beryl in syngenetic (facies) miarolitic pegmatites

Paragenesis of minerals in miarolitic cavities	Inner structure of pegmatite and the development of replacement phenomena	Analogous paragenetic types of intruded pegmatite
Quartz, potassium feldspar, aquamarine	Pegmatite essentially graphic. Replacement phenomena not developed	Graphic biotite-microcline pegmatites
Quartz, potassium feldspar clusters, albite, tourmaline, topaz, phlogopite, aquamarine, beryl, or heliodor	Pegmatite essentially graphic or coarse-grained. Albitization phenomena weakly developed around cavities	Coarse-grained and small-block muscovite-microcline pegmatites with beryl
Quartz, potassium feldspar, albite, topaz, zinnwaldite, beryl (or heliodor)	Pegmatite has a well-developed zone of coarse-grained pegmatite of pegmatoid structure, which passes into the zone of block pegmatite. Albitization and micatization phenomena are more obviously developed	Block and fully differentiated muscovite-microcline pegmatites with beryl
Quartz, albite, potassium feldspar, topaz, green tourmaline, zinnwaldite or muscovite, white, and colorless beryl	Pegmatite is characterized by the development of strong albitization associated with the miarolitic cavities	Replaced muscovite-albite pegmatites with beryl
Quartz, albite, potassium feldspar, topaz, part-colored tourmaline, lepidolite, colorless or rose-colored beryl	Cavities are associated with strong albitization and lepidolitization	Replaced lepidolite-albite pegmatites with beryl

2. A higher fluorine content in the complex of minerals that fill the cavities of syngenetic (facies) pegmatites; the normal absence of appreciable concentrations of fluorine in the intruded beryl-bearing pegmatites (topaz is a very rare mineral).

3. A wide development of the lithium-ferrous micas of zinnwaldite type in miarolitic pegmatites; the absence of such micas in intruded pegmatites, in which muscovite is the main mica of the replacement complexes.

4. A local development of replacement phenomena in the syngenetic miarolitic pegmatites, in which there is a close relationship between the replacement complexes and the miarolitic cavities; a wide development of replacement in the intruded pegmatites, in which the distribution and conditions of formation of the replacement complexes conform to other regularities.

In the pegmatites under consideration, beryl is principally related to miarolitic cavities. Much less commonly, its crystals occur in the albitized parts of the pegmatites, which surround the cavities. Miarolitic pegmatites have long been known as the source of the most beautiful precious beryl used for jewelry. The transparent, well-formed, variously colored beryl crystals from the cavities of miarolitic pegmatites are the ornaments of all mineralogical museums in the world.

In the USSR the miarolitic granitic pegmatites containing accessory beryl occur relatively widely in eastern Transbaikalia (Borshchevochnyi Mountains, Adun-Cholon, etc.) and in the Urals (Murzinskii rock mass, etc.). Of considerable interest are the chamber pegmatites of Volhynia (UkrSSR), which are a valuable source of piezo-quartz raw material and contain large crystals of olive-green alkali-free beryl.

The miarolitic pegmatites of the Borshchevochnyi Mountains, known for a long time as a source of high-grade gems (topaz, aquamarine, beryl, vorobyevite, rubellite), are a typical example of the pegmatites under consideration. The pegmatite district of the Borshchevochnyi Mountains is linked with a large granitic intrusion of Variscian age that consists mainly of normal porphyritic biotite granites with subordinate pegmatoid and aplitic granites. The porphyritic granites that form the deeply-eroded core of the intrusive mass are surrounded by an endocontact "aureole" of rose-colored medium-grained biotite granites, which pass in places into aplitic granites and contain large xenoliths of the roof rocks.

Pegmatites are abundant in granites and in the xenoliths of roof rocks enclosed in granites, but very rare in the enclosing country rocks. Aplitic veins also are widespread with the pegmatites.

The pegmatites in granites contain both the schlieren-type (syngenetic) bodies, without any distinct contact with the enclosing granites, and the typical fracture vein-type. One also commonly finds transional varieties that are facies formations of schlieren or stock-shaped form, from which the fracture vein-type bodies branch out.

In both the schlieren-type pegmatites and the transgressive bodies, there is preponderant development of the zone of graphic pegmatite, which commonly forms the entire mass of the pegmatite. The miarolitic cavities are associated mainly with the schlieren-type (syngenetic) pegmatites, but they also occur in large transgressive bodies at the contact between the granites and the enclosing rocks or their xenoliths.

Within the pegmatite district of the Borshchevochnyi Mountains, we find all types of miarolitic pegmatites, enumerated in Table 91. The most widespread are varieties in which albitization is very weak (Peshkovskoe, Zolotaya Mountains, Zolotaya Strelka, etc.). In the pegmatites of this group the paragenesis of minerals in the cavities is quartz, microcline (orthoclase)-perthite, aquamarine, topaz, and zinnwaldite (albite is not commonly abundant). Less common are pegmatites in whose central part intense albitization and lepidolitization has taken place around the cavities. Here, the paragenesis of minerals filling the cavities is quartz, albite (cleavelandite), lepidolite, pink or green tourmaline, vorobyevite (Savvateevo, Mokhovoe), and sometimes topaz (Kiberevskoe, Voron'ya).

Within the pegmatite field, the most interesting is the Savvateevo (Usovskoe) deposit; it has long been famous for its beautiful colored tourmalines and gem-quality vorobyevite, which was mined by prospectors from cavities in the initial period of exploitation.

The largest pegmatite in the Usovskoe deposit fills the bulge of the anticline at the contact between biotite gneisses and a thick lamprophyre dike.

The shape of the pegmatite body is irregular and very nearly stockwork-shaped; toward the southeast, it passes into an aplite vein. The total length of the body is about 400 m, of which 150 m belongs to the stockwork-shaped bulge, and 250 m to the aplite vein. The mean thickness of the stockworkshaped vein bulge is about 50 m.

The peripheral parts of the pegmatite consists of graphic pegmatite which is replaced towards the center with coarse-grained quartz-microcline pegmatite of pegmatoid structure. The miarolitic cavities are associated mainly with the zone of partly albitized coarse-grained pegmatite and are usually joined with one another by veins.

In the course of many years, during the exploitation of the Savvateevo deposit, the following interesting facts about the vertical zoning of the pegmatite body were noted.

1. In the first stage of exploitation the deposit was typically a thick albite zone with pockets of lepidolite in the central portion of the body containing large miarolitic cavities coated with lepidolite and beautiful crystals of rubellite and vorobyevite.

2. When the first pit reached a shallow depth (5–8 m) the lepidolite zone disappeared and the area of the albite zone was considerably reduced; in the cavities coated with albite the rubellite was replaced with green tourmaline and vorobyevite and light-green beryl.

3. A marked decrease in the size of the albite zone was noted on further deepening.

In the pit at 10 to 12 m the pegmatite consists of a thick graphic zone and a weakly developed zone of coarse-grained quartz-microcline pegmatite, which contains miaroles with crystals of quartz, schorl, and accessory aquamarine.

Thus, in the vertical section of the Usovskoe pegmatite body there are virtually all types of paragenetic associations, which fill the miarolitic cavitites in pegmatites.

Finally, the miarolitic pegmatites of Volhynia have very large cavities containing gigantic crystals of quartz, feldspar, topaz, and large crystals of olive-green beryl.

The cavity-bearing pegmatites of Volhynia have been recently studied in detail by L. P. Chernyshkova (1957); they are spatially and genetically associated with the so-called Korosten porphyritic granites of rapakivi-type that occur within the Korosten pluton (the northwestern part of the Ukranian crystalline shield).[4]

The zone of pegmatite-bearing porphyritic granites rings the older basic rocks (gabbro-anorthosites). The pegmatites, containing large miarolitic cavities, occur in a band near the contact between the granites and the basic rocks. The granites that enclose the pegmatites are usually modified by postmagmatic processes, so that the new formations are fluorite, albite, gilbertite, and black quartz; they also have a granophyric structure and a micropegmatitic structure of the basic mass.

The shape of the miarolitic pegmatite bodies is usually irregular—oval, pyriform, sometimes even widely ramified. The separate adjoining bodies are in many places connected by thin leaders or mineralized fissures. However, in many places such connections are not established even when the entire pegmatite has been mined. According to L. P. Chernyshkova (1957), who studied this region, the observed distribution of cavities in the pegmatites under examination is determined to a large extent by the level of erosional exposure. Thus, for example, she notes a sudden decrease in the number and size of the cavities in pegmatites occurring in the more deeply eroded parts of the pegmatite-bearing zone.

The outer zone (0.1 to 0.3 m thick) of the pegmatite deposits usually consists of graphic quartz-microcline pegmatite, which toward the center is replaced by typical block pegmatite; sections of unevenly grained pegmatite of apographic and pegmatoid structure lie in between. In the most highly differentiated pegmatite there are monomineralic zones of microcline-perthite and quartz, whose dimensions attain 20 to 30 m.

In the central part of pegmatite bodies the replacement processes (muscovitization, albitization, replacement with lithium micas and topaz) form

[4] It should be noted that, unlike other varieties of granitoids which form the Ukrainian crystalline shield, the Korosten granites have a somewhat higher (compared with the mean content of the granites) beryllium content (6×10^{-4} percent Be).

widespread replacement complexes, mainly at the expense of block microcline and the pegmatoid zone. As L. P. Chernyshkova notes, intensive replacement contributes to the formation of large cavities, which form the special areas where crystals can grow freely. In the pegmatites of Volhynia the dimensions of cavities vary from 1–2 to 10–20 m. Usually the large stockwork-shaped bodies contain one large cavity, which occupies the central part of the pegmatite; the cavity is filled with fine loose mica and argillaceous masses in which are embedded giant crystals of quartz, large topaz, and beryl crystals. On the floor of the cavity are deposits of black, yellow, and green argillaceous stratified formations.

In the cavities, beryl is usually found in association with violet or green lithium mica (lepidolite, protolithionite). In small cavities beryl and topaz are antipathetic, but in large chambers these minerals are commonly found together. Beryl occurs as the alkali-free variety, most characteristic of the miarolitic pegmatites (analysis 7, Table 39), is typically olive-green to honey-yellow, and shows abundant solution of the crystals. Some crystals are transparent and without cracks and can be used as a high-grade jewelry material. Cases of regeneration (completion of crystals by growth) of beryl crystal fragments in the free cavity are quite common. Table 92 shows the typical paragenesis of the different zones of Volhynian miarolitic "chamber" pegmatites.

Table 92 Paragenesis of minerals in the miarolitic "chamber" pegmatites of Volhynia

Zones	Minerals	
	Main	Accessory
Outer zone of graphic pegmatite	Quartz, microcline	
Pegmatite of apographic and pegmatoid structure	Quartz, microcline-perthite	In apographic pegmatite long laths of green and black lithium-ferrous micas. In the pegmatoid zone—lamellar segregations of dark lithium-ferrous and light potassium-lithium micas
Block microcline	Microcline-perthite (segragations up to 50 cm in diameter)	Plates of potassium-lithium mica and of muscovite are found between microcline-perthite crystals
Block quartz	Quartz (massive)	
Replacements	Albite, quartz	Topaz, muscovite, lithium micas
Cavity (chamber)	Smoky quartz (crystals); minerals of "cavity filling" – finely scaled potassium and lithium micas, clay minerals	(a) topaz; (b) topaz, lithium-ferrous micas; (c) topaz, beryl, lithium micas; (d) beryl, potassium-lithium micas

Judging from both the nature of inner structure and the paragenetic features of the pegmatites under consideration, we can see that the formation of large cavities is a prolonged and complex process closely related to the action of residual emanations and solutions forming in the late stages of pegmatites as the result of the crystallization of the pegmatite melt in a closed system.

The earliest signs of the actions of these emanations and solutions were expressed in the replacement of the potassium feldspar by albite, micas, and topaz. During this period the large beryl crystals probably grew freely in the cavity filled with the residual mineral-forming solution.

The activity of fluorine-containing solutions enclosed in the cavity in the pegmatite resulted in the caving of the chamber walls and the loosening of the quartz, topaz, and beryl crystals that grew on these walls. There was also the regeneration (or corrosion, given other conditions) of crystals immersed in the loose mass of the disintegration products of feldspar. Mineral genesis terminated in the deposition on the floor of the cavity of clay products of feldspar disintegration from the late hydrothermal solution.

Block and Fully Differentiated Biotite-Microcline Pegmatites

Block and differentiated biotite-microcline pegmatites, which contain rare-earth minerals, are a fairly widely occurring type, but only a few of them contain gadolinite or beryl.

The block or fully differentiated biotite-microcline pegmatites enriched in rare-earth minerals usually occur in the fractures of gneisses or of small masses of ultrabasic rocks, near the contacts of granitic intrusions, or else directly in the fractures of the endocontact zone of the same intrusions. In a number of places there is an association between such pegmatites and the alkalic varieties of granites.

The outer zone of the pegmatite bodies is composed usually of graphic (sometimes medium-grained) quartz-microcline or quartz-oligoclase pegmatite, and inward there is a zone of block pegmatite that surrounds the central quartz core. At the boundary between the quartz core and the microcline segregations there are accumulations of large tabular biotite in a number of places. Books of biotite are also scattered in the outer pegmatite zone. In some places, muscovite occurs near the contact with block quartz, but in a very subordinate quantity. Green microcline (amazonite) occurs in deposits associated with alkalic granites.

The pegmatite deposits with the highest content of rare-earth minerals have been markedly albitized. Here, the albite replacement complex composed of lamellar (cleavelandite) or granular albite is segregated in separate pockets or else forms separate albitized zones in which the highest concentrations of rare-earth minerals are usually found.

Gadolinite may be associated with various paragenetic complexes of pegmatites. Its crystals occur in the peripheral portions of the quartz core and in the blocks of potassium feldspar, near their boundary with the quartz core. A close relationship commonly exists between segregations of gadolinite and the albite replacement complex. In addition, gadolinite is usually in close association with biotite and sometimes with muscovite. In paragenesis with it, there occur thalenite, allanite, cyrtolite, fergusonite, samarskite, and other yttria tantalo-niobates. In a number of places, the gadolinite-containing pegmatites contain notable amounts of fluorite.

The beryllium content, combined with the rarity and small sizes of the deposits under consideration, makes them of no practical importance, although examples of the industrial mining of gadolinite from such pegmatites, with the ultimate aim of extracting the rare earths of the yttrium group, is widely known. In the Iveland and Setersdalen regions of southern Norway, gadolinite was obtained as a by-product during the mining of pegmatites for ceramic raw material; in the Baringer Hill deposit, Texas, U.S.A., gadolinite was mined from a large pegmatite which contained considerable accumulations of rare-earth minerals. It should be noted that in both places the total amount of material mined was very insignificant as a beryllium source material.

Examples of block biotite-microcline pegmatites containing accessory gadolinite include the known deposits of the Llano region, Texas, U.S.A., of the Kola Peninsula, West Kievy, USSR, and of southern Norway

The Baringer Hill deposit, Llano region, Texas, known since 1887 and apparently now exhausted, was undoubtedly the largest deposit of gadolinite and other rare-earth minerals in pegmatites. The deposit consists of only one lens-shaped pegmatite body (75×30 m) occurring in the Proterozoic (Algonquin) porphryitic biotite granites. Its outer zone is composed of graphic quartz-microcline pegmatite, whose rather unusual nature enabled K. K. Landes (1932) to assume that such a structure can be formed as a result of the substitution of late quartz for microcline-perthite.

Towards the center of the pegmatite, the graphic zone passes into a pegmatite of large-block structure, composed of giant idiomorphic monocrystals of rose-colored microcline-perthite, cemented together with massive milky quartz. In the center of the pegmatite body is a monomineralic zone of block quartz or a quartz core, in the neighborhood of which there is segregated a vertical albite replacement zone. The albite replacement complex composed of coarse-grained and thin-tabular brownish-red albite is associated with the basic mass of rare-earth minerals of the pegmatite, namely allanite, gadolinite, fergusonite, cyrtolite, and the rarer yytialite, rowlandite, polycrase, and mackintoshite. Along with the rare-earth minerals, one also notes in the albite zone uraninite (nivenite) and its alternation products.

A characteristic accessory mineral of the albite replacement complex is biotite, which in places forms considerable accumulations. There is also an unusual amount of magnetite, fluorite, and ilmenite. Gadolinite was observed as large irregular monocrystals weighing up to 80 kg and closely associated with albite, fergusonite, and cyrtolite. The outer part of the gadolinite segregations is covered with a dense brick-red crust which is probably a late-stage alteration product of the mineral.

The uranium and rare-earth minerals occur also in the form of inclusions in the peripheral parts of the quartz core; radial fissures ("stars") commonly occur around the inclusions of these minerals. The mean content of rare-earth minerals in the Baringer Hill pegmatite was measured in orders of tenths of 1 percent.

Examples of partly albitized block biotite-microcline (amazonite) pegmatites containing accessory gadolinite and associated rare-earth minerals are the vein-like pegmatites of West Kievy (Kola Peninsula) that are associated with a large intrusion of alkalic granites; these vein-like bodies were studied by I. V. Bel'kov (1958).

The pegmatite formations of West Kievy are in the contact zone between granitized gneisses and alkalic granites; they occur as short, thin, transgressive veins. The largest vein-like bodies have a length of 70 to 80 m and a thickness of 2.5 to 3 m. Near the contact with the pegmatites, biotite has been introduced into the gneisses and in places there is amazonite in the microcline. The pegmatite deposits containing an increased content of accessory rare-earth minerals, including gadolinite, have a small-block texture and have been noticeably albitized.

As a rule, the vein selvedges are composed of fine-grained albitized pegmatite of quartz-plagioclase composition [plagioclase-albite-oligoclase, No. 12 (Ab_{88} An_{12}, Ed.)], which contains magnetite and, in a number of places, segregations of younger fluorite. Next is the zone of medium-grained differentially albitized pegmatite of apographic or pegmatoid structure, composed of quartz, microcline-perthite, and albite [cleavelandite, Nos. 5 to 12 (Ab_{88-95} An_{5-12}, Ed.); to a lesser extent, fine-grained albite]. Biotite is common. Microcline-perthite usually occurs as amazonite; much less common is rose-colored microcline-perthite, which usually passes into green amazonite towards the center of the vein. In the albitized parts of the zone there is commonly an abundance of fluorite which in places forms noticeable accumulations. The central zone of the pegmatite bodies is composed of small-block quartz-amazonite pegmatite, commonly with large biotite books. The monocrystals of amazonite are idomorphic against the cementing quartz; in a number of places they are surrounded by a fringe of tabular cleavelandite that replaces microcline. Segregations of fluorite occur in block quartz along fractures.

The rare-earth minerals are usually located near the most intensively albitized zone of the medium-grained pegmatite that surrounds the block

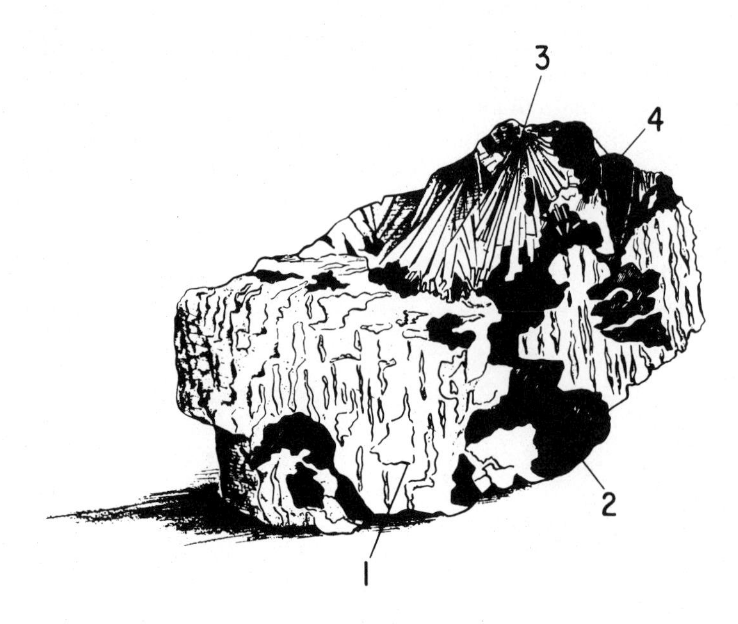

Fig. 23. Gadolinite with cleavelandite in amazonite pegmatite. (1) Graphic amazonite pigmatite; (2) quartz; (3) cleavelandite; (4) gadolinite.

core of the pegmatite, or else they are disposed within the limits of the albite replacement complex in the zone of the block quartz-amazonite pegmatite. Among the relict grains of amazonite in albite are scattered plates of biotite; crystals of magnetite, crytolite, risorite, gadolinite, hematite; allotriomorphic segregations of fluorite.

The large, poorly formed gadolinite crystals are disposed among cleavelandite blades or as inclusions in amazonite in the immediate vicinity of the segregations of the albite replacement complex (Fig. 23). In the albitized sections of the pegmatite, risorite, in association with gadolinite, forms large tetragonal crystals and peculiar radiating intergrowths with octahedral to rounded magnetite grains accompanied by fine and poorly formed cyrtolite crystals. The last mineral of the replacement complex is violet fluorite, whose elongated allotriomorphic segregations corrode the cleavelandite plates. In general, the concentration of gadolinite in the veins is not high, even in the most intensively mineralized pegmatites.

The gadolinite-containing pegmatites of Hittero, Iveland, Setersdalen, and other districts of southern Norway, are very interesting, but unfortunately we lack a detailed general description of these pegmatites. The pegmatites usually occur in the fractures of small masses of preCambrian ultrabasic rocks and belong to the types of block biotite-microcline and biotite-oligoclase-microcline pegmatites usually with the zonal structure. In a number of places there is a transition to muscovite-microcline pegmatite varieties.

Schetelig (Brögger, Vogt, and Schetelig, 1922) distinguishes three varieties of gadolinite in the southern Norwegian pegmatites:

1. Fine, well-developed separate crystals in quartz and feldspar, in the outer graphic zone of the pegmatite.
2. Larger crystals of thick-prismatic habit in quartz and feldspar, in the zone of coarse-grained pegmatite.
3. Very large, poorly formed crystals and irregular masses (sometimes their weight exceeds 1 kg), associated with muscovite and occurring in the zone of block pegmatite in the central part of the pegmatite bodies.

Listed below are the most characteristic associations of accessory minerals which accompany gadolinite in the southern Norwegian pegmatites.

Ollenstad:	(*a*) in graphic pegmatite—malacon, monazite, allanite, pyrochlore;
	(*b*) in block pegmatite—topaz, insignificant quantities of beryl;
Frikstad:	priorite, polycrase, topaz, apatite;
Birkeland:	lepidolite, topaz, bismuthinite;
Ivedal:	allanite, fergusonite, alvite;
Hameland:	chrysoberyl; and
Onnerod:	samarskite, columbite, bröggerite, monazite, rarely beryl.

PARAGENETIC FEATURES OF THE GADOLINITE-CONTAINING PEGMATITES. On analyzing the geochemistry and paragenesis of gadolinite-containing pegmatites, we note a number of common geochemical features of the pegmatite deposits of this group in various places in the world.

Common to all pegmatite deposits of gadolinite are the important role of rare-earth elements,[5] iron,[6] and flourine,[7] and the absence of boron in the pegmatitic process. Tourmaline, which could be an absorbent of iron, is not characteristic of gadolinite-containing pegmatites. All gadolinite-containing pegmatites also contain a notable development of albite, which is distinctly associated with the presence of higher concentrations of the rare-earth elements.

Data are lacking for the final solution to the problem of genesis of gadolinite in pegmatites. This is especially true of the fine well-formed gadolinite crystals, described by Schetelig (Brögger, Vogt, and Schetelig, 1922), which are found in the outer graphic zones of pegmatite veins,

[5] A wide occurrence in all deposits of the yttrium-earth tantalo-niobates, allanite, rowlandite, and other rare-earth minerals, along with gadolinite.

[6] Biotite, magnetite, ilmenite are highly characteristic minerals of gadolinite-containing pegmatites.

[7] In all deposits fluorite or topaz occurs.

the earliest formation of this paragenetic complex. Unfortunately, there is no detailed description of the sections where the presumed early gadolinite occurs (such description would give an idea of the degree of importance of later processes, especially albitization in these sections); therefore the problem of the early or late formation of this occurrence of gadolinite remains unsolved.

Judging from the paragenesis of known deposits, we can assume that the larger gadolinite crystals, which appear in the medium-grained or block pegmatite, are associated with replacement phenomena.

As proof of the early formation of gadolinite, some investigators (Schetelig, Bel'kov) quote the fact that crystals of gadolinite usually occur in the monocrystalline segregations of microcline-perthite. However, a

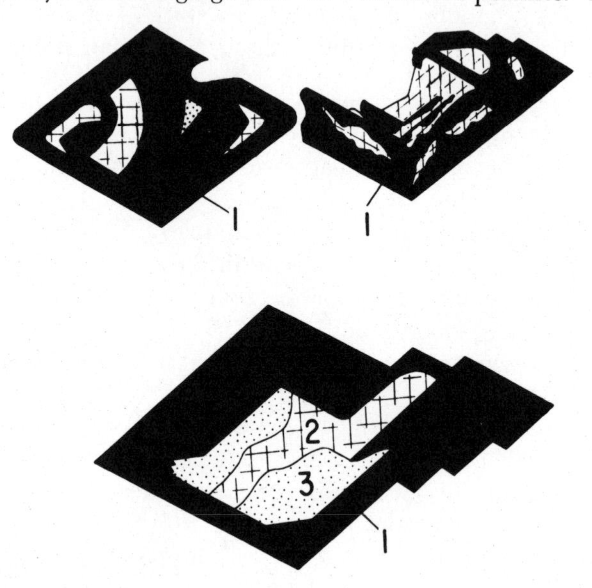

Fig. 24. Skeletal gadolinite crystals (according to Schetelig). (1) Gadolinite; (2) microcline relics; (3) quartz relics.

detailed analysis of this problem shows that such formations are observed mostly near the boundary with segregations of the albite replacement complex. Besides, Schetelig cites highly interesting facts which illustrate the structure of idiomorphic gadolinite crystals from the block-pegmatite zone, which he has studied and which have been found to be peculiar skeletal formations, apparently analogous to crystals of "stuffed" beryl (Fig. 24). The inner part of such idiomorphic crystals is filled with microcline, quartz, and albite.

It is possible to postulate correctly a metasomatic origin for the skeletal gadolinite crystals, which apparently immediately preceded or accompanied the development of albite. On the basis of the available facts, it is highly doubtful that gadolinite formed earlier than block microcline. A close paragenesis of albite and gadolinite occurs in the pegmatites of Baringer Hill, the Kola Peninsula, and other regions. In the pegmatites of Hittero and Iveland one notices also various (parallel and other) intergrowths of gadolinite and muscovite.

It should be noted that in pegmatites where replacement phenomena are not abundant, higher concentrations of gadolinite are unknown.

Thus the development of replacement phenomena, especially albite and to a lesser extent muscovite, is one of the most interesting geochemical features of the gadolinite-containing pegmatites.

Block and Fully Differentiated Muscovite-Microcline Pegmatites

Block and fully differentiated muscovite-microcline pegmatites, with beryl and tantalo-niobates, usually occur in metamorphized rocks (most abundantly in crystalline schists) of the exocontact zone of pegmatite-bearing granitic intrusions, or else they occur directly in granites, filling contraction and shear fractures developed in the apical part of the granitic intrusions.

Despite numerous differences in the details, the internal structure of the pegmatite deposits of this group is characterized by fairly constant common features.

At the contact between the pegmatite and the enclosing rocks there usually occurs a relatively thin aplitic margin, which is the result of the physico-chemical reaction between the pegmatite melt and the enclosing rocks (Beus, 1950). Its composition is not constant and depends on the peculiarities of its development. Usually the aplitic margin contains increased concentration of iron- and magnesium-containing minerals resulting from the assimilation of these elements from the enclosing rocks. In a number of places the aplite may be absent or its composition may be altered during subsequent replacement processes.

The next inner zone of the pegmatite body, as a rule, is composed of graphic and medium-grained quartz-microcline pegmatite. Then the graphic pegmatite either occupies the outermost part of the pegmatite (being further replaced by medium-grained pegmatite of apographic structure), or else it occurs in the form of separate pockets in the preponderant mass of medium-grained pegmatite.

Depending on the degree of differentiation of the pegmatite, the zone of medium- and coarse-grained pegmatite is replaced towards the center either by a zone of block pegmatite, composed of giant crystal blocks of microcline-perthite and enclosed in massive quartz, or else by a zone of block microcline. In the most completely differentiated pegmatites, the central part of the pegmatite is virtually a monomineralic quartz core composed of massive grey or rose quartz. In rare cases the core of the pegmatite is composed of a zone of block microcline-perthite.

In the poorly differentiated pegmatite bodies the quartz core, including large crystals of microcline-perthite, may directly follow the zone of graphic or medium-grained pegmatite.

Between the quartz core and the surrounding feldspar zones is a group of separated pockets and, less commonly, an irregular margin of a muscovite replacement zone (quartz-muscovite or quartz-albite-muscovite replacement complex). In a number of places, there is a noticeable albitization of block microcline and especially of medium-grained pegmatite, but the primary apographic structure of the latter is always preserved.

In the block muscovite-microcline pegmatites, beryl concentrates mainly at the boundary between the central block-quartz zone and the surrounding zone of block microcline or medium-grained pegmatite, usually in association with muscovite. Beryl crystals more rarely occur directly in quartz blocks (which is mainly characteristic of the poorly differentiated pegmatite bodies), and still more rarely in block microcline at some distance from the quartz core. Individual higher beryllium concentrations associated with a muscovite replacement complex are found at the boundary between the zone of block pegmatite (or block microcline) and the zone of partly albitized medium-grained pegmatite of apographic structure.

In the pegmatites of this type, the paragenesis with beryl is well-formed crystals of columbite-tantalite, triphylite, graftonite, manganophyllite, less frequently samarskite, and zircon (cyrtolite). In a number of deposits a characteristic mineral is black ferrous or ferrous-magnesian tourmaline.

The main characteristic of block-muscovite-microcline pegmatite is the coarsely crystalline beryl with low alkali content. This variety of beryl occurs wholly or partly in the block quartz as well-developed hexagonal crystals of long-prismatic habit, that sometimes have a complex cap. The crystals leave clear imprints of faces in the massive block quartz. There are several known cases of beryl crystals occurring in block quartz that are fractured and recemented by the same quartz (Fig. 25). The rupture between the individual parts of the crystal amounts in places to 2 to 3 cm. In various deposits, the color of the crystals varies from blue (aquamarine) to green and brown. Light-green and yellowish-green beryl is most common. The size of crystals varies from a few centimeters to 1.2 to 2 m (rarely more) along the *c*-axis, and from fractions of a centimeter to 1 m across. The mean dimension of crystals in most deposits does not fall below 2×5 cm, and in such deposits one rarely finds crystals of 0.5 cm and less along the *c*-axis.

An interesting feature of this variety of beryl is its highly irregular, pocket-like distribution in the beryl-bearing zone, which borders the quartz core of the pegmatite body. The larger these crystals or crystal pockets of beryl, the more pronounced is the irregularity of its distribution in the pegmatite. When examining beryl deposits of this type, one commonly finds places where several tons of beryl concentrate have been derived from a pocket consisting of one or a few beryl crystals, after

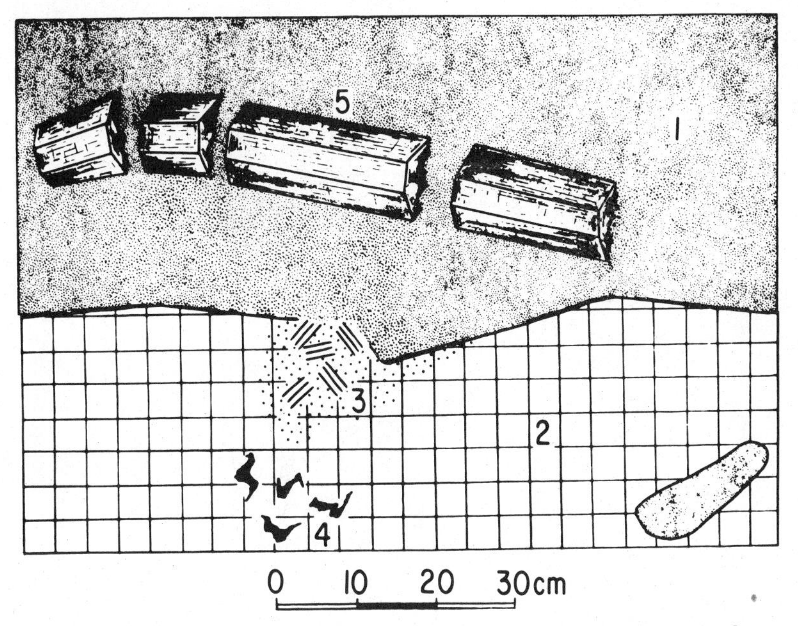

Fig. 25. A ruptured beryl crystal in block quartz, eastern Siberia. (1) Quartz; (2) microcline; (3) muscovite in albitized microcline; (4) quartz growths in microcline; (5) beryl.

which the mining has followed for tens of meters completely or almost completely barren rock until a new pocket has been reached. In a number of deposits there is a regular association of the largest beryl crystals and crystal pockets with the footwall of the block-quartz zone.

There are somewhat different features for the sodium variety of beryl (Figs. 10, 11), which is rarer in the block muscovite-microcline pegmatites and usually appears in pegmatites that are more or less affected by albitization. The sodium beryl crystals, which have a conical or pyramidal habit and poorly formed faces, usually concentrate at the following:

(*a*) the boundary between the zones of block and medium-grained pegmatites, occurring in the albitized and muscovite medium-grained pegmatite of apographic structure;

(*b*) the boundary between the zones of block quartz and block microcline, occurring in albitized microcline.

Unlike the earlier alkali-free beryl, whose crystals usually contain no alien inclusions, sodium beryl commonly forms the so-called "stuffed" compound crystals, whose central part is filled with albitized medium-grained pegmatite, albite or quartz, and muscovite. It is not uncommon to find irregular intergrowths of beryl with quartz and albite.

The color of sodium beryl varies from pale-green to yellow-green and

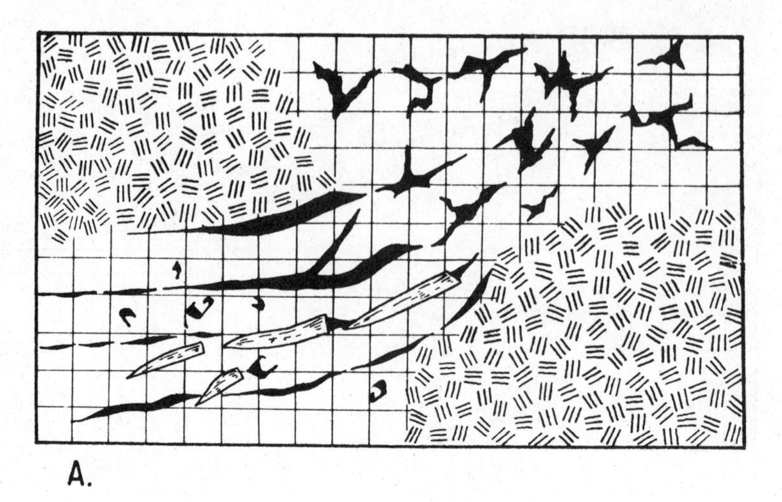
A.

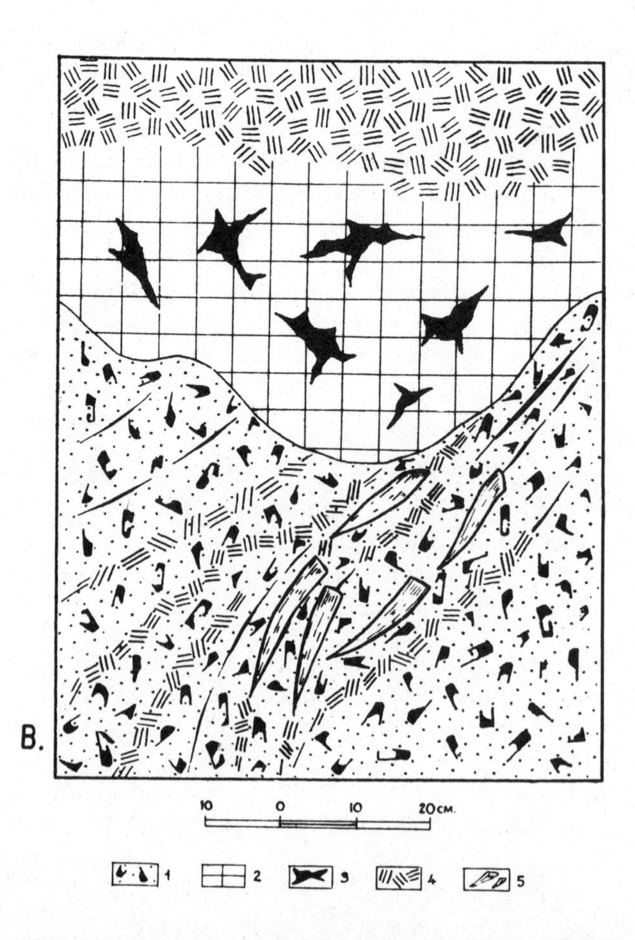
B.
10 0 10 20CM.
1
2
3
4
5

greenish-yellow. The size of crystals varies roughly within the limits noted above for the alkali-free variety, although the giant crystals, more than 1 m along the *c*-axis, occur here much less frequently.

A feature of the sodium variety of beryl is its more regular distribution in the beryl-bearing zone, which is especially typical of relatively small crystals associated with the albitized parts of the medium-grained pegmatites (at the boundary with the block zone). In a number of deposits there is a relationship between sodium beryl and the jointing that transgresses the zones of medium-grained pegmatite and block microcline (Fig. 26); the association of this beryl variety with albitized and muscovitized rock is very constant.

The thickness of the beryl-bearing zone in industrial deposits of block muscovite-microcline pegmatites varies from 0.5 to 2 m (rarely more), depending on the size and morphology of the pegmatites. The thickest and most sustained beryl-bearing zones are noted in large, well-differentiated pegmatites of isometric or lenticular shape.

On the basis of world-wide data, the beryl content in industrial pegmatites of this type varies between 0.2 and 0.5 percent, seldom exceeding this limit.

In a number of places, when block and fully differentiated muscovite-microcline pegmatites are mined in depth, the thickness of the zone of graphic and medium-grained pegmatite increases as the importance of the block zones decreases (Beus, 1951, 1953a, 1956a).

Decreasing degrees of differentiation of the pegmatite are accompanied simultaneously by a noticeable decrease in beryl content, down to its complete disappearance. The poorer the differentiation at depth of the investigated pegmatite, the lower the beryl content. However, the trend of zonal changes depends entirely on the nature of the erosional exposure of the pegmatite. In places where erosional exposure reveals the apical part of a pegmatite body whose thickness increases in depth, there is commonly a reversed zonal change—namely, as thickness increases, the poorly differentiated pegmatite at depth is followed by large-block or even fully differentiated pegmatite with a higher beryl concentration than that at the surface. Quite important also is the change in the mode of occurrence of the pegmatite body. For example, one encounters at depth step-like or cupola-like parts of poorly differentiated pegmatite veins, generally of low beryl concentration; these cupola-like parts in a number of places show a complete differentiation and contain large industrial accumulations of beryl.

Fig. 26. Crystals of sodium beryl

(A) In block microcline with fissures filled with quartz and beryl. (B) Associated with jointing in the zone of medium-grained pegmatite of apographic structure. (1) Medium-grained, albitized pegmatite; (2) block microcline; (3) quartz; (4) muscovite; (5) beryl.

Block muscovite-microcline pegmatites with beryl are known and worked in many pegmatite districts in the world. However, a majority of deposits were worked only at the surface, because the irregular distribution and generally low beryl content made it unprofitable to work the beryl-bearing pegmatite bodies in both. Only the largest single deposits of this type were worked to a depth of 40 to 60 m (Beus, 1956a).

Deposits composed of fully differentiated pegmatites that have an independent monomineralic zone of block microcline perthite are rarer. These beryl deposits have relatively large dimensions and a more constant beryl-bearing zone.

Examples are known of deposits of this group being worked to a depth of 40 to 80 m along the dip. Fully differentiated pegmatite in many places is replaced at depth with block pegmatite.

The peculiar features of the internal structure and of the paragenesis of beryl-bearing block muscovite-microcline pegmatites, which are characteristically weakly albitized, are illustrated by a typical pegmatite in one of the central Asian fields (Fig. 27).

The pegmatite, of clearly defined lenticular shape, is conformable in quartz-biotite schists of Upper Silurian age. The length of the lens is 50 m and the thickness at the bulge is 12.6 m. The direction of dip is 145°; the angle of the dip of the hanging wall is 25°, and of the floorwall, 40°.

Near the contact with the pegmatite is altered quartz-biotite schist in a band as much as 0.5 m thick, containing newly formed muscovite, cordierite, tourmaline, and garnet.

The effect of the pegmatite on the enclosing rocks was shown by the enrichment in potassium of the quartz-biotite schists near the contact (muscovitization of biotite) and in the impoverishment in iron and magnesium (due to the migration of these elements into the pegmatite) (Beus, 1950).

No systematic investigation of the range of beryllium in the contact zone has been carried out, but individual analyses indicate a weak migration of beryllium into the enclosing rocks, which occurred during the interaction between the pegmatite melt and the quartz-biotite schists.

In particular, muscovite and cordierite, which formed during the contact metamorphism at the contact with the pegmatite, have a higher beryllium content (be up to 16×10^{-4} percent and 52×10^{-4} percent, respectively). The mean beryllium content in the altered schists of the

---

Fig. 27. Geological plans of block microcline pegmatite with beryl, Central Asia (according to A. A. Beus). (1) Zone of block microcline; (2) zone of graphic pegmatite; (3) muscovite; (4) albite zone; (5) tourmaline; (6) beryl; (7) fissures with tectonic breccia; (8) line of tectonic dislocations; (9) opening of adits.

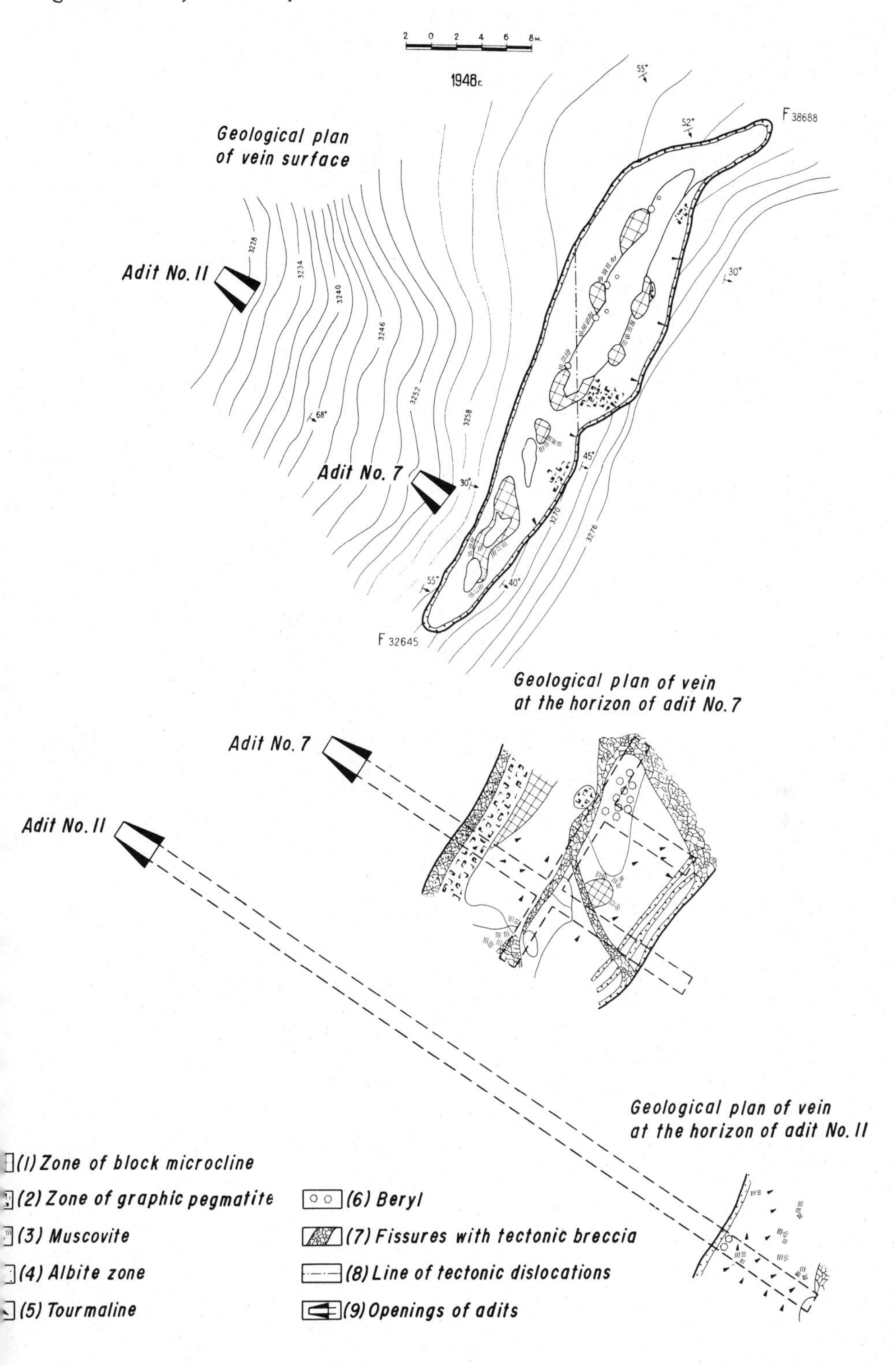

2 0 2 4 6 8м.
1948г.
Geological plan of vein surface
Adit No. 11
Adit No. 7
3228
3234
3240
3246
3252
3258
3270
3276
55°
52°
30°
68°
45°
30°
55°
40°
F 38688
F 32645
Geological plan of vein at the horizon of adit No. 7
Adit No. 7
Adit No. 11
Geological plan of vein at the horizon of adit No. 11
(1) Zone of block microcline
(2) Zone of graphic pegmatite
(3) Muscovite
(4) Albite zone
(5) Tourmaline
(6) Beryl
(7) Fissures with tectonic breccia
(8) Line of tectonic dislocations
(9) Openings of adits

contact zone is, as can be estimated from analyses of single samples, three to four times as high as that of the unaltered quartz-biotite schists taken from the pegmatite (Table 93).

The aplite-like zone of the vein, is characterized by a banded structure and by higher concentrations of iron- and magnesium-containing minerals (almandine, black tourmaline), and a thickness of from 4 to 30 cm. The rock-forming minerals of the zone are quartz, oligoclase No. 16-20

Table 93 Beryllium content of the enclosing rocks of pegmatite vein

Name of rock	Be content in $10^{-4}\%$
Biotite quartzite, 50 m from the vein	1
Quartz-biotite schist, 50 m from the vein	3
Quartz-biotite schist with andalusite, 10 m from the vein	3
Quartz-muscovite schist, 10 cm from contact	8
Quartz-muscovite schist with cordierite, 3 cm from contact	14

($Ab_{84}An_{16}$ – $Ab_{80}An_{20}$, Ed.), and microcline. Within the zone, hybridism is clearly reflected in the structure and mineralogical composition (Beus, 1950).

Towards the center of the vein, the aplite-like zone passes into a zone of medium-grained quartz-feldspar pegmatite which consists mainly of albite-oligoclase, whose number (anorthite content, Ed.) decreases towards the vein center, microcline, and quartz. In the outer portions of the zone are long laths of biotite showing replacement by muscovite. Large conical crystals of black tourmaline usually occur, mostly at the boundary with the aplite-like zone, their pointed ends directed towards the plane of contact between the vein and schists. Other tourmaline crystals are dispersed in groups across the medium-grained zone, their pointed ends oriented either towards biotite partly replaced by muscovite, or around the small xenoliths of the enclosing rocks in the vein.

At this level of erosion, the graphic zone of quartz-microcline composition is poorly exposed and occurs in separate places in the mass of the medium-grained pegmatite of apographic structure.

In the central part of the pegmatite there are large (up to 10 m^3) monocrystalline blocks of greenish microcline-perthite, which surround the core (zone) of block quartz. However, no continuous zone of block microcline can be observed in the vein.

The core of the pegmatite consists of separate quartz blocks as much as 3 to 4 m thick, arranged bead-like in the central part of the vein. In the mass of solid grey quartz are irregularly arranged portions of quartz of a beautiful rose color. Between the block-quartz zone and the surrounding feldspar zones there is an intermittent quartz-muscovite fringe (zone), 10 to 20 cm thick, which contains a small amount of albite.

On the footwall of the block-quartz, at the boundary with the zone of medium-grained pegmatite and microcline-perthite blocks, there are large (up to 1 m in length and 30 cm across) prismatic crystals of green and yellowish-green beryl. Smaller green beryl crystals occur directly in block quartz, also mainly in the footwall of the zone. The crystals occurring in block quartz are commonly semi-transparent and have a compound cap, unlike the larger opaque crystals associated with the boundary between the quartz core and the surrounding zones. The largest of these crystals are usually disposed so that their long axis is roughly parallel to the contact plane of the zone, whereas the fine crystals may be randomly oriented. In the small segregations of block quartz, surrounded with medium-grained pegmatite, interesting drusy formations of beryl crystals are oriented roughly at right angles to the plane of contact between block quartz and the medium-grained pegmatite.

The beryl crystals at the boundary between the quartz core and the feldspar fringes are usually in close paragenesis with the quartz-muscovite replacement complex. The separate beryl crystals commonly form various intergrowths with the muscovite books; the muscovite crystals always leave distinct imprints on beryl faces. The beryl crystals show, in turn, a distinct effect on the form of muscovite crystals occurring in the intergrowths.

In the muscovite zone and at its boundary with the block-microcline zone, black crystals of cyrtolite and pockets of triphylite (and other phosphates transformed into heterosite occur in association with beryl.

Thus, it is possible to distinguish in the pegmatite two fairly close forms of beryl segregations that differ only in the degree of perfection of the crystals and partly in their paragenesis:

1. Well-formed prismatic crystals (usually with a cap), occurring wholly in block quartz and leaving in it distinct imprints of their faces; they are most abundant towards the footwall of the zone and do not display any relationship to any other minerals.
2. Larger prismatic crystals (usually capless), occurring at the boundary of the block-quartz zone and of the surrounding feldspar zones; they are paragenesis with quartz-muscovite replacement complex in association with cyrtolite and triphlite.

Compared with both beryl varieties, block quartz is a later formation that joins them along fissures and cements the individual broken crystals. There is no albite zone in the vein, and albitization is weak.

The mean beryl content along the pegmatite does not exceed 0.04 percent, which corresponds to a beryllium content of about 16×10^{-4} percent.

The calculations of the ratios of beryllium occurring in the pegmatite concentrated in beryl and of beryllium dispersed in the rock-forming and accessory pegmatite minerals (Table 94) show that, in this case, not more than 20 percent of the total beryllium is found dispersed in the pegmatite.

Consequently, the pegmatite referred to above can be cited as an

Table 94 Content of dispersed beryllium in the rock-forming accessory minerals of the pegmatite vein

Name of mineral	Quantitative content in in pegmatite, %	Be content in 10^{-4}%
Quartz	34	0.5
Microcline-perthite	57.4	4
Oligoclase-albite	8	6
Muscovite	3	25
Black tourmaline	1	13
Biotite }	0.3	11
Garnet }		6
Cyrtolite	<0.01	40
Other minerals	ca. 0.3	–
Mean content of dispersed beryllium		4
Mean content of beryllium due to beryl		16
Total beryllium content of vein		20

example of widespread beryl-bearing pegmatites of block structure, which show evidence of both a poor development of the replacement phenomena, especially muscovitization, and poor beryl mineralization.

In another deposit of the same pegmatite district there are abundant replacement phenomena, including albitization. This vein is 70 m in length, the bulge thickness being 12 m; it is a typical lenticular body dipping towards the southeast at an angle of 35 to 45°, conformable with the enclosing quartz-biotite schists.

Along its contacts with the enclosing schists, there is a rather thin, partly albitized aplite-like fringe, which passes into an outer zone composed of medium-grained quartz-microcline pegmatite, which is strongly albitized in places. At this level of erosion, the central part of the pegmatite consists mainly of giant (up to 4 m across), strongly albitized blocks of microcline-perthite. Quartz blocks, which appear here and there within the block-microcline zone, are very small and surrounded by thick quartz-albite-muscovite fringes (Fig. 28).

The beryl found at the surface was white and had a conical crystal habit

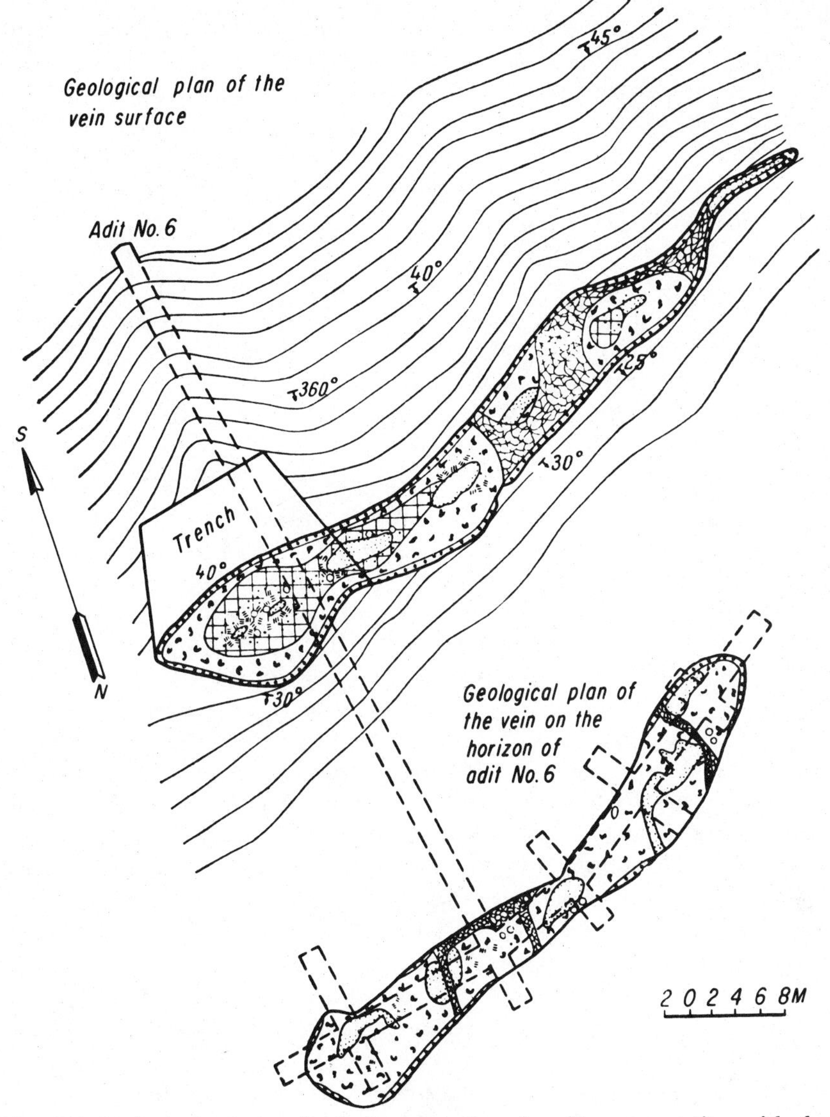

Fig. 28. Geological plans of block muscovite-microcline pegmatite with beryl, Central Asia (according to A. A. Beus). See Fig. 27 for designations.

(the sodium-lithium variety of beryl); the crystals occurred mainly in the albitized microcline sections in close paragenesis with muscovite.

At a depth of 5 m from the surface was a solid zone of block quartz as much as 3 m thick, surrounded by a muscovite zone which was particularly thick ($<$ 1.5 m) in the hanging wall of the pegmatite. The block microcline zone, which surrounds the entire central part as a continuous belt, is highly albitized, and near the contact with the quartz core, it is transformed into a solid aggregate of roughly tabular albite. In these sections are accumulations of very large crystals of sodium beryl and columbite.

At this level the color of beryl varies from white to dirty-green. There are also zoned crystals with a pale-green center and snow-white peripheral parts. The crystals are particularly characterized by numerous inclusions of black tourmaline, muscovite, and albite.

The crystals of black tourmaline commonly pierce beryl in all directions. In other places tourmaline produces "investment" pseudomorphs after the hexagonal beryl crystals. Fairly common also are peculiar zoned crystals of the following habit: crystal center—quartz or albitized microcline; zone of beryl with regular hexagonal outlines; zone of black tourmaline which coats beryl; outer hexagonal shell composed of beryl.

Peculiar intergrowths of beryl and large cyrtolite crystals are also very interesting.

At the same level beryl is replaced by manganese and iron phosphates of pallite and other types. In the replacement complex there is also late fine-grained albite and arsenopyrite. Distinct traces of corrosion are observed in individual crystals.

In association with beryl, at the boundary between the muscovite zone and the block-quartz zone, there are abundant large crystals and pockets of triphylite, arrojadite, magniophilite, other manganese and iron phosphates—partly altered by supergene processes—as well as cyrtolite.

With increasing depth, the degree of differentiation of the pegmatite gradually decreases, albitized rock is less common, and the beryllium content noticeably decreases. At a depth of 40 m down dip, the fundamental mass of the pegmatite is composed of medium-grained pegmatite. The block-quartz zone consists of separated blocks that are adjacent to the central part of the vein. Beryl, in crystal pockets and as separate pale-green prismatic crystals, as much as 4×10 cm, is associated with the peripheral portions of the block quartz; it also occurs in muscovite pockets dispersed in the medium-grained pegmatite. At a level of 40 m from the surface, the beryl content is one-third of that at the well-differentiated horizon exposed by erosion at the surface.

In the typical example under consideration, vertical zonal distribution of beryl in the pegmatite body should be emphasized. The highest concentration of beryl is at the upper, well-differentiated levels of the pegmatite lens, in the sections where albitization and muscovitization have been intense. Here beryl occurs in the albitized parts of block microcline and is represented by the sodium-lithium and sodium varieties; within the albitized and muscovitized coarse-grained pegmatite the "stuffed" varieties of sodium beryl are abundant.

It has already been noted that, along with the lessening of the differentiation of the pegmatite and the noticeable weakening of albitization, the beryl content also decreases with depth. At the same time, the alkali content in beryl decreases (Table 95). Beryl found in the pegmatite body at a depth of 40 m down dip, and adjoining the separate quartz blocks in the central part of the vein, was similar in habit to the alkali-free variety.

One of the Central Asian deposits can be used as an example to illustrate an even more distinct relationship between the process of beryl concentration in block pegmatites and the peculiarities of the geological position of the pegmatite, its inner structure, and the nature of development of replacement phenomena.

This deposit is within the exo- and endo-contact zone of a granitic mass that breaks through a mass of metamorphosed and dislocated deposits of Middle Devonian age. The mass is mainly medium-grained porphyritic biotite granite with noticeable signs of having assimilated the enclosing rocks.

Most pegmatite formations within this deposit are associated with gently pitching fissures, which are developed in the border zones of the grantic mass. The pitch of the fissures is northwest and the angle of dip is 20 to 30°.

Table 95 Decrease of alkali content in beryl down the dip of the pegmatite vein

Characteristic of beryl	Place of sampling	Total
White conical sodium-lithium beryl from albitized block microcline	Surface of vein	2.31
Dirty-green, "stuffed" beryl from muscovite zone	At a depth of about 10 m down dip	0.92
Dirty-green beryl with inclusions of black tourmaline from muscovite zone	At a depth of 40 m down dip	0.69
Yellowish-green beryl from quartz blocks	At a depth of 40 m down dip	0.54

The length of individual pegmatites is 200 m, the thickness 0.2 to 4 m; in the intersections of fissures, there are bulges as much as 7 to 12 m thick (Fig. 29). These bulges have the form of convex-concave lenses (domes) and have perfect and clear zonal structure, intensive development of replacement units, and a high content of beryl and tantalo-niobates. From an economic point of view the dome-shaped bulges are very valuable.

Especially interesting in this respect is the dome-shaped bulge of the "Nizhnyaya" vein, which contains an abnormally high beryl concentration. In the center of the bulge there is a quartz core as much a 5 m thick, which includes separate idiomorphic crystals of microcline-perthite up to 1 to 3 m across. Towards the contacts of the body, the quartz core passes abruptly into the zone of strongly albitized, medium-grained pegmatite of apographic structure, which constitutes outer portions of the bulge. In this zone microcline is almost completely replaced by albite.

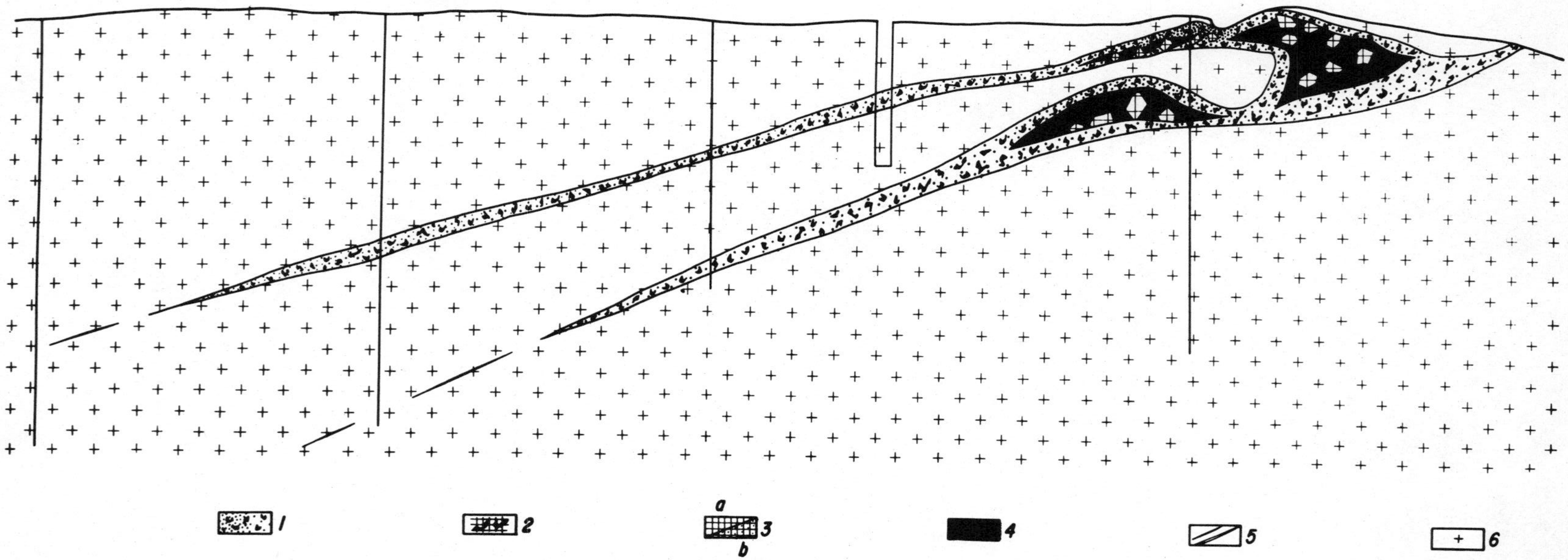

Fig. 29. Section through the dome-shaped part of the pegmatite body; enriched with beryl. (1) Medium-grained pegmatite, albitized to a various extent; (2) small-block pegmatite; (3a) microcline-perthite; (3b) partly albitized microcline-perthite; (4) quartz; (5) pegmatite veins; (6) granite.

The characteristic accessory mineral of the zone of albitized, medium-grained pegmatite is light-green beryl whose poorly formed crystals attain 10 cm along the *c*-axis and are 2 to 3 cm across. In the dome-shaped bulges in this zone there have occurred interesting parallel growths of flattened beryl and albite crystals, and the characteristic "stuffed" beryl crystals whose center consists of granular albite. It is interesting to note that the degree of idiomorphism of the beryl crystals depends directly on the degree of albitization of the pegmatite. The distribution of the mineral in the zone of the albitized medium-grained pegmatite is fairly uniform.

The highest beryl concentrations are associated with the central part of the dome-shaped bulge, which is composed of large-block pegmatite. In the block quartz, whose color varies from dark-gray to bright-rose, there are, along with the giant blocks of white microcline-perthite, pockets of large tabular muscovite with herringbone structure up to 1.5 m across. In these parts of the hanging wall of the block zone are giant pockets of very large prismatic and truncated pyramidal crystals of light-green beryl, some of which attain 1.5 m along the *c*-axis and as much as 60 cm across.

Strongly albitized microcline is observed near the muscovite pockets at the boundary between the microcline and quartz blocks. The albitized portions are at times pierced with numerous thin prismatic crystals of greenish-yellow beryl, 1 to 4 mm across and as much as 4 cm along the *c*-axis. In a number of places, the slender prismatic beryl crystals penetrate the albitized microcline, starting from thin fissures filled with quartz and small garnet crystals.

In another part extremely fine, slender prismatic beryl crystals penetrate into a thin fissure of poorly albitized block microcline-perthite. Some of the beryl crystals are disposed parallel to the walls of the fissure, the individual crystals even curving conformably with the curves of the fissure; other crystals are disposed at right or other angles to the fissure, growing into microcline. Under the microscope the complete idiomorphism of beryl with respect to the replaced microcline (Fig. 30) is seen; if no supplementary observations are available, this may result in erroneous conclusions regarding the relative ages of beryl and microcline.

Another characteristic feature of the dome-shaped bulge is the occurrence of rare cavities in the footwall of the block-pegmatite zone; these cavities are filled with brownish clay, in which are free semitransparent and completely transparent beryl crystals overgrown with fine bertrandite crystals.

The cavities contain well-developed prismatic beryl crystals from 0.4×2 to 8×12 cm, whose color varies from light-green to wine-yellow and brown. In the same cavity, the beryls are usually the same color. Highly interesting are zoned beryls in which the turbid, opaque lower part of the crystal changes suddenly, along a plane parallel to the pinacoid, into a completely transparent beryl suitable for jewelry (Fig. 31). The transition

Fig. 30. Late idiomorphic beryl crystals in block microcline. Magnification ×15.

Fig. 31. Boundary between the turbid part of a beryl crystal, filled with gaseous-liquid inclusions, and the transparent part, which contains only single inclusions. Magnification approximately ×150.

from turbid into clear portions and vice versa can occur several times in the same crystal.

The microscopic investigation of the zoned beryl crystals indicates that there is a close relationship between the arrangement of zones of varying transparency within the crystal and the distribution of the gas-liquid inclusions. The turbid, opaque lower parts of the crystals are full of gas-liquid inclusions, most of which are cylindrical in form and are oriented parallel to the *c*-axis of the beryl crystal. Highly characteristic of such crystals are three-phase inclusions which contain carbon dioxide.

Fig. 32. Zoned beryl crystals from a cavity.

Near the boundary of the transparent zone the number of inclusions suddenly decreases and within the transparent part of the crystal only single fine cylindrical inclusions (Fig. 32) occur.

A noticeable corrosion of beryl is found in the cavities. This corrosion results in numerous cavities parallel to the sixfold beryl axis; thus it is most probably determined by the characteristic features of the crystal structure of beryl.

The beryl found in cavities belongs to the alkali-free variety (Table 39, the chemical analysis of heliodor).

Bertrandite is sometimes in association with this variety of beryl in fine (1 mm) tabular crystals growing on the faces of beryl.

Thus, four varieties of beryl, differing in crystal habit and paragenesis, are distinguished in the pegmatite body.

The earliest generation, represented by large prismatic crystals, is associated with the zone of large-block pegmatite. The paragenesis is block quartz and coarse, tabular muscovite. Albite cements the fissures in beryl crystals and is of later formation.

The crystals that developed in the zone of the albitized medium-grained pegmatite are apparently contemporaneous with albitization, as can be concluded from the various skeletal intergrowths between beryl (the sodium variety) and albite. The close association of beryl of this generation with struverite is also quite interesting.

Finally, the slender prismatic beryl is the latest generation with respect to albitization. The association of this generation of beryl (characterized by complete idiomorphism) with jointing, which is developed not only in quartz and non-replaced microcline, but also in portions composed of albite, indicates a later formation of beryl compared with the other mentioned minerals.

We have here a very clear example of the fact that idiomorphism of beryl crystals with respect to microcline and other minerals is not certain proof of their earlier formation.

This generation of beryl belongs to the alkali-free or low-alkali varieties. In particular, in the examined deposit this generation is apparently an analogue of that which crystallizes in cavities when conditions permit free growth of crystals.

As already mentioned, an interesting feature of beryl from the cavities is the peculiar zoning caused by the regular distribution of gas-liquid inclusions in the crystal. The origin of such zoning can be explained by a change during beryl crystallization, most probably related to a change in the physico-chemical state of the system. We assume that the formation of the upper transparent beryl crystal zones is related to slow crystallization from aqueous solutions during the final stage of the pegmatite process. The alteration of zones with sharply different concentrations of the gas-liquid inclusions points to the rhythmic nature of mineral formation in the miarolitic cavities.

Besides beryl and the much rarer bertrandite, there is also a third beryllium mineral in the pegmatite vein—phenacite, which crystallized in the fissures in block microcline, forming druses of small (0.1 $\times$ 2.5 mm) acicular crystals on the leached surface of the microcline crystal.

Away from the bulge of the pegmatite body, its inner structure and paragenetic features undergo a sharp change. On the sides of the dome the thickness of the block-pegmatite zone gradually decreases. The block size also decreases, the large-block pegmatite being gradually replaced along the vein dip by a small-block pegmatite (block size 0.3 to 0.5 m), and this in turn by coarse-grained pegmatite. At the same time, the importance of the medium-grained pegmatite increases considerably with depth, and the replacement phenomena become noticeably less abundant. At a depth of 50 to 60 m down dip, the vein consists wholly of medium-grained pegmatite in which, along with granular albite, microcline relics commonly form half the rock. Moreover, in these sections there are fairly common lath-shaped relics of biotite that have only partly been replaced by muscovite.

The rare-metal minerals are also less abundant. In the medium-grained albitized pegmatite, fine crystals of yellowish and light-green beryl occur in small quantities (in the order of hundredths of 1 percent).

Thus the highest concentration of beryl (and of other rare-metal minerals) in the deposit is in the dome-shaped bulges of pegmatite bodies. The accumulations of beryl are associated, as a rule, with sections in which the evidences of replacement (muscovitization and albitization) are most abundant.

This deposit is a very clear example of the part played by volatile compounds in the formation of the rare-metal (including beryllium) minerals of pegmatites. Indeed, the dome-shaped folds of pegmatite bodies, which, owing to their morphology, should be the collectors of the volatile compounds of the pegmatite melt-solution, serve in this particular deposit as the reservoirs of the main mass of the rare-metal minerals and as the parts in which the replacement phenomena attain their maximum development. These phenomena and the rare-metal (including beryllium) minerals sharply decrease outside the dome-shaped folds, and with increasing depth.

As an example of the fully differentiated muscovite-microcline pegmatites with a more complex distribution of beryl, we can cite a large pegmatite in the same pegmatite district, whose formation took place under complex tectonic conditions that brought about a number of peculiar features in its internal structure.

The body is shaped like an irregular dike and occurs in quartz-biotite schists of lower Paleozoic age, 500 m from the contact with the intrusive bi-mica granite. The strike of the pegmatite coincides with that of the metamorphic mass; the dike transgresses the steeply dipping schists at various (sometimes very sharp) angles, and produces the typical step-like body (Fig. 33). The dike was traced for 380 m in length; its true thickness varied from 8 to 10 m in the gently dipping portions to 30 to 35 m in the steeply dipping portions. At the exposed level are large xenoliths of the enclosing micaceous schists that taper out in depth.

The body is a fully differentiated pegmatite with a peculiar irregular zoning. The type of pegmatite is determined by the predominance of the zones of block microcline and block quartz. Also the muscovite replacement complex is widely developed. At places there is a noticeable medium-grained albitized pegmatite and block microcline.

The zone of medium-grained albitized pegmatite is developed mainly at the extremities of the body. In the central and most completely differentiated part at the surface, this zone is poorly developed and occurs as

Fig. 33. Crystal relic of alkali-free beryl in the core of a sodium beryl crystal (the c = axes of the crystals are roughly perpendicular to each other).

small pockets in the near-contact portions of block microcline. The results of geological exploration show that medium-grained pegmatite increases with depth, owing to the decrease in thickness of the block zones.

A characteristic feature of the zone of medium-grained pegmatite is its strong albitization, which is distinctly displayed in the surface level; in places microcline is completely replaced by albite.

Judging from the microcline relics, the zone was first composed mainly of microcline and quartz, but the subsequent alteration, accompanied by intensive replacement of microcline, changed its composition considerably.

From the extremities towards the center of the vein, the medium-grained pegmatite gradually passes into block microcline.

The block-microcline zone, composed of almost monomineralic microcline-perthite, is the basic mass of the pegmatite, and varies in thickness from 8 to 20 m. The separate parts of the zone are strongly albitized, especially the contact of the body with the schists and the boundary with the segregations of block quartz. Such portions are commonly associated with pockets of large beryl crystals. In the block microcline are fairly common streaks and small pockets of albite-muscovite replacement complex, with which the columbite-beryl minerals are also associated.

The interrelations between block microcline and block quartz are highly distinctive, and this is the characteristic feature of this body compared with the usual fully differentiated pegmatites. As shown in Fig.

34, block quartz transgresses the zone of block microcline along fractures which are roughly comformable with the layering in the pegmatite dike. Block quartz also forms vein-like segregations that can be traced at the contact between pegmatite and country rocks and the large xenoliths in the central part of the pegmatite. Along the dip of the pegmatite the number and thickness of the vein-like quartz segregations noticeably decreases. In particular, at a depth of 30 to 50 m along the dip, quartz occurs as thin streaks. Taking into account the diminution of quartz down the dip, we can expect its complete disappearance in deeper levels.

On the whole, the segregations of block quartz are monomineralic. Only rarely does the dark block quartz contain idiomorphic segregations of microcline-perthite, pockets of large crystals of light-green beryl, and irregular segregations of red garnet (< 10 cm across). At the boundary, with the albitized portions of block microcline, in the quartz are rare tabular crystals of columbite; in albitized and muscovitized microcline near the boundary with block quartz are nest-like accumulations of beryl, and segregations of triphylite and related secondary iron and manganese phosphates.

Sharp contacts are a very characteristic feature of the block quartz zone.

The most characteristic replacement zone which, along with the block zones, determines the pegmatite type is that of muscovite. The albite-muscovite replacement complex is predominant in the body, while the quartz-muscovite complex is much less significant.

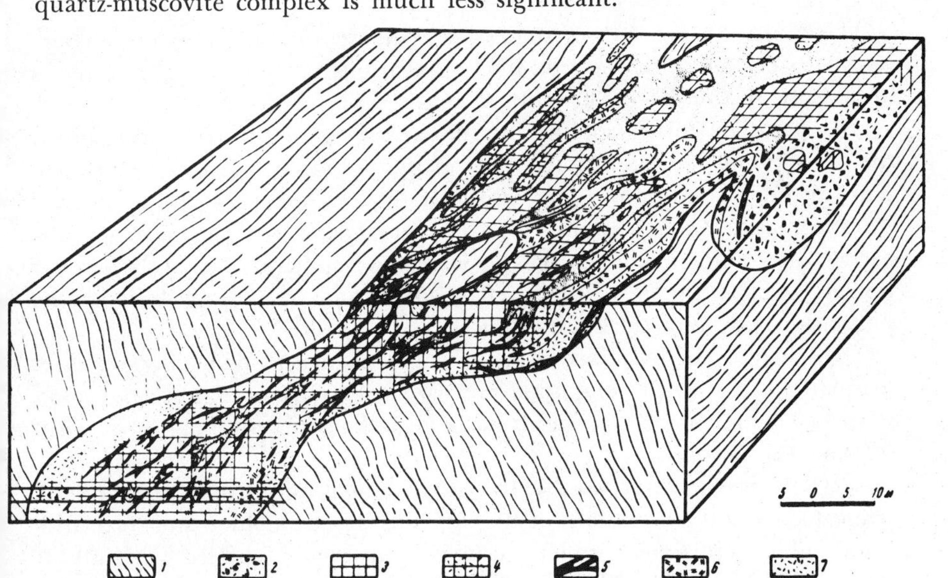

Fig. 34. Block quartz transgresses the zone of the block microcline-perthite. (1) Quartz-biotite schists; (2) albitized medium-grained pegmatite; (3) block microcline-perthite; (4) albitized block microcline-perthite; (5) block quartz; (6) muscovite; (7) albite replacement complex.

The albite-muscovite complex, characterized by higher concentrations of beryl and columbite, is mainly in streaks and as small pockets in the zone of block albitized microcline, especially near its boundary with the block quartz. The streaky segregations of the muscovite replacement complex are usually spatially associated with quartz streaks and sometimes form their natural extension.

Albitization has occurred both in block microcline and in medium-grained pegmatite, but there is no albite zone as a separate structural unit.

The peculiar features of the structure and position of various varieties of albite in the pegmatite, their interrelations, and the paragenesis with secondary and accessory minerals enabled N. E. Zalashkova (1957) to distinguish three albite replacement complexes of different ages when he studied the deposit.

Most common is the early replacement complex composed mainly of granular albite, with which the beryl is paragenetically associated. Of lesser significance are later fine-grained and saccharoidal albite.

At the surface exposure, granular albite is segregated in the following sections of the pegmatite body:

1. As a fringe on the periphery of the vein-like and block segregations of quartz—after block microcline and medium-grained pegmatite.
2. In the outer part of the body, where it replaces the zone of medium-grained pegmatite.

The albitization decreases somewhat with depth. In particular, the intensity associated with the vein-like segregations of block quartz decreases noticeably at a depth of 30 to 40 m down dip.

The peculiar features of the internal structure of the pegmatite allows the assumption that, at various stages of its formation, there existed turbulent tectonic conditions. The effect of the tectonics caused numerous intrapegmatite transgressions of later paragenetic complexes across the earlier ones and, in particular, the wide development of vein-like quartz bodies, which transgress the earlier zones and even pass beyond the pegmatite body into the country rocks.

Two varieties of beryl are present in the pegmatite body. Beryl I is in prismatic, transparent, and semitransparent crystals of light-green color, from 1×5 to 3×8 cm in size. It has a low alkali content, ranging between 0.4 and 0.7 percent.

Beryl II is characterized by the development of opaque conical and truncated-pyramidal crystals of light-green, greenish-blue, and brownish color. There are some "stuffed" crystals whose core is filled with albite, quartz, and muscovite. The crystal dimensions are as much as 0.6 m across and 1 m along the *c*-axis. In composition, this is a typical sodium beryl, containing about 1.2 percent alkalies (Table 40, analysis 18).

Beryl I, which is relatively rare, is associated spatially with block quartz segregations and usually crystallizes in the peripheral portions of these segregations. Its highly irregular distribution is only controlled by vein-like segregations of block quartz, which transgress block microcline.

Beryl II, which occurs much more frequently, is associated spatially with the following sections of the pegmatite body:

1. The largest crystals (as much as 1 m in length and 0.6 m across) and crystal pockets of light-green beryl with conical and truncated-pyramidal crystal habit are closely associated with intensely albitized aureoles that accompany vein-like bodies of dark block quartz that transgress block microcline. Beryl accumulations are also disposed near the quartz streaks

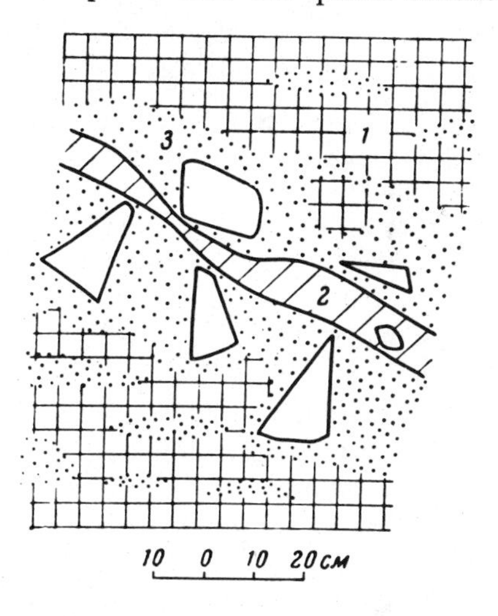

Fig. 35. Crystals of conical beryl in albitized block microcline, Altai. (1) Microcline; (2) quartz; (3) albite.

and veins that penetrate to the contact between pegmatite and large xenoliths of country rocks, which act as a screen in this case. The largest crystals predominate near albitized block microcline adjacent to the footwall of the fissure segregations of quartz. The beryl crystals tend to be oriented with their sharp ends towards the quartz body, and the dimensions of large crystals are commonly incommensurable with those of the thin vein-like quartz segregations (Fig. 35). Pockets of large tabular muscovite are usually in close association with beryl.

2. The small crystals of yellowish-green beryl, 1 to 10 cm across, are found in the endo-contact zone of the pegmatite body near vein-like quartz segregations (Fig. 36) and also in pockets and streaks of muscovite replacement complex in albitized block microcline. There commonly occur in the albite-muscovite streaks large tabular crystals of columbite and small (1.5 to 2 mm), well-formed crystals and intergrowths of crystals of brown zircon in paragenesis with beryl.

It should be noted that the transgressive position of block quartz with

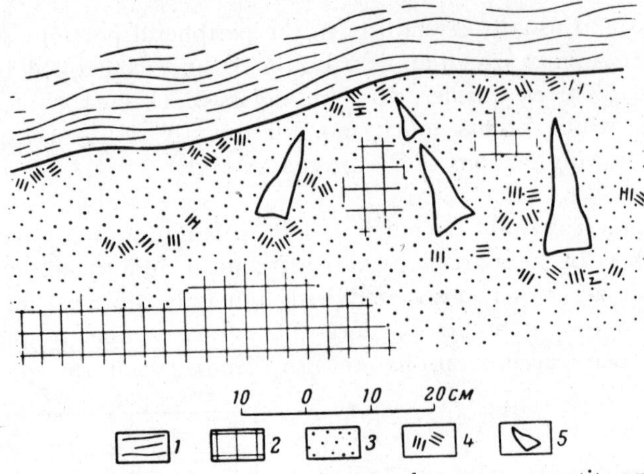

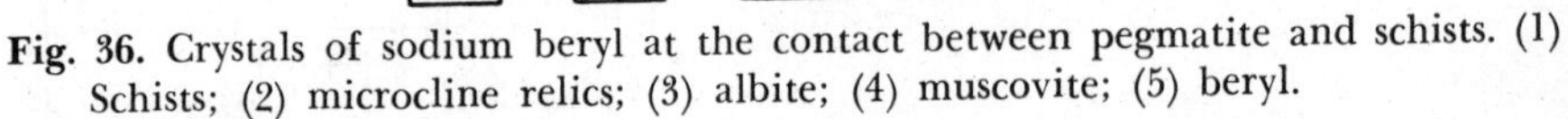

Fig. 36. Crystals of sodium beryl at the contact between pegmatite and schists. (1) Schists; (2) microcline relics; (3) albite; (4) muscovite; (5) beryl.

respect to the earlier zones, the random orientation of muscovite and albite replacement complexes in the vein, and the occurrence of large schist xenoliths have caused a complex distribution of beryl in the pegmatite body. The main mass of the beryl and its highest concentration are found in the apical part of the body. With increasing depth, the beryl content drops to hundredths of 1 percent (30 to 40 m down dip); this is probably related to the decrease in number and thickness of the quartz streaks, the decrease of albitized rock, and a certain decrease in the degree of differentiation of the pegmatite.

The study of the distribution of beryllium disseminated in the rock-forming and accessory minerals of the body (Table 96) established that only about 8 percent of the total beryllium content is found in disseminated form at the surface levels, which are enriched in beryl, whereas 92.23 percent of beryllium is found as beryl.

BALANCE OF DISSEMINATED AND CONCENTRATED BERYLLIUM IN THE PEGMATITE VEIN (CONTENT IN 10^{-4} PERCENT)

Calculated mean content of beryllium disseminated as isomorphous impurity in various minerals (p)	6
Mean beryllium content due to beryl (k)	72
Total beryllium content (p + k)	78
Ratio of the amount of beryllium concentrated in the form of beryl to that of disseminated beryllium	(k:p = 12:1)
Coefficient of dissemination $(\frac{p}{p+k} \times 100)$	7.7

Block Muscovite-Oligoclase Pegmatites with Chrysoberyl

Block muscovite-oligoclase pegmatite with chrysoberyl is a fairly rare type of beryllium-bearing pegmatite in which contamination by alumina is important. Such pegmatites usually occur in fields of normal granitic pegmatites, specifically in areas of alumina-enriched micaceous schists containing, in addition to micas, the aluminum silicates (sillimanite, kyanite, andalusite) characteristic of such rocks.

The main feldspar of this type of pegmatite is oligoclase or albite-oligoclase No. 10-14 ($Ab_{10}An_{90}$ —$Ab_{14}An_{86}$, Ed.); microcline is usually of subordinate significance. In the outer zones of pegmatite formations,

Table 96 Beryl content of the minerals in a pegmatitic vein (analyst S.N. Fedorchuk)

Mineral	Mean Be content in 10^{-4}%
Block microcline-perthite	5
Block quartz (crushed)	0.5
Granular albite	7
Saccharoidal albite	4
Garnet	20
Muscovite	26

oligoclase and quartz form apographic intergrowths which, towards the center of the pegmatite, are gradually replaced by coarse-grained pegmatite of pegmatoid structure, and further by small-block pegmatite consisting mainly of monocrystalline oligoclase blocks cemented with gray quartz. In the central part of the most fully differentiated pegmatites, there is a quartz core, near which can be observed a decrease in the plagioclase number (anorthite content, Ed.) and the replacement of oligoclase with later granular and roughly tabular albite.

A characteristic feature of the block muscovite-oligoclase pegmatites is the abundance of muscovite, which is a component of the quartz-muscovite replacement complex and also occurs as pockets of large tabular crystals in block pegmatite. The frequently observed association of zones of muscovite with endocontact sections of these pegmatite bodies underlines the substantial part played by aluminous contamination in their formation; these pegmatites are very important as sources of commercial muscovite.

It should be noted that beryllium minerals very rarely occur in the muscovite-oligoclase pegmatites, but some individual deposits may serve to illustrate the effect of wall rock assimilation on the nature of beryllium mineralization in pegmatites. In pegmatites with aluminous contamination, beryl, which occurs in normal pegmatites, is replaced by chrysoberyl, which is often the only beryllium mineral present. Beryl, which at times is present in small quantity along with chrysoberyl, is usually of an earlier generation and is characteristic of slightly contaminated pegmatites.

In pegmatites rich in chrysoberyl, there are also aluminum silicates (kyanite or sillimanite, rarer andalusite) and the lazulite-type aluminum phosphates.

In these pegmatites, chrysoberyl is a relatively late mineral, being most probably contemporaneous with the quartz-muscovite replacement complex. The light-green tabular chrysoberyl crystals are usually disposed in fissures in oligoclase and quartz; in a few places they occur between the cleavage flakes of muscovite.

Some veins on the fourth level of the Taseev muscovite deposit may serve as a characteristic example of block muscovite-oligoclase pegmatites with accessory chrysoberyl.

The pegmatites with crysoberyl occur in bimicaceous schists containing staurolite, kyanite, and sillimanite. The length of the bodies are as much as 140 m, their thicknesses range up to 4 m; each has a small-block structure with a central quartz core.

The outer zones of the pegmatite bodies are composed of coarse-grained quartz-oligoclase pegmatite whose structure (texture, Ed.) is at times close to apographic. The increase in the size of feldspar and quartz segregations towards the vein center results in the formation of the pegmatoid structure, most characteristic of the veins, which passes into small-block structure. The pockets of the quartz-muscovite replacement complex sometimes occur at the endocontact of the pegmatite, although the strongest development of muscovite is characteristic of sections adjacent to the quartz core of the pegmatite body.

Near the contacts in pegmatites, irregular segregations of black tourmaline and almandite crystals occur with pockets of large, columnar sillimanite crystals; kyanite is rarer, sometimes occurring near the contact.

A characteristic mineral of the zones of coarse-grained and small-block pegmatites is bright-blue lazulite which forms irregular segregations in oligoclase and quartz or between the muscovite plates.

Associated with lazulite are small segregations of sulfides (pyrite, pyrrhotite) and green, poorly formed crystals of apatite which are fairly common in the plagioclase and quartz; at places, near the axial part of the bodies in block pegmatite, there are accumulations of sillimanite.

Chrysoberyl is fairly widespread in zones of coarse-grained and small-block pegmatite and is also found in the quartz-muscovite replacement complex. Its light-green tabular crystals, as much as 10 cm in the pinacoid plane and 0.3 to 0.5 cm in thickness, occur in quartz segregations, along fissures in small oligoclase blocks, and at the boundary between oligoclase and quartz segregations. Single chrysoberyl crystals are disposed between the cleavage plates of muscovite books.

In some bodies, accessory beryl also occurs with chrysoberyl in irregular light-green segregations in feldspar. The interrelation between beryl and chrysoberyl seems to point to the later formation of chrysoberyl, associated with the final stages of pegmatite formation.

Replaced Muscovite-Albite Pegmatites

Replaced muscovite-albite pegmatites are closely related, by gradual transitions, to the block muscovite-microcline pegmatites referred to above; they are characterized by the dominance of an albite zone superposed on the zone of block microcline and also on the presence of medium- and coarse-grained pegmatite.

Depending on the geological conditions of formation, the beryl-bearing albite zone is either in the central part of the pegmatite around the quartz core, or else it occurs at the endocontact as the outermost zone of the pegmatite body.

In the albite replacement complex there are usually relics of block microcline and albitized medium-grained pegmatite of apographic structure. At the same time the internal structure of such albitized pegmatites is irregular in a number of places (Beus, 1951, 1953a, 1956_1) (Figs. 37, 38).

The most common varieties of beryl in the replaced muscovite-albite pegmatites are the alkali sodium and sodium-lithium beryl, closely related to the albite replacement complex. Owing to its light (even white) color and the generally irregular crystal form, this beryl is difficult to recognize in many deposits and at times has been overlooked by geologists whose examination was not careful enough. Besides large crystals of conical, pyramidal, and irregular form, alkali beryl usually forms very fine crystals disseminated in albite.

The beryl-bearing zone in the replaced muscovite-albite pegmatites is always related to the albite replacement zone. The parts of the pegmatite body where beryl is concentrated may be the following:

1. Sections of the albite zone at the boundary with the quartz core or with the separate quartz blocks.
2. Sections of the albite zone near the contact with country rocks or their xenoliths.
3. Pockets of quartz-muscovite and albite-muscovite replacement complexes, scattered in the albite zone or disposed near the contact with the pegmatite body.

In well-differentiated pegmatites with a distinct quartz core surrounded with an aureole of albitized rock, superposed on the zone of block microcline or coarse-grained quartz-microcline pegmatite, the conical or ir-

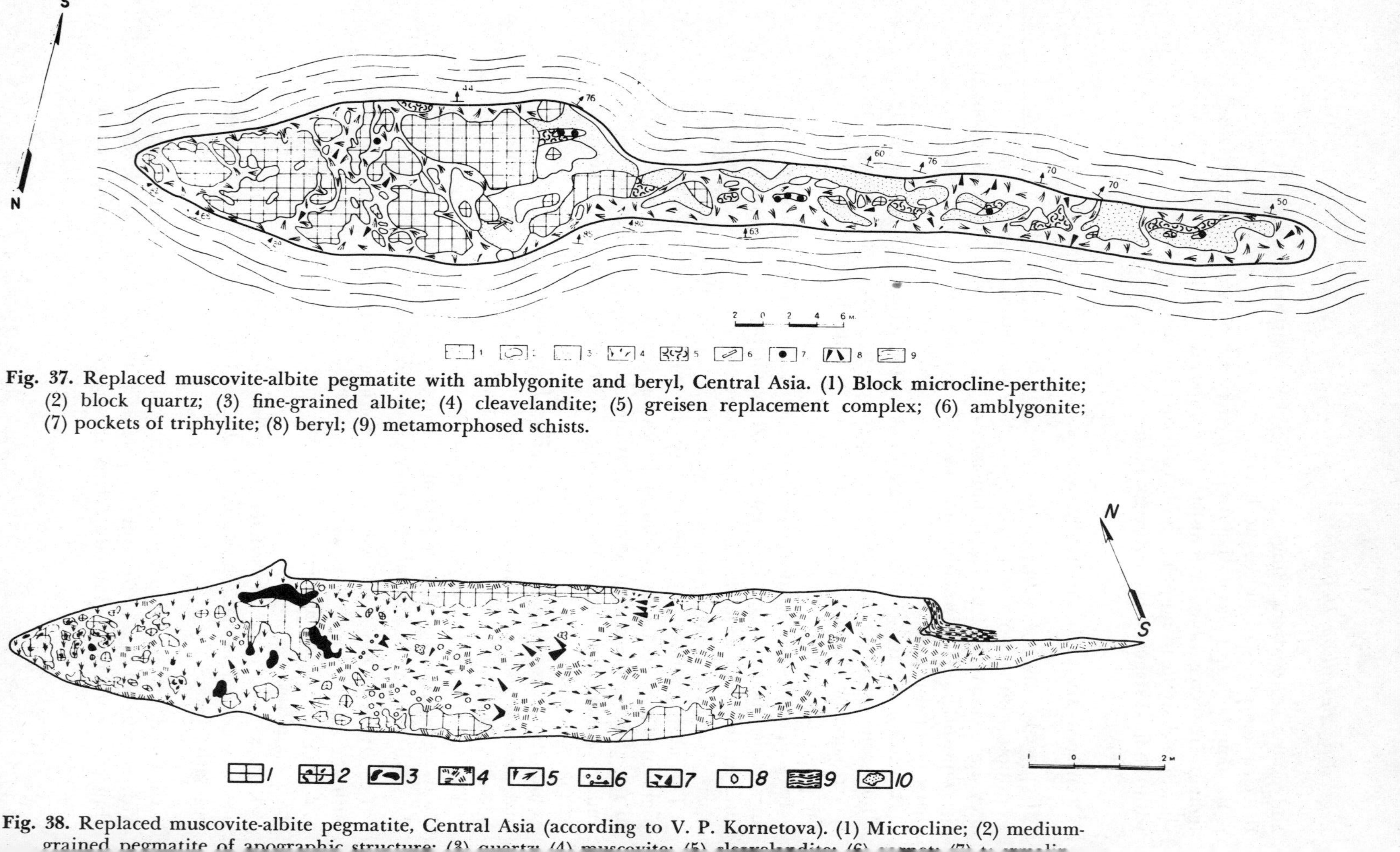

Fig. 37. Replaced muscovite-albite pegmatite with amblygonite and beryl, Central Asia. (1) Block microcline-perthite; (2) block quartz; (3) fine-grained albite; (4) cleavelandite; (5) greisen replacement complex; (6) amblygonite; (7) pockets of triphylite; (8) beryl; (9) metamorphosed schists.

Fig. 38. Replaced muscovite-albite pegmatite, Central Asia (according to V. P. Kornetova). (1) Microcline; (2) medium-grained pegmatite of apographic structure; (3) quartz; (4) muscovite; (5) cleavelandite; (6)

regular crystals of alkali beryl occur in the albitized pegmatite zone near its contact with the quartz core. In a number of places the sharply-pyramidal beryl crystals are regularly orientated, about normal to the plane of contact with the quartz core.

Pegmatites with an albitized zone in their endocontact parts commonly contain conical alkali beryl. These beryl crystals are usually oriented with their narrow end towards the contact with the country rocks, normal to the contact plane.

In individual deposits there is a fairly uniform distribution of beryl in the albite zone. These beryl crystals are usually small and difficult to identify macroscopically. In general, this group of beryl-bearing pegmatite deposits has a more uniform distribution of beryl and (usually) a higher content than the muscovite-microcline pegmatites in which the evidences of albitization are poorly shown. In addition to the usual greenish muscovite in the albitized zone in paragenesis with beryl, there are the manganese garnet, spessartite, triphylite-lithiophilite, green tourmaline, columbite-tantalite (which is sometimes of great economic importance), and cassiterite.

During exploitation of the replaced muscovite-albite pegmatites in depth, it was possible in many places to note a decrease in the degree of albitization and the transition of the pegmatite into partly albitized block muscovite-microcline pegmatite. In other places, there was a more complex change of zoning of the replaced muscovite-albite pegmatite at depth, determined by the nature of the pegmatite body and its morphology. This applies in particular to pegmatites that formed during turbulent tectonic conditions.

The down-dip zonal change in the replaced muscovite-albite pegmatites is described in the literature (Beus, 1951, 1953a, 1956a), where it is illustrated by concrete geological examples.

Replaced Spodumene-Albite and Lepidolite-Albite Pegmatites

Replaced spodumene-albite and lepidolite-albite pegmatites, which are joined by gradual transitions with the muscovite-albite pegmatites referred to above, contain considerable concentrations of spodumene whose crystals usually occur in the quartz core of the pegmatite body (the quartz-spodumene zone), which is commonly albitized to a large extent (the quartz-albite-spodumene zone). Characteristic features of the pegmatites of this group are the intense development of albite and, in a number of places, a distinct concentric zonal structure.

In pegmatites with a similar zonal structure, the central quartz-spodumene core is usually an albite zone, which is mostly composed of tabular albite (cleavelandite). This zone contains the white, (more rarely) colorless, or rose-colored alkali beryl disseminated in cleavelandite as large crystals of irregular or short-prismatic form. Beryl is usually most abundant near the boundary between the albite zone and the quartz-spodumene pegmatite core. The characteristic accessory minerals of the beryl-containing albite zone are these: greenish muscovite, spessartite, green tourmaline, lithiophilite, and amblygonite. Mangano-columbite, mangano-tantalite, microlite, and cassiterite are observed in a number of deposits in association with beryl. The outer albitized zone of the pegmatite body also can contain alkali beryl of white or light-green color (sodium or sodium-lithium variety). The distribution and nature of the beryl associated with the outer zones are the same in the replaced muscovite-albite pegmatites.

In many distinctly zoned spodumene-albite pegmatites there are rudimentary formations of lepidolite or greisen-like replacement complexes, whose abundance usually is greatest in the upper part of the pegmatite body and decreases abruptly with increasing depth. As the lepidolite or greisen-like zone becomes more important, there is a transition to the replaced lepidolite-albite (or to the relatively rare greisen-like albite) pegmatites.

Of special significance is the highly distinctive group of spodumene-albite pegmatites that were formed under turbulent tectonic conditions. The vein-like bodies and dikes of pegmatites of this group are usually associated with definite fissure zones and form characteristic plate-like bodies with lengths ranging up to 1000 m.

The geological disposition and mineralogical composition of such pegmatites have been studied and described in detail in a series of papers by A. I. Ginzburg (1952a, 1952b, 1955a, 1955b), who designated them as the group of epigenetic (pinched) pegmatites that crystallized under variable pressure.

This group of pegmatites is interesting because of the close paragenesis of most of the beryl occurring in veins with fine-grained varieties of albite whose occurrence is governed by the jointing, widely developed in the peripheral sections of the pegmatite bodies.

The zoning of these spodumene-albite pegmatites is usually of a simple nature. The outer parts of bodies are composed of a rather thin zone of fine-grained albitized pegmatite of aplite-like habit, which towards the center of the pegmatite deposit is usually replaced by a thin zone (less than 1 m) of medium-grained albitized pegmatite. Between the outer zones and the central quartz-spodumene core of pegmatite bodies there usually occurs a muscovite-albite zone, which is developed very irregularly and contains the most significant concentrations of finely-crystalline beryl. The quartz-spodumene zone, which includes large crystals (blocks) of microcline-perthite, is a main unit of the pegmatite bodies, and its thickness as a rule substantially exceeds that of all the outer pegmatite zones.

The zone is usually partly albitized and greisenized, and has a peculiar streaky texture that is the result of the late albitization and greisenization processes which develop in the fissures of the quartz-spodumene zone and in the weakened, near-contact parts of the bodies.

The distribution of beryl in pegmatites is determined by the distribution of the albite and quartz-muscovite replacement complexes; as mentioned before, these complexes are to a large extent related to the intrapegmatite jointing, which occurred after the zones had formed by primary crystallization. In a number of places a fairly uniform distribution of beryl is noted within the albitized and muscovited zones. The characteristic feature of these deposits, which usually contain large proportions of beryl, in addition to lithium minerals, is the small dimensions of the beryl crystals; they rarely exceed a few millimeters.

In the zones of coarsely-crystalline spodumene pegmatite, there are rare crystals of sodium-lithium beryl, attaining in size 6 × 10 cm. Such beryl is not of uniform color and may be pale-bluish, colorless, white, or, more rarely, greenish. Single portions of crystals may be turbid or semitransparent. In many places, beryl crystals contain inclusions of quartz, albite, muscovite, tantalite-columbite, and apatite. On the other hand, most of the beryl associated with the albite and quartz-muscovite replacement complexes consists of very fine crystals ranging from fractions of one millimeter to a few millimeters, rarely as much as 1.5 × 2 to 3 cm. The crystals are mostly colorless or are of pale bluish-green hues. The beryl content usually varies between 0.3 and 0.6 percent.

The beryl distribution in the spodumene-albite pegmatites, which crystallized under turbulent tectonic conditions, shows a positive relation with the late replacement solutions, which arrived along fissures from the deep levels of the pegmatite mass.

The lepidolite-albite pegmatites have strongly developed lepidolite zones (the quartz-lepidolite or albite-lepidolite replacement complexes), which usually separate out in the central part of the pegmatite body; the spodumene-containing zones are either absent or subordinate. Crystal segregations of rose-colored (vorobyevite) or colorless, transparent (rosterite) lithium or lithium-cesium beryl are usually associated with the lepidolite replacement complex. A characteristic accessory mineral of the zone in a number of deposits is rose-colored, colorless, or multicolored tourmaline. The rare-metal minerals, found in association with beryl are microlite, manganotantalite, stibiotantalite, cassiterite, and pollucite. As in the spodumene-albite pegmatites, the central lepidolite zone is usually surrounded by an albite (cleavelandite) zone; this is followed by the outer zones, which are usually albitized to a greater or lesser extent. As in the previously described varieties of replaced pegmatites, some albitized outer zones may be beryl-bearing; the alkali content of the beryl increases as one passes from the outer to the central zones.

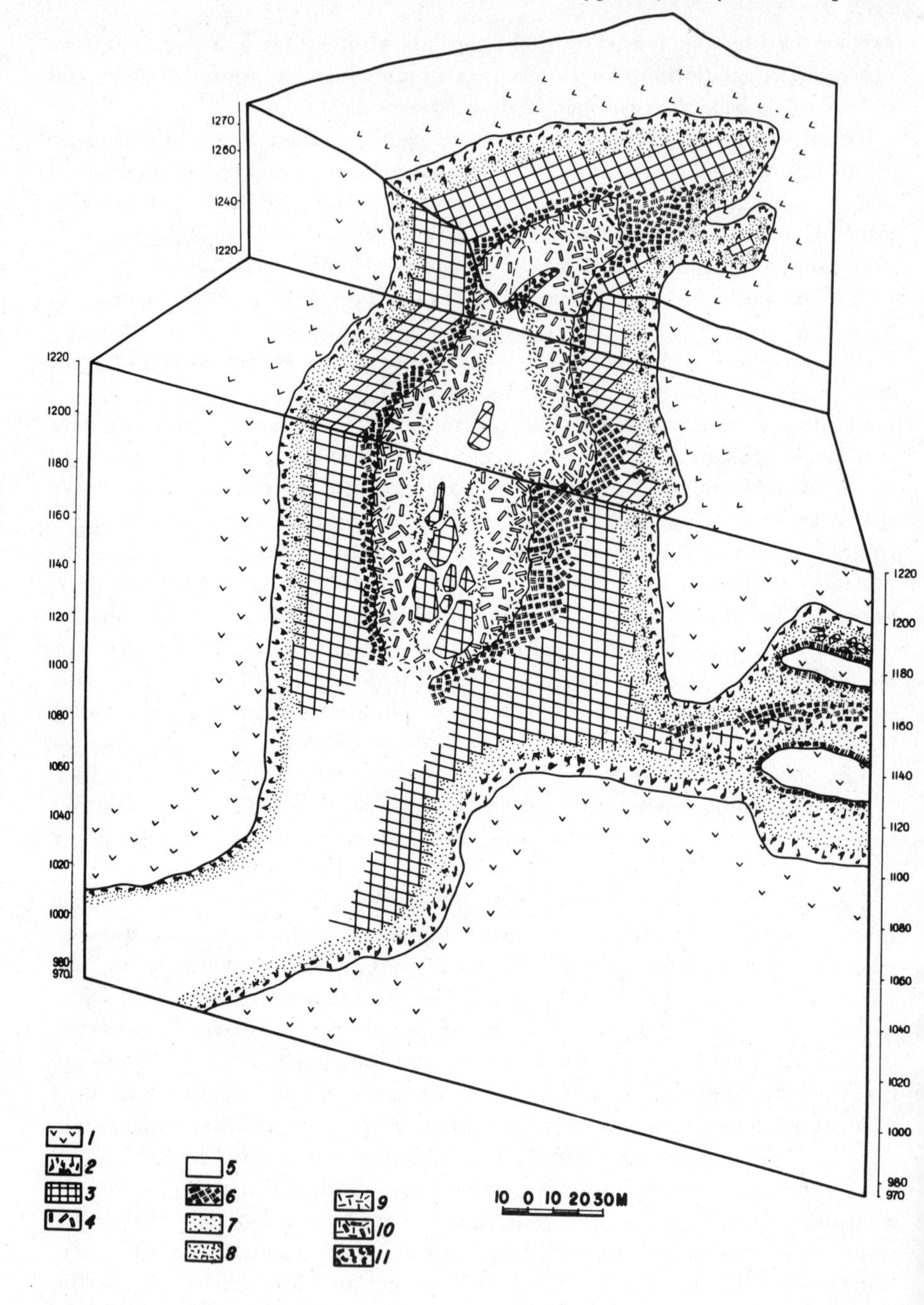

Fig. 39. Block diagram of a large stock of replaced spodumene-albite pegmatite with very distinct zonal structure (from the data of I. A. Smirnov and N. A.

Cited below are characteristic examples of beryl-bearing pegmatites of the group under consideration.

One of the most interesting deposits is associated with a basic mass of gabbroic composition, which is a huge xenolith in the roof of a granitic intrusion. The structure of the deposit is determined by the presence in the gabbro of two major fissure systems that govern the distribution and the morphological features of pegmatite bodies within the area.

The first system consists of gently dipping fissures of northwest strike dipping towards the southwest. The fissures of the second system are characterized by steep (at times almost vertical) angles of dip, the strike being roughly the same as in the fissures of the first system.

Stepped veins or, more rarely, gently dipping veins with thick stock-shaped bulges are associated with the intersections of these fissure systems. The bulges form as a result of the relative displacement of blocks in the area where two or more fissure systems intersect.

The largest of the gently dipping veins with a thick dome-shaped bulge, having the shape of a stockwork with an elliptical shape in plan, is a characteristic example of the replaced spodumene-albite pegmatites with beryl, tantalite, and microlite.

The stock-shaped bulge is 250 $\times$ 150 m in plan and possesses a distinct concentric zonation which is sustained down dip to a depth of more than 200 m (Fig. 39).

Distinct zones can be noted from the contacts to the center of the stock; each is characterized by a definite paragenesis of minerals (Table 97).

The main beryl-bearing zone of the pegmatite body is that containing pockets of saccharoidal albite, spaced between the outer zone composed of graphic and medium-grained pegmatite and the monomineralic annular zone of microcline-perthite. The occurrence of relict blocks of quartz and microcline-perthite indicates that the zone containing pockets of saccharoidal albite was formed mainly by the replacement of the block pegmatite zone, which was transitional between the zones of graphic pegmitite and monomineralic microcline-perthite.

Besides saccharoidal albite, there is within the zone widespread earlier granular albite, which in general was formed as a result of the replacement of microcline in the graphic and medium-grained pegmatite during the early stages of albitization. Granular albite is transgressed and intensely replaced by the late saccharoidal albite.

The pockets of saccharoidal albite in the medium-grained and graphic

---

Solodov). (1) Gabbro; (2) zone of albitized medium-grained pegmatite of apographic structure; (3) zone of block microcline; (4) quartz-spodumene zone; (5) zone of block quartz; (6) muscovite zone (quartz-muscovite replacement complex); (7) fine-grained albite, saccharoidal; (8) fine-grained albite, fine-tabular; (9) cleavelandite complex (with sections of thin-tabular albite); (10) quartz-spodumene-cleavelandite complex; (11) lepidolite zone.

Table 97 Mineralogical composition of the pegmatitic vein zones

Zones	Minerals			
	Rock-forming	Accessory	Rare-metal	Other Accessory
Outer zone of graphic and medium-grained pegmatites of apographic structure (partly albiteized)	Microcline, albite, quartz	Muscovite	–	–
Pockets of saccharoidal albite	Saccharoidal and granular albite	Muscovite, quartz, garnet	Beryl, tantalite, lithiophilite	Apatite, bismutite
Block microcline	Microcline-perthite	–	–	–
Quartz-muscovite	Quartz, muscovite	Garnet, tourmaline	Beryl, bismutotantalite, tantalite	Bismutite, apatite
Spodumene-cleavelandite	Cleavelandite, spodumene, quartz	Muscovite	Lithiophilite, alkaline beryl, columbite	–
Quartz-spodumene	Quarts, spodumene	Albite	–	–
Pockets of fine-tabular albite	Albite	Lithiophilite	Microlite, tantalite	Apatite
Block quartz with blocks of microcline-perthite (core)	Quartz, microcline-perthite	–	Pollucite, tantalite	
Lepidolite (developed in the upper horizons of the stock)	Lepidolite, albite	–	Colorless alkaline beryl-rosterite mangantantalite	–

pegmatite and the zone of block microcline do not contain any beryl accumulations. The highest beryl concentration is characteristic of albite pockets occurring in small-block pegmatite at the boundary between the zone of graphic and medium-grained pegmatite and that of block microcline. Thus, there is segregated a 0.5 to 3 m thick band enriched with beryl, which extends along the boundary of the above textural complexes. It should be noted that the beryl-bearing zone is more continuous and thicker in the hanging wall of the stock. In the footwall of the stock, the zone is intermittent and thinner, and has a lower concentration of beryl. Beryl is distributed in the zone in pockets; the content does not decrease with depth. The highest beryl concentration was noted in the step-like bends of the contact of the hanging wall of the stock, where there are solid accumulations of beryl crystals under the flatter surface of the bends; the beryl concentration exceeds 5 percent.

Within the zone, light-green and yellowish-green sodium beryl (Table 42, analyses 13, 14, 24) predominates and usually is in prismatic crystals with indistinct faces, commonly quite corroded by saccharoidal albite. The crystal size varies from very fine to 3 × 10 cm. The "stuffed" crystals are very characteristic. Their primary skeletal habit has been destroyed, in part, by the superimposed later albitization, which has resulted not only in the replacement of the beryl-enclosing minerals, but also in the dissolution of the beryl crystals. Regular skeletal intergrowths of beryl with the earlier generation of albite are rare in areas not subjected to an intense late albitization.

The next beryl-bearing zone is the quartz-muscovite zone, which occurs in the form of irregular pockets along the inner boundary of the monomineralic zone of block microcline. It is developed in greatest quantity in the hanging wall of the stock, where it is 13 m thick. In the footwall the thickness of the zone varies between 1 and 4 m. The ratio of the pockets of the quartz-muscovite replacement complex to the relics of block microcline scattered within the zone varies between 1 to 1 and 1 to 4 in the footwall, and within 1.5 to 1 and 1 to 1 in the hanging wall of the stock.

The beryl found in the quartz-muscovite replacement complex is usually semitransparent, is greenish-blue, and has distinct crystal faces; the crystal size varies between 0.5 × 2 and 1.5 × 10 cm. The distribution of beryl in the zone is not uniform. It is interesting to note that the beryl content drops to one-fifth at a depth of 30 to 40 m. As in the zone consisting of pockets of saccharoidal albite, the beryl here also is predominantly concentrated in the hanging wall of the stock.

Alkali lithium and lithium-cesium beryl of white, light blue, or rose color, genetically closely related to cleavelandite, is characteristic of the cleavelandite-spodumene zone of the stock, which results from the superposition of the albite (cleavelandite) replacement complex on the outer part of the quartz-spodumene zone. The habit of beryl crystals is short-prismatic to tabular, and the faces are poorly formed; they are commonly isometric segregations of irregular form. The size of individual crystals varies from two-tenths to several tenths centimeters across. The distribution of beryl is irregular and in pockets. Many beryl crystals are associated with the boundary between segregations of relict block quartz and the surrounding cleavelandite. The beryl content decreases with depth. It also decreases from the hanging wall to the footwall of the stock-shaped bulge.

The occurrence of crystals of water-clear rosterite also is characteristic of the lepidolite zone in the upper horizons of the stock-shaped bulge, which is in a cross-cutting intrusive body that overlaps the apical part of the quartz core. The crystals occurring in lepidolite are highly irregular in form and are as much as 2 × 3 cm long.

Unlike the stock-shaped bulge, the gently dipping part of the pegmatite body is weakly differentiated and is mostly composed of medium-grained albitized pegmatite with disseminated beryl. The higher beryl concentrations in the pockets are in sections of the quartz-muscovite replacement complex and in the central part of the body in block pegmatite.

When analyzing the features of beryl distribution in the pegmatite body, we must first take into consideration that all generations of beryl in the pegmatite are related both spatially and genetically to the replacement complexes. Depending on the paragenetic features and the chemical composition of the mineral, four generations of beryl can be distinguished in the body; each is related to a definite paragenetic complex.

It is very difficult to establish the interrelation between the main rock-forming minerals of the pegmatites and the main generations of beryl related to the zone with pockets of saccharoidal albite. Here the superposition of the late albite replacement complex has masked the natural relationship between the earlier generation of beryl and the associated minerals. However, a detailed study of the mineralogy of the zone makes it possible to relate the formation of sodium beryl in the zone with pockets of saccharoidal albite, to the earliest stages of albitization, during which the microcline in the graphic and medium-grained pegmatite zones was replaced with early granular albite. An assumed close paragenetic relationship exists between sodium beryl and granular albite, the latter having been formed either simultaneously with beryl, or somewhat later. Both granular albite and beryl are corroded and replaced by saccharoidal albite.

The ensuing beryl genetically is closely related to the quartz-muscovite replacement complex which formed during the replacement of block microcline.

It is, however, possible that the beryl of the quartz-muscovite replacement complex may be the redeposited beryl of an earlier generation, which separated at the boundary between the zone of block microcline and the central quartz-spodumene core of the pegmatite.

The third generation of beryl is related paragenetically to the cleavelandite replacement complex and is represented by sodium-lithium and lithium-cesium varieties of alkali beryl (Table 43, analyses 27, 35, 36). It stands out sharply, owing to the peculiarities of its chemical composition. Rosterite is close to this generation also and is characteristic of the albite-lepidolite replacement complex (Table 43, analysis 31). It is highly probable that rosterite formed as a result of recrystallization of the earlier lithium-cesium beryl when the lepidolite replacement complex was superposed on the spodumene-cleavelandite zone.

Notwithstanding the very considerable concentration of beryllium in the pegmatite body, the phenomena of its dissemination do not play any noticeable role in the process of formation of pegmatites. It can be seen from Tables 98 and 99 that only 6 percent of the total amount of beryllium is presented in the disseminated form in pegmatites.

Table 98 Beryllium content of the rock-forming and accessory minerals of a pegmatite vein

Mineral or complex	Be content in 10^{-4}%
Graphic pegmatite	2.6
Microcline-perthite	
From the zone of pockets of saccharoidal albite	3
From the zone of block microcline	4
From the quartz core	5
Quartz	
From the zone of pockets of saccharoidal albite	2
From the quartz-muscovite zone	2
From the quartz-spodumene zone	2
From the quartz core	2
Saccharoidal albite from the zone of pockets of saccharoidal albite	12
Fine-grained albite from the quartz-muscovite zone	11
Cleavelandite	18
Fine-tabular albite	7
Muscovite	
From the quartz-muscovite zone	32
From the cleavelandite-spodumene zone	46
Spodumene	20
Lepidolite	48
Garnet	12

An example of the beryl-bearing lepidolite-albite pegmatites is the complex tantalum-beryllium pegmatite of the Harding deposit in the Taos district, New Mexico, U.S.A. The deposit is mined for microlite, tantalite, and beryl; it has a high content of beryl and tantalum combined as microlite. The pegmatites of the Harding deposit are related genetically to the so-called Dixon granites and occur in amphibolites and micaceous schists of preCambrian age. The most interesting pegmatite bodies, which contain beryl and microlite, occur in amphibolites. The main pegmatite is a flat lens 305 $\times$ 183 m and 18 m thick.

The pegmatite has a zonal structure with a separated quartz core that contains large crystals of albitized microcline-perthite and pockets of albite-lepidolite replacement complex.

The central core is surrounded by a zone composed of spodumene, albite, and muscovite, with large pockets of albite-lepidolite complex containing much disseminated brown-black microlite and tantalite.

The outer zone of the pegmatite is composed of a coarse-grained quartz-albite-muscovite aggregate including large crystals of white beryl and relics of albitized microcline-perthite.

Abnormal concentrations of cesium-containing rose-colored beryl are also associated with the quartz core of the pegmatite, where beryl is the essential component of the albite replacement complex. In the solid quartz of the core, the latter forms a series of stockworks governed by fissures and consisting of cleavelandite, quartz, and rose-colored lithium-cesium beryl.

Exploitation of the replaced spodumene-albite and lepidolite-albite pegmatites, exposed the following changes of zoning, which occur with increasing depth and which control the distribution and content of beryl (Beus, 1951, 1956a):

1. The substitution of spodumene-albite pegmatite for replaced lepidolite-albite (or greisen-albite) pegmatite.
2. The substitution of muscovite-albite pegmatite for replaced lepidolite-albite (or greisen-albite) pegmatite.
3. The substitution of muscovite-albite pegmatite for replaced spodumene-albite pegmatite.

Large, dike-shaped bodies of spodumene-albite pegmatites which formed in turbulent tectonic conditions have the most continuous zoning in depth. A highly characteristic internal structure of such pegmatites, in which the quartz-spodumene zone plays the dominant part, is continuous down to a depth of 200 m and more down the dip; however, there is a change of zoning, namely disappearance of the quartz–spodumene zone and the transition to the replaced muscovite-albite pegmatites. In a number of places such a transition is accompanied by an increase in sodium-lithium beryl, which is the main rare-metal component of the replaced muscovite-albite pegmatites.

Table 99 Beryllium distribution in the pegmatite body (k–amount of beryllium combined in beryl; p–amount of beryllium disseminated in the rock-forming and accessory minerals)

Zones	Occurrence in the vein by volume, %[a]	Coefficient of concentration Be $\frac{k}{k+p}$ 100%
Graphic and medium-grained pegmatite	11	0
Of pockets of saccharoidal albite	11.4	98
Block microcline-perthite	35	0
Quartz-muscovite	8	96
Cleavelandite-spodumene Quartz-spodumene Thin-tabular albite	27.3	94
Quartz core with blocks of microcline-perthite	7	0
Albite-lepidolite	0.3	58
average for the body	100	94

[a] According to N.A. Solodov

In the replaced pegmatites of various types there is a distinct and regular tendency for the highest beryllium concentrations to be in the top levels of pegmatite intrusions and in those parts which can be considered as special "traps" for the volatile compounds. Such traps—for example, various types of bulges which alternate with pinches up the dip, domes of all kinds, sudden bends of pegmatite bodies down the dip, etc.—have, as a rule, an abundance of replacement features and in many places an abnormally high content of beryllium minerals.

In studying these beryllium deposits in pegmatites, we must pay special attention to the problems of vertical zoning of pegmatite deposits and of pegmatite districts as a whole. These problems, which will be briefly analyzed in the following section, play an especially important part in the exploration and appraisal of beryl-bearing pegmatites, and commonly determine the prospects of deposits and of whole regions as well as the trend of prospecting and exploration.

Zoning of Beryl-Bearing Pegmatite Districts and the Distribution of Beryllium Minerals within a Pegmatitic Intrusive Complex

In the analysis of the geological structure, mineralogical composition, and geochemistry of the rare-metal (including beryl-bearing) granitic pegmatites, the concept of the pegmatitic intrusive complex (called "injection" by author, Ed.) is highly important. In the following, this term will denote a series of coeval pegmatite deposits combined with a single pegmatitic source and occupying a definite place in the structure of the pegmatite district or region.

The spatial position of the pegmatitic intrusive complex is obviously determined by both the area and vertical range of the pegmatite deposits of one period of injection. It is borne out by the facts that although individual pegmatite bodies may be joined by leaders along vertical planes within the intrusive complex, they may also be completely isolated, depending on the nature of the pegmatite-enclosing cavities and on the jointing of enclosing rocks.

The concept of a pegmatitic intrusive complex should not be identified with that of a pegmatite district, because the latter is only that part of a pegmatitic intrusive complex exposed by erosion.

Within one pegmatitic intrusive complex there can be developed all paragenetic types of pegmatites, among which we can trace a distinct relationship through numerous transitional varieties.

Because spatially the pegmatitic process operates mostly along the vertical parameter, the concept of a pegmatitic intrusive complex enables one to analyze the entire process as a whole, namely, to distinguish the phenomena occurring in the roots of the pegmatitic intrusive complex from those characteristic of its apical sections.

Practice has shown that this approach to the study of each pegmatite district is most fruitful, as it makes it possible to treat correctly the zoning of pegmatite districts and to plan geological exploration and prospecting for rare metals, including beryllium.

The zoning of the rare-metal pegmatite districts has been attracting for a considerable time the attention of investigators of the pegmatitic process, who are trying to find, in the characteristic zonal regularities established for a number of pegmatite districts, the key to the laws governing the process of pegmatite formation (Fersman, 1940; Heinrich, 1953; Varlamoff, 1953-1954).

References to the zoning of a pegmatite field, are usually to the horizontal zoning that is shown in the disposition of various types of pegmatites within the district with respect to the outcrops of the assumed parent granites. However, the horizontal zoning of the pegmatite district does not exist alone; it is the reflection of the vertical zoning of the pegmatitic intrusive complex, of which each partial horizontal exposure is a pegmatite district. It is obvious that a true reflection of the vertical zoning of a pegmatitic intrusive complex in the horizontal zoning of the pegmatite district can occur only under favorable geological and geomorphological conditions, which are rarely found. That is why clear horizontal zoning is noted only in a limited number of the most characteristic rare-metal pegmatite districts, although this phenomenon exists in all pegmatite regions.

The regularities of horizontal zoning of pegmatite districts are generally reduced to the fact that with distance from the parent granitic intrusion, regardless of the composition of the enclosing rocks, a regular change in the paragenesis of minerals takes place in pegmatites. This most commonly finds its expression in the replacement of the graphic and medium-grained biotite-microcline pegmatites with block muscovite-microcline pegmatites succeeded by the replaced muscovite-albite, and later by the spodumene-albite and lepidolite-albite pegmatites. Such a change in the paragenesis of minerals corresponds roughly to the vertical zoning of the individual pegmatite formations, which show, with increasing depth, a regular change of zonal structure and a gradual substitution of less developed pegmatite types for the more developed ones (Beus, 1948, 1951, 1953a). It is obvious that the normal vertical zoning and the horizontal zoning of which it is a function, commonly are considerably complicated by the effect of various geological (mainly structural-tectonic) factors; however, the general trend referred to above remains constant. In the roots of the pegmatitic intrusive complex there develop, as a rule, the undifferentiated varieties of pegmatite formations, with virtually no traces of replacement, whereas the upper horizons of pegmatitic intrusive complex consist of series of substantially replaced pegmatite bodies, the largest of which have a high degree of differentiation (Fig. 40).

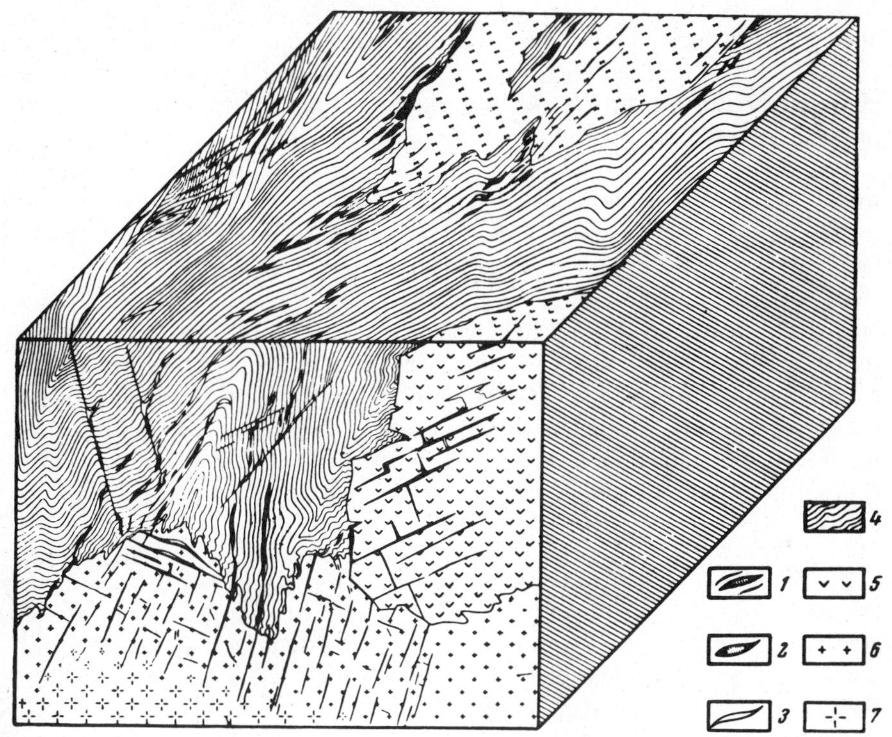

Fig. 40. Zoning scheme of a pegmatite intrusive complex. (1) Undifferentiated pegmatites (in the central part of the lens is the zone of block pegmatite); (2) block pegmatites; (3) replaced pegmatites; (4) metamorphic rocks; (5) gabbro; (6) granitoids; (7) parent granites.

A detailed analysis of problems related to vertical zoning of pegmatitic intrusive complexes requires a special study; here, only those related directly to the beryllium minerals of pegmatites, and which might help us further in solving some genetical and geochemical problems, will be considered.

It has already been noted that the nature of the vertical zoning of the pegmatitic intrusive complex is closely related to the geological position of the component pegmatite deposits within the pegmatite structure. Thus, when analyzing the regularities of zoning of pegmatitic intrusive complexes, it is necessary in each individual case to take into account the special geological conditions that substantially affect the formation of pegmatites. Thus, for example, a sudden change of position of the pegmatite bodies, or the appearance of bulges or pinches, have a considerable effect on the zoning of the pegmatitic intrusive complex.

In general outline such deviation from normal zoning is expressed in the following:

1. With a sudden flattening of pegmatite bodies up dip, the more

developed (that is, more perfectly differentiated and more intensely replaced) types of pegmatites appear. These are characteristic of the upper layers of the intrusion complex. In a number of places there is also a sharp increase in beryllium concentration (Beus, 1956a).

2. A sharp increase in the angle of dip of pegmatite bodies usually results in the appearance of less developed pegmatite types characteristic of the lower parts of the pegmatitic intrusive complex. At the same time, the beryl concentration usually drops sharply.

3. The appearance of bulges in pegmatite bodies usually results in the formation of a more complicated pegmatite type with a higher concentration of rare-metal minerals, including beryl. Yet, in pinches there is usually a sudden transition to poorly developed pegmatite types characteristic of the lower levels of the pegmatitic intrusive complex. In nonreplaced pegmatites such a transition is usually accompanied by a sharp decrease in the concentration of the rare-metal minerals, until their complete disappearance.

It should be noted that vertical zoning is particularly manifested in the steeply dipping strata of the pegmatitic intrusive complex, whereas the gently dipping sections are usually characterized by a relative constancy of paragenesis for a considerable distance down dip. The shape of pegmatite bodies is always an important factor.

A classical example of zoning of pegmatite fields within which the replaced pegmatite varieties are widely developed is one of the large pegmatite fields in eastern USSR.

The geological structure of this pegmatite district consists mainly of metamorphosed Lower and Middle Jurassic conglomerates, sandstones, coaly clay shales, and effusive formations.

In the central part of the pegmatite district, the Jurassic conglomerate series is cut by two small masses of bimica granites, which are apparently the apical protrusions of a large pluton, not yet exposed by erosion. Most pegmatite bodies occur in Jurassic conglomerates and shales; only a few are in granites.

The pegmatite district is associated with the southwestern limb of an asymmetrical anticlinal fold of the second order, whose axis has a northwestern trend. The fold plunges gently towards the southeast. In the core of the anticlinal fold is a large intrusive body whose apophyses are the separate outcrops of bimica granite that mark the axial part of the anticline. The southwest limb of the fold and the core of the fold are complicated by disjunctive dislocations. The pegmatite bodies are associated mostly with the systems of westnorthwest (270–310°) shear fissures, and, to a lesser extent, with northeast and submeridional systems.

The vein-like bodies of pegmatites usually have an irregular dike-shaped form; they are accompanied by bulges, pinches, and apophyses, and

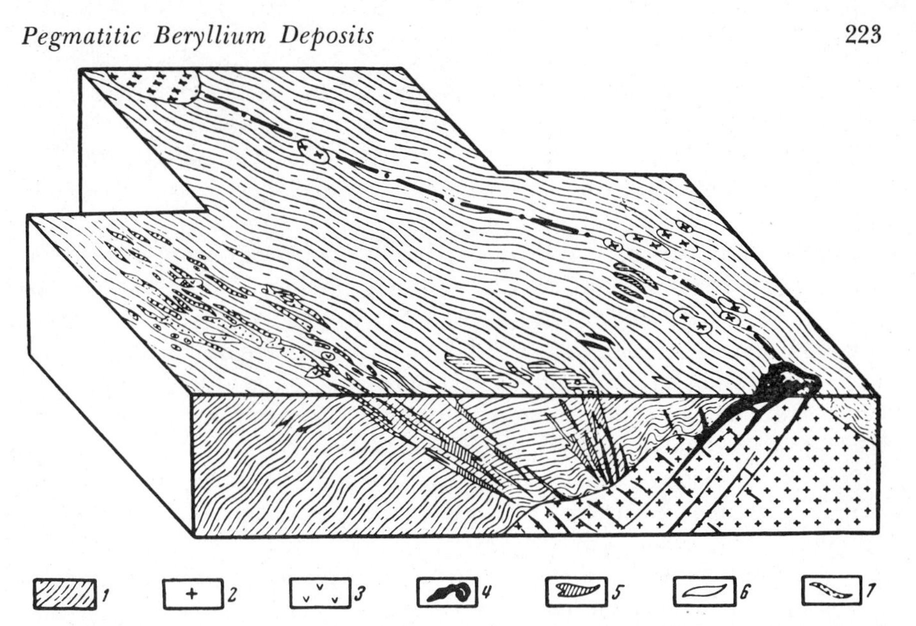

Fig. 41. Block diagram of a pegmatitic intrusive complex with a clearly outlined horizontal and vertical zoning, Transbaikalia. (1) Sandstones and shales; (2) bimica granites; (3) amphibolites; (4) graphic biotite-microcline pegmatites; (5) block muscovite-microcline pegmatites, partly albitized; (6) replaced muscovite-albite pegmatites; (7) replaced spodumene-albite pegmatites.

they transgress the country rocks along strike and dip. The largest bodies attain lengths of several hundred or even several thousand meters; the thickness is 20 to 30 m. The angles of dip of the pegmatite dikes and vein-like bodies that occur in various parts of the district vary from gentle (20 to 30°) to steep (75 to 85°); the common trend of dip is northeast in the direction of the core of the anticlinal fold.

In general, the pegmatite bodies have a tendency towards flattening from the axial part of the dominating anticlinal structure to its southwestern extremity.

All basic paragenetic types are known among the pegmatites of the district in question:

1. poorly differentiated graphic biotite-microcline
2. block muscovite-microcline
3. replaced muscovite-albite
4. replaced spodumene-albite and lepidolite-albite.

A highly characteristic zoning (Fig. 41) is observed in the disposition of various paragenetic types of pegmatite bodies across the extent of the pegmatite district, and in the intensity of replacement processes in them.

Thus, for example, the pegmatites in the near-axial part of the anticlinal structure, near the intrusive body in the core of the anticline, are composed of weakly differentiated pegmatites of graphic and medium-grained structure with very little evidence of albitization.

The pegmatites that are not very far from the axial part of the fold are composed of partly albitized medium-grained and block muscovite-microcline pegmatite.

Further towards the southwest, replaced muscovite-albite pegmatites are associated with the more gently dipping system of fissures that transgress the southwest limb of the anticlinal fold at some distance from its axis.

Finally, the pegmatite dikes of the area farthest removed from the axis are composed mainly of spodumene-albite pegmatite, and, on the extreme southwest limb, of replaced muscovite-albite pegmatite. Here albitization and greisenization are most strongly manifested.

Thus, away from the intrusive core of the anticline, the degree of differentiation of pegmatites and the intensity of the replacement processes (albitization, greisenization, and lepidolization) increase. In the same direction the size and complexity of rare-metal pegmatites (lithium, beryllium, tantalum, tin, etc.) also increase. Within the pegmatite district, the vertical zoning of pegmatites, corresponds to the horizontal zoning referred to above. As depth increases, the thick dikes branch out into a series of vein-like bodies composed of undifferentiated medium-grained pegmatite of apographic and graphic structure. At a depth of between a few tens and 150 m, replaced muscovite-albite pegmatites are substituted for the spodumene-albite pegmatites. The depth at which the spodumene-rich units occur increases away from the axis of the anticline from northeast to southwest. Exploratory drilling has shown that the greatest depth of spodumene-rich units (150 m) is at the extreme southwest limb of the deposit.

Within the district a peculiar zoning of beryllium minerals in the pegmatites was noted.

Near the core of the anticline in the weakly albitized pegmatites of block structure [texture, Ed.] there are large crystals of pale-blue or light-green beryl, with regular prismatic form. These crystals are commonly grouped in pockets and distributed irregularly.

Along with the coarsely crystalline beryl referred to above, which is abundant in the block pegmatite of the unreplaced parts, there is, in the pegmatites at some distance towards the southwest, finely crystalline beryl, whose crystals, measuring from fractions of a millimeter to 1.5 cm, are rather uniformly distributed in the replaced sections of pegmatites.

In the most intensely albitized and greisenized pegmatites of the extreme southwest part of the deposit, beryl occurs only as small crystals, measuring from fractions of a millimeter to 1.5 cm, and distributed relatively uniformly in areas composed of albite replacement complex. The only exceptions are the rare separate resorbed crystals of earlier beryl, as much as a few centimeters in size.

The beryllium concentration in replaced spodumene-albite pegmatites situated farthest from the pegmatitic source is fifteen to twenty times as great as that in the graphic and small-block pegmatites disposed within the granite outcrops and forming the root of the pegmatitic intrusive complex.

By analyzing data relating to many beryl-bearing pegmatite districts throughout the world, it is possible to conclude definitely that the vertical zoning of each pegmatitic intrusive complex is one of the main factors that determine the distribution of rare-metal (including beryllium) minerals.

Beryllium minerals, as a rule, are not found in the roots of pegmatitic intrusive complexes, which are composed of pegmatite bodies of graphic and apographic structure, virtually without any replacement phenomena. Only rare single crystals of alkali-free greenish-blue or light-green beryl (very rarely pockets of crystals) are found in the thickest sections of pegmatite bodies in which the rudiments of the coarse-grained and block pegmatites appear. In a number of places, the beryl crystals in such pegmatites are found in miarolitic cavities that are associated with areas where coarse-grained pegmatite of pegmatoid structure is developed. Even in the most interesting representatives of this pegmatite type the beryl content, as a rule, is negligible and does not exceed a few thousandths of 1 percent (in the mineral).

The level in which undifferentiated, substantially graphic pegmatites predominate is down dip from the level in which the zone of block pegmatite is most important. In the apical sections of the pegmatite bodies at this level there are, in places, the first signs of the albitization stage, which is superimposed on the zone of quartz-microcline pegmatite of apographic structure. The largest pegmatite bodies usually have a perfect degree of differentiation, including the formation of a thick quartz core surrounded by giant blocks of microcline-perthite.

It can be seen from available data that the beryl distribution in pegmatites at this level is wholly determined by the degree of differentiation and by the internal structure of pegmatite bodies. The beryl concentrations in these pegmatites varies from thousandths and hundredths (in small-block pegmatites) to tenths of 1 percent (in large-block and completely differentiated pegmatites). Very characteristic is the association of beryl accumulations with completely defined parts, namely:

1. In small-block pegmatites—with the zone of block pegmatite.
2. In large block and completely differentiated pegmatites—with parts disposed at the boundary between the zone of block quartz (quartz core) and the surrounding feldspar zones.

In the most general case, when there are no sharp changes of geological conditions up the dip of the pegmatitic intrusive complex, there is, away from the pegmatitic source, an increase in the degree of differentiation and beryl concentration in these bodies. In the upper levels of pegmatite deposits of block texture, noticeable evidences of albitization determine the appearance of a new variety of beryl that is located near the replacement zones. Thus, there is a gradual transition to the formations of the upper level of the pegmatitic intrusive complexes, which are composed of substantially albitized pegmatites enriched with a number of rare elements, including beryllium. It can be seen from available data that the distribution of beryllium minerals (mainly alkali beryl) in replaced pegmatites is wholly determined by the development of replacement phenomena and is not directly dependent on the degree of differentiation of the given level of a specific pegmatite body, as it is in the pegmatite deposits of the preceding level. The concentration of the main beryllium mineral—beryl—in replaced pegmatites varies within wide limits, attaining at times 0.6 to 1 percent. Compared with pegmatites of the lower levels of the pegmatitic intrusive complex, the replaced pegmatites have not only higher beryllium concentrations, but also more voluminous accumulations of beryllium minerals.

Thus, in a pegmatitic intrusive complex, beryllium accumulates in the well-differentiated pegmatite bodies of the middle intrusive level and particularly in the bodies of the top level, where it is concentrated, together with lithium and tantalum, in replaced pegmatites of various types.

Peculiarities of the Formation and Paragenesis of Beryllium Minerals in Beryl-Bearing Pegmatites

Unlike the previously described block biotite-microcline pegmatites with gadolinite and other rare-earth minerals, the beryl-bearing pegmatites usually do not contain any increased concentration of rare-earth elements. Iron, also, plays a much less important part in the formation of such pegmatites, because boron, which is usually present in them, is a strong precipitating agent for iron, which is thus removed from the process of mineral formation by being captured in the ferrous tourmalines. Quite naturally, the formation of gadolinite in these pegmatites meets with difficulties; this mineral, usually absent in most deposits, occurs only in a few places, and in negligible quantities.

From the above characteristics of a number of typical deposits of block and fully differentiated muscovite-microcline pegmatites, it is concluded that these pegmatites contain three generations of beryl, related to various paragenetic complexes and differing in a number of physical properties and features of chemical composition:

1. alkali-free beryl from block quartz;
2. sodium beryl, related to quartz-muscovite, muscovite-albite, and albite replacement complexes;
3. alkali-free beryl from cavities and late fissures.

The relationship between beryl I and block quartz, and the habit of its crystals, allows the assumption that beryl of this generation was formed earlier than the quartz of the block zone and of the quartz core of the pegmatite deposits. It has already been mentioned that, in many places, crystals of beryl I are split along planes parallel to the pinacoid, and are "healed" with block quartz (Fig. 25).

The disposition of the beryl I crystals in the block quartz, and the occurrence of compound caps in these crystals in a number of places indicate that these crystals might have been formed by free growth in the central sections of pegmatite bodies before the block quartz crystallized.

Unlike the alkali-free beryl I, the crystals and crystal growths of sodium beryl II[8] are most common in the partly albitized pegmatites, where they are spatially related to those albitized parts composed of the relatively early albite that is the result of the initial stages of albitization (Beus and Zalashkova, 1956).

In all investigated deposits, the formation of solid conical sodium beryl is characteristic of the parts of the albite replacement complex that were formed from the block microcline or the coarse-grained pegmatite composed of pegmatoid segregations of potassium feldspar and quartz as much as 5 cm and more in diameter.

When albitization is superposed on the zone of graphic pegmatite or medium-grained pegmatite of apographic structure, the solid conical beryl gives place to "stuffed" conical beryl.

The most abundant accumulations of "stuffed" beryl are observed in pegmatite bodies in which the zone of partly albitized graphic or apographic pegmatite[9] directly adjoins the quartz or quartz-microcline pegmatite core or the zone of quartz-muscovite replacement complex that surrounds the core. It has already been mentioned that a characteristic feature of the "stuffed" beryl is its relatively uniform distribution in the beryl-bearing zone.

The analysis of material gathered during many years of study of pegmatite districts, and partly discussed in this book and some of the author's earlier papers (Beus, 1948; Beus and Zalashkova, 1956), makes it possible to treat the relationships between sodium beryl and the main minerals of pegmatites as follows:

1. With respect to microcline and microcline-perthite of all zones of primary crystallization, the generation of beryl in question has been found later; this is proved unequivocally by the relationship (observed in a number of deposits) between sodium beryl (both solid and "stuffed")

[8] A detailed characteristic of the morphology of sodium beryl crystals is given in Chapter 2.

[9] The incomplete albitization in these cases is expressed by the almost complete replacement of microcline by albite, only fine relics remain of microcline; at the same time the effect of albitization in quartz is very slight. The quartz intergrowths recrystallize only partly and preserve the relict apographic structure of the zone.

Fig. 42. Rough outline of the faces of "stuffed" beryl where in contact with quartz ichthyoglypts.

and the jointing in the zones of block microcline-perthite and of albitized apographic pegmatite (see Fig. 26), and by the occurrence of microscopic microline relics in the beryl enclosed in albite:

2. The distinct allotriomorphism of beryl, with reference to the graphic and apographic quartz intergrowths (Fig. 42), and the phenomena of beryl crystals bending round the quartz growths and other aggregates, also suggest that the sodium beryl formed later than the quartz of the graphic and apographic pegmatite and hindered the normal growth of beryl crystals.

3. The relationships between the conical sodium beryl and the early albite generation of which the beryl-bearing zones (granular albite) are composed are fairly distinct. As a rule, the allotriomorphism of granular albite with beryl is the most common type; more rare are regular intergrowths between granular albite and beryl. From a summary of numerous mineralogical observations and analyses of thin sections, we may assume that the basic mass of albite was formed simultaneously with beryl, or somewhat later.

Quite characteristic are the relationships to the medium- and large-tabular muscovite, which is the essential component of the beryl-bearing albite zones. Muscovite is usually allotriomorphic with respect to sodium beryl, but the prismatic planes of beryl crystals bear clear inductive imprints of the ribbed muscovite faces where the crystals touch the mica books. The penetration of muscovite into beryl is less frequent.

The problem of the origin of the solid and "stuffed" varieties of sodium beryl is very interesting.

The typical disposition of crystals of conical sodium beryl near the contact of the pegmatite body, observed in a number of deposits, and the orientation of crystals normal to the plane of contact caused many investigators to conclude prematurely that this generation of beryl occurred earlier than or almost simultaneously with the crystallization of the main minerals of the pegmatite, microcline-perthite and quartz. The spatial relationship between beryl and the albitized sections of the pegmatite was considered to be accidental, especially because in a series of substantially albitized pegmatites there was corrosion of beryl by late saccharoidal albite. The formation of "stuffed" beryl crystals was explained from this view as a capture by the growing crystals of small batches of the mineral-forming melt-solution, whose crystallization took place within the beryl crystal.

Similarly, other investigators, who considered that sodium beryl was of relatively early formation, explained the formation of "stuffed" crystals as due to the replacement of beryl by the enclosed minerals (Crookshank, 1948; *et al.*).

It should be noted that the actual observed relationships between sodium beryl II and the early paragenetic complexes of pegmatites contradict the conclusions about its early crystallization; this inference can be made, in particular, from the facts given above, which illustrate the commonly observed relationship between this generation of beryl and jointing. Thus, the formation of "stuffed" beryl crystals cannot be explained by the capture of batches of liquid pegmatite melt by the growing crystal.

The observed facts make it also impossible to explain the origin of "stuffed" beryls by albite replacement of the inner part of beryl crystals along the sixfold axis. As a rule, there is no corrosion of the well-formed faces of the internal cavity of beryl crystals by early albite, which is in close paragenesis with "stuffed" beryl. Albite is an allotriomorphic mineral with respect to the outer and inner faces of the "stuffed" beryl crystals (Fig. 43). The corrosion of sodium beryl by albite is observed only when a later stage of albitization is superposed on the beryl-bearing zone. However, the late beryl-replacing albite usually sharply differs morphologically from the earlier albite related paragenetically to beryl (Fig. 44).

The generalization of numerous mineralogical observations on the relationships between sodium beryl and the accompanying minerals has enabled us to arrive at the conclusion favoring the metasomatic origin of the solid and "stuffed" sodium beryl varieties during the beginning stages of albitization (Beus and Zalashkova, 1956). This origin is wholly borne out by the fact that the spatial arrangement of the albitized zones in pegmatite bodies also determines the distribution of sodium beryl. At the same time, the solid composite crystals of sodium beryl are, as a rule, associated with the replacement of the monomineralic blocks or large segregations of

Fig. 43. Allotriomorphism of early albite with respect to the crystal faces of sodium beryl, Altai. Magnification ×10. (Crossed nicols.)

microcline, whereas the formation of the "stuffed" variety is spatially and genetically closely related to the incomplete albitization of the graphic and apographic pegmatite. The origin of these "stuffed" composite beryl crystals is satisfactorily explained by the heterogeneity of the replaced medium and by selective metasomatism, which does not affect, or only slightly affects, the quartz of the apographic intergrowths. Any obstacle encountered by the growing conical beryl crystals (for example, a grain of quartz) unavoidably results in the heterogeneous growth of monocrystals that form the cluster. In the deposits examined, three types of disturbance of the homogeneous growth of sodium beryl crystals were noted at the contact between beryl that replaced microcline and quartz of the apographic pegmatite:

1. The quartz grain touches the lateral part of the growing beryl crystal or crystal cluster; here beryl curves around the quartz grain, and an embossed imprint of the quartz ichthyoglypt remains on crystal faces.
2. The quartz grain is wedged deeply into the beryl crystal; behind the quartz grain, beryl separates into several flat crystals that surround the quartz grain and continue to grow independently.
3. The quartz grain shields the growth of the inner part of the composite conical beryl crystal; behind the quartz grain, the growth of

beryl predominates on the outer walls of the crystal. The result is a peculiar hollow skeletal crystal form; its growth peculiarities are determined by the heterogeneity of the medium in which the growth of beryl takes place.

From the presence of rare relics of microcline partly replaced with albite, albitized medium-grained pegmatite, we may assume that beryl developed directly after the microcline was replaced with albite. It is possible that the replacement of microcline by albite took place with the albitization. Of particular interest is the paper by B. Shaub (1937) who, by detailed study of the crystal of "stuffed" beryl, arrived at the conclusion that the crystallization of the beryl and the included albite took place simultaneously.

The interrelations between alkali-free beryl I and sodium beryl II make it easy to determine more accurately the place and time of their formation in the pegmatitic process.

In some pegmatite deposits there are both the alkali-free and sodium beryl. The alkali-free prismatic beryl is associated with the zone of block quartz, whereas the sodium variety is always related to those parts of the pegmatite body that are replaced with albite. A comparison of the partly albitized beryl-bearing pegmatites with various degrees of development of the replacement complex suggests a decrease in the importance of prismatic alkali-free beryl with a parallel increase in the abundance of the alkali varieties related to the replacement zones. When albitization is superposed on those parts of the pegmatite that contain the early alkali-

Fig. 44. Corrosion of sodium beryl by late albite, Altai. Magnification ×10. (Crossed nicols.)

free beryl I, the latter recrystallizes and sodium beryl is formed. In particular, relics of the crystals of semitransparent green alkali-free beryl were noted in the core of the conical crystals of sodium beryl (Fig. 33.). The sharp difference in orientation between the beryl crystal and the enclosing beryl of a later generation does not provide any foundation here for assuming a zonal growth of the beryl crystal and a successive deposition of zones of varying composition.

To complete the study of the paragenesis of sodium beryl, it is necessary to give a brief description of the multi-phase micro-inclusions which are very characteristic of this generation. Sodium beryl in a number of deposits typically contains inclusions of rectangular habit, orientated in agreement with the crystal elements of the beryl and containing in the solid phase relatively large crystals of the cubic system (Fig. 45). These crystals are probably chlorides or fluorides of alkali metals, according to data available from special studies of gaseous-liquid inclusions in beryl and in other pegmatite minerals. It should be noted that such inclusions are absolutely not characteristic of alkali-free beryl, and are undoubtedly related to the formation of the generation in question.

Considering the paragenesis of sodium beryl, it is possible to assume that Na, Be (OH), CO_3, Cl, and F took an active part in the process of mineral formation, whereas Si, Al, and K were relatively passive.

PARAGENESIS OF SODIUM BERYL

	Replacement complex
Beryl	$Al_2Be_3[Si_6O_{18}]$
Albite	$Na[AlSi_3O_8]$
Muscovite	$KAl_2[AlSi_3O_{10}](OH)_2$
Alkali chlorides or fluorides (inclusions)	(Na, K) (Cl, F)
Water (inclusions)	H_2O
Quartz	SiO_2
Microcline (relics)	$K[AlSi_3O_8]$

Turning to the paragenesis of the late generation of alkali-free beryl III, which normally crystallizes in cavities or fissures, we should note that these well-formed prismatic to thin-prismatic crystals can form under conditions of free growth, as in the cavity or fissure, and of metasomatism, as replacement of microcline. This has been illustrated above in the description of deposits.

In outline, the paragenesis of this generation of beryl is with late saccharoidal albite (however, the presence of albite is not essential), and at times with fluorite and fine tabular muscovite. In a number of places, the late alkali-free beryl related to jointing is found in complete isolation.

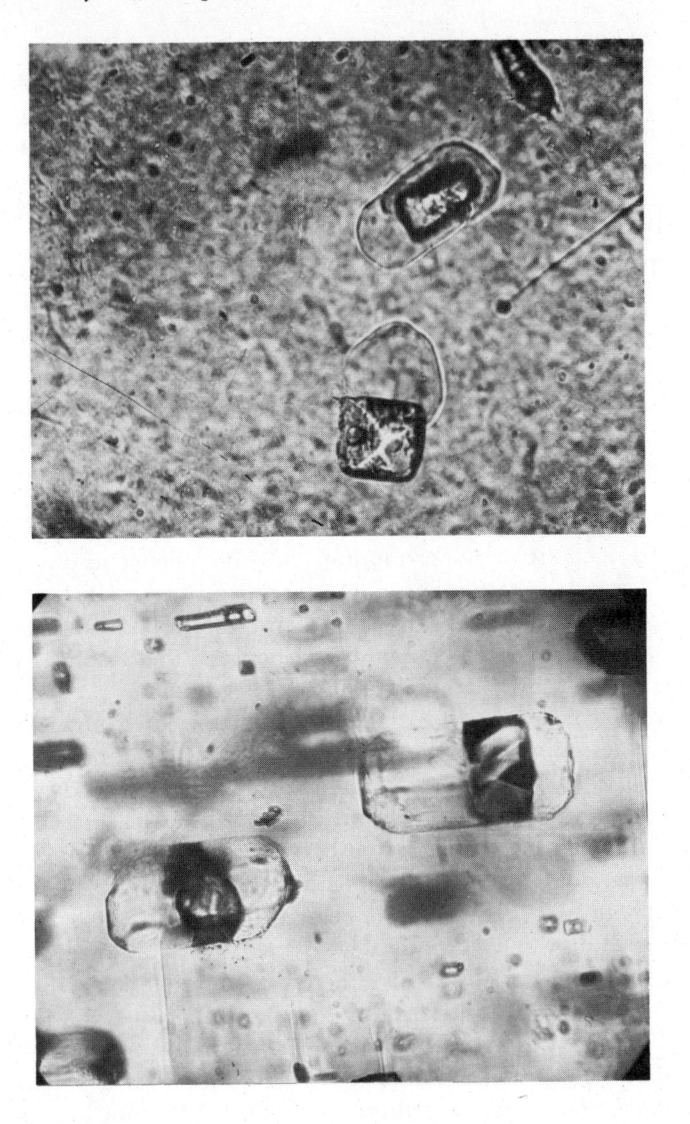

Fig. 45. Gaseous-liquid inclusions in sodium beryl containing cubic crystals of alkali metal chlorides. Top, solid conical sodium beryl (magnification $\times 39$). Bottom, "stuffed" conical sodium beryl (magnification $\times 365$).

Very characteristic of this generation of beryl is the wide occurrence of free carbon dioxide in the gaseous-liquid inclusions and the presence of a solid phase in the form of alkali halide crystals.

The analysis of the paragenesis of this generation of beryl permits the assumption that, apart from Be^{2+}, Si^{4+}, and Al^{3+}, such cations and complexes as Na^{1+}, $[HCO_3]^{1-}$, $[CO_3]^{2-}$, and F^{1-} also take an active part in its crystallization.

Beryl is virtually the only beryllium mineral of the block and fully differentiated pegmatites to have a wide occurrence. Other beryllium minerals present in the pegmatites of the type under consideration, including chrysoberyl, phenacite, and bertrandite, have a very limited occurrence and their quantity is usually very small.

Chrysoberyl usually occurs in pegmatites slightly enriched in aluminum, owing to the assimilation of the enclosing aluminous rocks. The peculiarities of its paragenesis in such pegmatites were given during the discussion of muscovite-oligoclase pegmatites in which the "crossing" (assimilation, Ed.) phenomena are noticeably developed. Phenacite and bertrandite are found in normal pegmatites. They are always the latest minerals to form and are localized in cavities and fissures transgressing various zones of pegmatites. The tabular crystals of bertrandite or the prismatic (to acicular) crystals of phenacite usually crystallize on the faces of crystals of beryl III, quartz, or feldspar, whose surfaces are commonly corroded by later solutions. Fine scaly muscovite (more rarely albite and late quartz) is observed in paragenesis with bertrandite and late phenacite.

In some places, the formation of phenacite and bertrandite in preceded by the dissolution of beryl by late hydrothermal solutions; however, usually a direct relationship cannot be established between the dissolution of beryl and the crystallization of late phenacite and bertrandite.

When passing from the block and fully differentiated muscovite-microcline pegmatites to the substantially replaced pegmatites, the nature of beryl paragenesis and its typomorphic features change regularly along with the paragenesis of the main rock-forming minerals and the internal structure of the pegmatite deposits. Alkali-free beryl, which crystallizes in the zone of block quartz, does not occur in replaced pegmatites.

The common link between two genetically closely related groups of pegmatites is sodium beryl, whose development (as has already been mentioned) begins in the block and fully differentiated pegmatites simultaneously with the earliest stages of albitization.

In the replaced pegmatites, sodium beryl usually occurs in the least albitized, near-contact zones composed (prior to albitization) of pegmatite of graphic and apographic structure. The habit of sodium beryl, which is characteristic of these sections of replaced pegmatites, is analogous to that previously described for pegmatites with block and fully differentiated texture and with dominant primary crystallization zones. In many places very small beryl crystals occur within a zone that has a gradual transition from "stuffed" to homogeneous crystals. This transition is determined by the intensity of albitization which may result in a complete substitution of albite for the graphic and medium-grained pegmatite and the transformation of the primary quartz-microcline zone into an almost monomineralic albite aggregate containing solid crystals of sodium beryl.

The formation of sodium-lithium beryl in pegmatites is closely related to the intensity of albitization, which, in the first place, results in the appearance of a generation of tabular albite (cleavelandite), to which sodium-lithium beryl always bears a clear paragenetic relationship. Along with the development of the cleavelandite replacement complex, the composition of the main paragenetic associations of the pegmatite changes, and lithium minerals, mainly spodumene, begin to play a noticeable part. Thus, the typical paragenesis of sodium-lithium beryl is cleavelandite, muscovite, lithium minerals, and tantalite-columbite.

In the most fully differentiated parts of the body usually associated with the apical parts of the pegmatitic intrusive complexes, lithium-cesium beryl (vorobyevite or rosterite)—the youngest generation of beryl in the replacement pegmatites—crystallizes along with the formation of the late cleavelandite segregations and the lepidolite replacement complex. In pegmatites where lepidolite has not formed, lithium-cesium beryl rarely occurs and is associated with small cavities in cleavelandite. It is much more common in pegmatite deposits with a wide development of the lepidolite replacement complex which, in many places, is accompanied by the accumulation of cesium in the form of pollucite. The most characteristic paragenesis of lithium-cesium beryl is lepidolite + cleavelandite, more rarely cleavelandite + lithium-bearing muscovite + spodumene, or cleavelandite + quartz (the latter is also the common constituent of the associations referred to above).

Of considerable interest are the interrelationships between the sodium variety of beryl and the alkali sodium-lithium and lithium-cesium varieties.

It has already been pointed out that the distribution of sodium beryl in pegmatites and the consideration of its paragenetic relationships with the surrounding minerals relates the formation of this generation of beryl to the early stages of albitization, which are shown by the gradual, commonly incomplete, replacement of microcline of the block, apographic, and graphic pegmatite zones with irregularly-grained, (more rarely) poorly tabular albite. In the intensely albitized parts of the pegmatite, composed of cleavelandite, sodium beryl is replaced by white and colorless sodium-lithium beryl or by rose-colored lithium-cesium beryl (vorobyevite). The latter is especially characteristic of the cleavelandite-spodumene and albite-lepidolite pegmatite zones. In a number of places, the formation of sodium-lithium and lithium-cesium beryl of the cleavelandite zone is considered to be a result of recrystallization of the alkali-free beryl during the inundation of poorly albitized sections of beryl-bearing pegmatites with alkaline sodium and sodium-lithium solutions. The incomplete recrystallization of the early generations of beryl, shown by characteristic zoned crystals, are fairly often observed in a number of deposits. The central part of these usually poorly formed crystals is composed of light-green sodium beryl, which gradually passes into white or almost white sodium-lithium beryl that forms the outer zone of the crystal.

The recrystallization of beryl of earlier generations also is indicated by a large crystal of dirty-green sodium beryl found in a pegmatite in the Altai; the smaller part of this crystal formed in the lepidolite zone and was transformed into pink beryl of vorobyevite type. The part formed outside the lepidolite zone is mostly dirty-green beryl.

The processes of dissolution of the beryl of the early generations (alkali-free and sodium beryl), is widespread in replaced pegmatites and, in the final stages of pegmatite formation, results in the forming of secondary beryllium minerals that crystallize in the small leached out cavities in albite. Unlike the block and fully differentiated mucovite-microcline pegmatites, the secondary beryllium minerals in the replaced pegmatites are composed almost exclusively of beryllium phosphates; the most widely represented is herderite. Much less common are bavenite and bertrandite, which only rarely occur in pegmatites poor in phosphorus.

Thus, beryllium starts to separate as a solid phase after the formation of the early paragenetic complexes (zones of graphic and medium-grained pegmatite, and block microcline) and during the initial stages of the replacement period, which precede the beginning of crystallization of the block-quartz zone. Beryllium partcipates in the process of mineral formation during the entire replacement stage up to the low-temperature hydrothermal phase, and this results in the formation of secondary beryllium minerals in fissures and leached cavitites in minerals of the replacement complexes.

Granitic Pegmatites of the Crossing Line

Granitic pegmatites of the "crossing line" differ considerably from the standard "pure-line" pegmatites referred to above and are characterized by a number of geological and mineralogical-geochemical peculiarities that separate beryllium deposits of this group of vein-like bodies into a clearly distinct genetic type. The "crossing-line" pegmatites are a fairly rare type of deposit, which form under peculiar geological conditions, but are highly important, from the industrial viewpoint, as a source of commercial beryl and emerald. Beryl and emerald deposits related to the "crossing-line" pegmatites are known, outside the USSR, in various regions of the world (Salzburg, Austria; the Oslo district, Norway; the Arabian Desert, Egypt; northeastern Transvaal, South Africa; the Puuna district, Australia).

The districts of "crossing-line" pegmatites are usually within the exocontact zones of pegmatite-bearing granitic intrusions in various basic and ultrabasic rocks that have been considerably altered by regional metamorphism. In the endocontact zone of such intrusions, in a number of places, there are schlieren-like pegmatites with some miarolitic cavities containing topaz and beryl crystals.

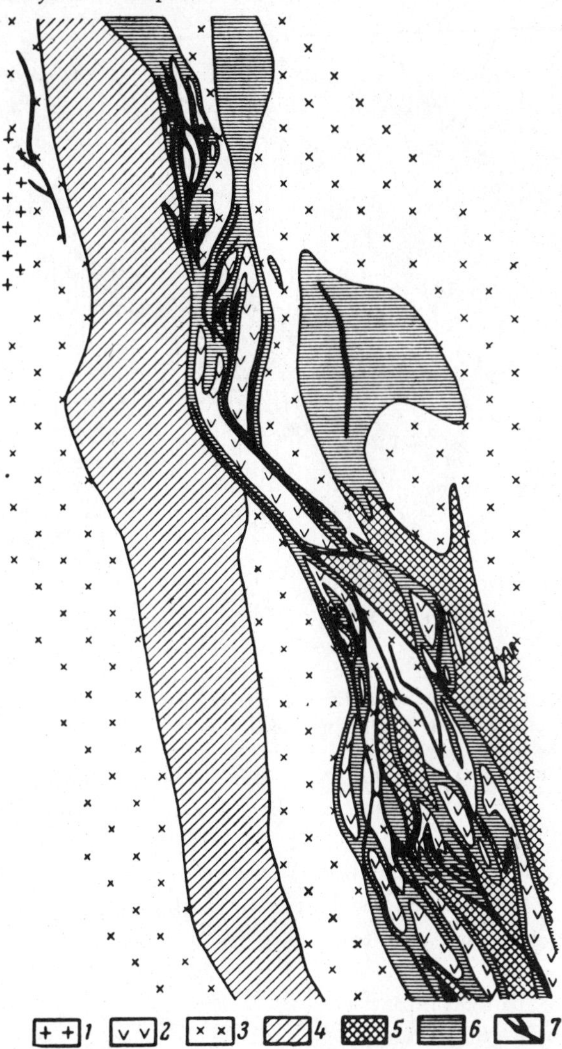

Fig. 46. A series of beryl-bearing mica-plagioclase veins transgressing ultrabasic rocks. (1) Binary granite; (2) serpentinites and talc-carbonate rocks; (3) amphibolite; (4) carbonaceous-amphibolite schist; (5) diorite porphyry; (6) talc, chlorite, and actinolite rocks; (7) beryl-bearing mica-plagioclase veins.

The altered basic and ultrabasic rocks that enclose vein-like bodies are usually composed of amphibole schists, amphibolities, diorites, and serpentinites, partly converted to talc, chlorite, actinolite, or tremolite schists.

The beryl-bearing deposits of one of the typical districts in the USSR have a complex structure and consist of separate veins and schlieren, sometimes anastomosing. Groups of these veins form thick suites (Fig. 46) that extend for hundreds of meters in length. Individual veins in the

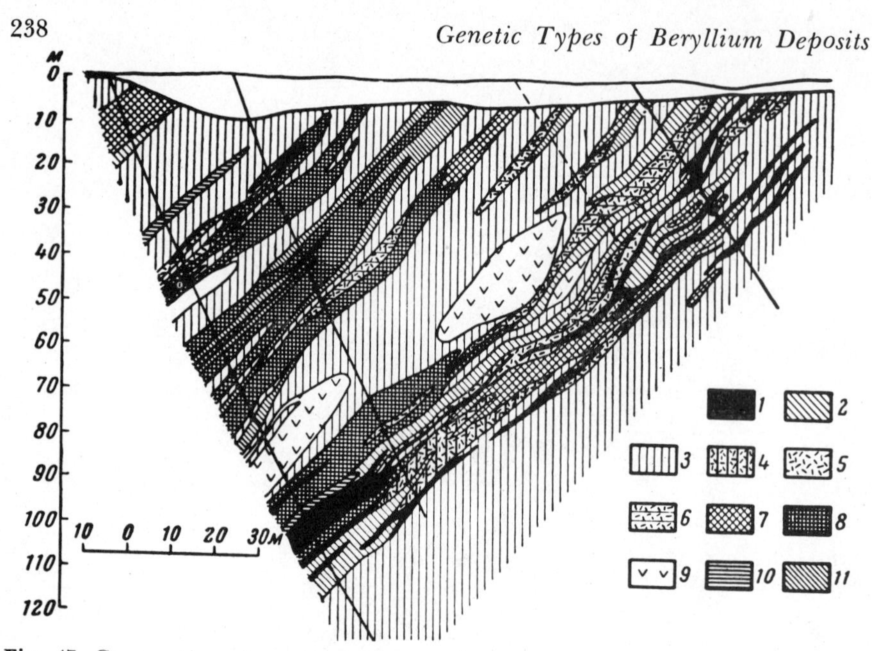

Fig. 47. Cross-section through a series of beryl-bearing mica-plagioclase veins. (1) Phlogopite veins with plagioclase cores; (2) phlogopite-talc, phlogopite-actinolite, and phlogopite-chlorite zones, (3) talc schists; (4) talc-actinolite schists; (5) actinolite schists; (6) actinolite-chlorite schists; (7) diorites; (8) amphibolites; (9) serpentinites; (10) chlorite schists; (11) carbonaceous schists.

suites are as much as 5 to 6 m thick, their length amounting to several tens of meters. The vein suites can be traced to a considerable depth (Fig. 47).

The "crossing-line" vein-like bodies are subdivided according to their mineralogical composition and structure, into the following main groups:

1. mica-plagioclase and mica veins with beryl (strictly the "crossing-line" pegmatites);
2. beryl-quartz-albite veins;
3. beryl-muscovite-quartz veins;
4. beryl-muscovite-fluorite veins.

Most interesting among deposits of the vein complex are the *mica-plagioclase and mica veins*, which combine all the characteristic features of this type of deposit. A. E. Fersman (1925b, 1940) and K. A. Vlasov (1938a, 1938b) previously studied and described in detail this vein type and gave the clear description of the structure and paragenesis of the mica-plagioclase bodies that assigned them to the category of desilicated pegmatites. The zonal structure is very characteristic of beryl-bearing veins of this type; however, they are not always clearly manifest. The central part of the veins is composed entirely of coarse-grained plagioclase (plagioclasite), which forms separate lenses (Fig. 48), and (more rarely) continuous vein-like bodies as much as 1.5 m thick. In veins in serpentinite, on either side of the plagioclase core, there are reaction zones: a phlogopite zone, as much as 6 m thick; an actinolite zone, much thinner (0.2 to 0.3 m) and intermittent; a chlorite zone, as much as 2 m thick; a talc zone. In several places the actinolite and chlorite zones are not present, and then the talc zone immediately follows the phlogopite zone.

Usually thin (3 to 10 cm) layers of beryllium-margarite occur at the contact between the plagioclase core and the phlogopite zone.

The quantitative ratio between plagioclase and quartz, and phlogopite and biotite is never constant in the veins and varies within wide limits. In individual veins the plagioclase cores are rather small or completely absent, and the vein is composed mainly of dense phlogopite mica. At places lens-shaped quartz segregations occur in the core of the veins.

Besides the medium plagioclase and phlogopite, the characteristic minerals of the mica-plagioclase and mica veins are these: beryl, phenacite, chrysoberyl, beryllium-margarite, fluorite, tourmaline, prochlorite, bavenite, gilbertite, fuchsite, molybdenite, native bismuth, chlorite, and talc.

Almost all beryl and emerald (the rarer, but characteristic mineral of such deposits) are associated with the phlogopite mica; a lesser proportion of these minerals is contained in the plagioclase cores and only single crystals are found in the chlorite zone.

The mineralogical composition of the quartz-plagioclase zone of the vein complex is relatively constant. The main mineral is medium plagioclase; of lesser importance are quartz and phlogopite, which are disseminated as inclusions in quartz and plagioclase.

Beryl, fluorite, apatite, and some sulfides (mainly molybdenite) occur relatively widely.

Beryl is distributed irregularly in the plagioclase part of the veins, commonly forming large accumulations in pockets.

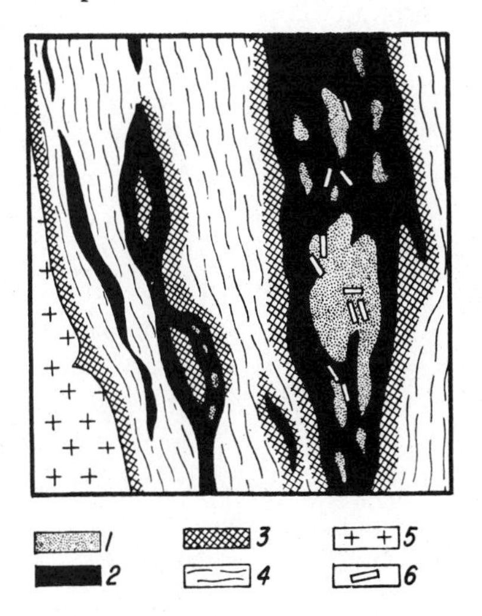

Fig. 48. Mica-plagioclase veins with beryl in mica-chlorite schist. (1) quartz-feldspar cores; (2) zone of fine-tabular biotite; (3) actinolite-chlorite zone; (4) dense mica-chlorite schists; (5) medium grained biotite granites; (6) beryl (emerald) crystals.

The commonest types are growths of irregular crystals and individual well-formed crystals of prismatic habit. The crystal size varies within wide limits from fractions of a millimeter to 10 cm in diameter. Crystals of medium size (0.5 × 2 cm to 1 × 5 cm) occur most widely. The color of beryl varies from light-green to turbid-white and yellowish. The crystals in plagioclase, as a rule, are opaque beryl, but those in the smoky quartz of the central zone are dense-green translucent and transparent prismatic emerald.

The proportion of crystals and accumulations of beryl as pockets in plagioclase increases toward the contact of plagioclase with quartz. As the thickness of the quartz-plagioclase core increases, so, in general, does its beryl content.

In addition to beryl, fluorite is another constant constituent of the plagioclase part of the veins. It is of various colors and forms disseminated crystals or large pockety accumulations. Molybdenite, another common mineral of the quartz-plagioclase zone, is associated mainly with the outer part of the plagioclase core. Rare minerals, present only as single grains in plagioclase or quartz, are apatite and topaz; even rarer are chalcopyrite and pyrite, as fine inclusions in solid quartz.

The most interesting of the secondary minerals is bavenite, discovered by E. I. Kutukova (1946). It forms during the hydrothermal alteration of beryl.

In the reaction zones around the veins, the zone richest in beryl is the mica zone of biotite or phlogopite-biotite composition. It contains, in addition to the rock-forming micas, the following typical minerals: emerald, beryl, beryllium-margarite, tourmaline, apatite, fluorite, chrysoberyl, phenacite, and molybdenite.

Unlike the beryl-bearing quartz-plagioclase core, the phlogopite-biotite zone is dominated by bright-green emerald. Pale-green beryl is not characteristic of the phlogopite-biotite zone. Some crystals from this part of the vein complex have an annular zonal coloration, which increases from the center to the periphery or vice versa. Another type of zoning is sometimes expressed by a sudden change in the intensity of the green coloration of crystals along the *c*-axis.

Morphologically, the beryl of the phlogopite-biotite zone substantially differs from the beryl of the quartz-plagioclase core of the vein-like bodies. In the fine scaly mica-rich mass, beryl forms separate elongated prismatic crystals or parallel growths of several crystals and no coarse-grained growths of irregular crystals are found. The beryl crystals are orientated with the schistosity of the micaceous enclosing layer. In this part of the vein the beryl content is markedly lower than in the quartz-plagioclase core.

Most crystals of brightly colored beryl in the phlogopite-biotite zone are cracked and translucent. The cracks of crystals are usually filled with fine, scaly micaceous material, more rarely with fluorite. The very transparent and fissure-free emeralds are high-grade gemstone material.

All geologists who have studied similar deposits note the irregular distribution of brightly colored transparent beryl varieties (emerald) within the surrounding reaction zones. However, in several places, a higher content of high-grade emerald occurs where the quartz-feldspar core tapers out.

It should be noted that emeralds of highest quality were found as single specimens in blue talc in the biotite-talc and actinolite-talc zones, although, as a rule, beryllium minerals are rare in these zones.

Phenacite, a very interesting accessory beryllium mineral of the "crossing-line" pegmatites, is usually related to the chlorite zone of the reaction complex, or else it is found at the contact between chlorite and phlogopite zones. Its crystals are, as a rule, colorless; more rarely, they are wine-yellow, and they vary between 1 and 10 cm in diameter. Phenacite is commonly associated with chrysoberyl.

Like phenacite, chrysoberyl is also associated with the chlorite zone; it occurs more rarely in the phlogopite zone and in the plagioclase cores. It is in tabular green and yellow-green crystals, usually occurring in the form of trillings characteristic of this mineral. The crystals vary between 0.5 and 6 cm in diameter.

In most places, chrysoberyl and phenacite occur in the pure mica veins, in which either there is no plagioclase core or the core has been replaced in the central part of the vein by lens-shaped accumulations of beryllium-margarite. Phenacite and chrysoberyl are considerably less abundant than beryl, and in deposits of this type they are only a very subordinate part of the total balance of beryllium combined in beryllium minerals.

In addition to the vein bodies of mica-plagioclase and mica, and their accompanying thick zones of altered wall rocks, referred to briefly above, there are within the vein district widespread *quartz-albite veins* with muscovite and thin biotite-phlogopite reaction selvedges, which contain high concentrations of beryl. The usual accessory minerals in veins of this group are fluorite, fluorapatite, molybdenite, and native bismuth. The same minerals also are present in very small quantities in the thin biotite-phlogopite selvedges.

Beryl is abundant in the quartz-albite veins; it is in the form of irregular crystals and large granular accumulations at the boundary of the albite and quartz masses, and in the form of inclusions in the albite mass, commonly in intergrowth with albite.

Beryl also occurs in small amounts in the quartz itself, where it concentrates mainly in the marginal parts of the quartz. Here it forms small crystals, inclusions, druses, streak, and small, fine-grained lenses. In places where the quartz-plagioclase core of the vein tapers out, the quantity of beryl generally sharply increases, so that sometimes beryl becomes the main mineral of the vein, forming a solid fine-grained aggregate with a little plagioclase.

The *beryl-muscovite-quartz veins,* which are commonly found within the vein district of the emerald area, are, unlike the veins of the preceding groups, mainly quartz (as much as 90 percent). Muscovite and albite are of much lesser importance. Individual bodies have a zonal structure: at the contacts, an albite zone (8 to 10 cm), next a muscovite zone with a small content of beryl, molybdenite, and chalcopyrite. The succeeding muscovite-beryl zone, which consists of light-blue beryl and muscovite (thickness 10 to 12 cm), rims the central, thickest zone, which is composed of quartz. At the pinches, the veins are usually composed of muscovite-beryl aggregate. Besides quartz, muscovite, and beryl, veins of this group have a small proportion of fluorite, margarite, molybdenite, and copper sulfides.

In several places the beryl-muscovite-quartz veins show an increase in the proportion of fluorite, associated with a decrease in the proportion of quartz, thus forming a transition between the veins of beryl-muscovite-fluorite and fluorite-beryl composition. Isolated vein bodies of this group have been traced for a distance of 100 to 120 m in length and down dip; the thickness varies from 1 to 5 m.

It should be noted that vein bodies of beryl-quartz-albite, beryl-muscovite-quartz, beryl-muscovite-fluorite, and fluorite-beryl composition, sometimes related to the "crossing-line" pegmatites, display a distinct similarity to hydrothermal-pneumatolytic formations; this is why many investigators consider the "crossing-line" pegmatites to be deposits related, in principle, not to pegmatitic, but to pneumatolytic and hydrothermal processes.

The various regions where beryl-bearing "crossing-line" pegmatites are developed all have similar geological conditions of formation and similar paragenetic associations of minerals.

The characteristic features of the Somerset Mine (Leisdorp, Transvaal), which is a sizeable deposit of emeralds, are virtually identical to those of analogous deposits in the USSR. The beryllium-bearing formations, represented by quartz-plagioclase and mica veins, occur in the roof pendants of the so-called "ancient granite" which crops out in the southern part of the Murchison Range. The roof pendants are composed mainly of hornblende-muscovite schists, partly converted into talc, chlorite, actinolite, and biotite schists. The veins consist of plagioclase (albite-oligoclase) and quartz, which sometimes interpenetrate, and are surrounded by a biotite reaction zone, analogous to the biotite-phlogopite mica of the Ural deposits. The plagioclase to quartz ratio in the veins varies within very wide limits; from pure plagioclase to almost pure quartz (van Eeden, et al., 1939).

The quartz-plagioclase vein-like bodies are lens-shaped. Usually, they are not continuous in length and occur as fragmented cores in a zone composed of biotite. This zone passes through the biotite-chlorite, chlorite, and talc zones, into hornblende schists. In a number of places, biotite is introduced along the schistosity with numerous quartz streaks.

As in the deposits described above, these quartz-plagioclase veins contain accumulations of opaque green beryl. Crystals of bright-green emerald are rare in veins composed of saccharoidal quartz. However, the biotite selvedges around the veins contain pockets and single crystals of emerald, oriented with the schistosity of the enclosing rock.

In addition to the rock-forming albite-oligoclase and quartz in the vein complex of Murchison Range, the following minerals are in association with beryl and emerald: garnet, fluorapatite, microcline, tourmaline (indicolite), topaz, sphene, epidote, molybdenite, chalcopyrite, chalcocite, and magnetite. In the zones around the veins, there also are biotite, chlorite (penninite and clinochlore), actinolite, scapolite, etc. The suite of minerals and their paragenesis are very close to those noted for analogous deposits in the Soviet Union.

Another emerald deposit, situated in the Arabian Desert (Jebel Zabara, Jebel Sikait), has not been adequately studied, although it has been known and mined for some three thousand years. The available fragmentary information (MacAlister, 1900) related this deposit to a series of altered ultrabasic rocks occurring in the exocontact zone of a large granite-gneiss mass. It should be noted that pegmatites proper are unknown in this area; at the same time there are widely distributed quartz veins, dikes of quartz porphyry, and thick greisen bodies. On the basis of the only available section through the deposit, the emerald-bearing zones are composed of a mica (apparently biotite-phlogopite) schist selvedge near the outcrops of the greisens and the quartz porphyry dikes. With the mica schists, within the altered ultrabasic rocks, are well developed talc, tourmaline, and garnet schists; however, the emeralds are associated only with the continuous zones of biotite schist, which are disposed symmetrically with respect to the greisen veins and quartz porphyry dikes.

A highly interesting emerald deposit is also known in the Puuna regions of Western Australia (Simpson, 1914). The emerald-bearing veins transgress altered dolerites in the roof of a granitic mass, and are fringed with thick zones of biotite. The veins are characterized by the predominance of quartz and a little feldspar (albite). Beryl is at the transition of beryl-bearing quartz-albite veins into quartz veins. Emerald is found in the biotite fringes of the veins and in the xenoliths of enclosing rocks in the veins. Faintly colored beryl occurs in the quartz-feldspar and quartz veins. Wolframite, scheelite, molybdenite, and cassiterite are the characteristic accessory minerals of the vein bodies. There are examples of the replacement of cassiterite by beryl.

In completing the description of so-called "crossing-line" pegmatites (or "desilicated" pegmatites), we must note that there is a certain degree of conventionality in relating beryl-bearing deposits of this type to pegmatites. It can be seen from the available data that most of the known deposits related to the desilicated pegmatites are apparently high-temperature hydrothermal-pneumatolytic formations formed by reaction with enclosing ultrabasic wall rocks.

Beryllium-Bearing Pegmatites of Nepheline Syenites

The occurrence of higher concentrations of beryllium in the alkalic pegmatites was first established by W. Brögger (1890), in southern Norway, from which he described a number of new beryllium minerals.

However, neither the paper by Brögger nor the later one by G. Flink (1900), which deals with the mineralogy of alkalic pegmatites of southern Greenland, contains any detailed description of the pegmatites in which the beryllium minerals were detected. For this reason, the characteristic features of deposits of these minerals remained unknown for a long time.

The discovery, between 1939 and 1950, of alkalic pegmatites with accessory beryllium minerals within the Lovozero and Khibinsk rock masses in the Kola Peninsula has markedly corrected and completed the concepts of the rare-metal (including beryllium) mineralization in the pegmatites of nepheline syenites.

Problems of the mineralogy and classification of the alkalic pegmatites of Lovozero and Khibinsk were dealt with in many investigations that described in sufficient detail their paragenesis, which in many respects is substantially different from the granitic-magma pegmatites referred to above.

One of the main characteristic features of the pegmatites of nepheline syenites, stressed in these papers, is the close relationship between their mineralogical composition and that of the parent alkalic rocks.

Unlike the granitic pegmatites, whose rock-forming and accessory minerals are not subject to sharp variations, the paragenesis of alkalic pegmatites varies substantially, depending on the composition of the associated alkalic rocks. This dependence is manifested both in the main minerals and in the common nature of the typomorphic accessory minerals of the pegmatites and their enclosing parent alkalic rocks.

Numerous examples illustrating this dependence are cited by all investigators of the pegmatites of the alkalic masses of the Kola Peninsula (Kostyleva, 1937; Gerasimovskii, 1939a, 1939b; Borodin, 1954). This dependence is also shown in the classification schemes of alkalic pegmatites, proposed in the above papers. In all classifications based on paragenesis or mineralogy, the number of segregated pegmatite types is determined to a large extent by the mineralogical composition of the pegmatite-bearing intrusive complexes.

However, besides many features shared with the parent nepheline syenites, the characteristic feature of the mineralogical composition of alkalic pegmatites is a noticeable enrichment in colored and ore minerals, and in those rare-element minerals that are either absent in the parent stocks or else occur in a considerably lower proportion.

Thus, the composition of the main part of pegmatites of nepheline syenites is determined by various combinations of the main rock-forming minerals (potassium feldspar, sodalite, nepheline, hackmanite, arfvedsonite, and aegirine) and of a number of accessory (including the rare-metal) minerals (eudialyte, eucolite, rinkolite, sphene, etc.).

When analyzing the regularities of the internal structure of alkalic pegmatites, M. V. Kuz'menko (1957) distinguished, by analogy with granitic pegmatites, three distinctly textural types, whose further subdivision is based on paragenesis. This author also substantiated the need for distinguishing pegmatites in which minerals of the replacement stage acquire a great importance. Thus, for example, the scheme suggested by M. V. Kuz'menko (Table 100) comprises the usual poorly differentiated pegmatites, whose composition is close to that of the parent rocks, and also the fully differentiated and multi-replaced pegmatites, which differ

Table 100 Textural-paragenetic types of alkalic pegmatites of the Lovozero mass (according to M.V. Kuz'menko)

Type	Sub-type	Facies (variety)
1. Uniformly grained	1. Nepheline-aegirine-feldspar	1. With eudialyte 2. With eudialyte and murmanite 3. With lamprophyllite and ramsayite
	2. Feldspar-sodalite	4. With chinglusuite and nordite
2. Block	3. Feldspar-aegirine	5. With eudialyte and murmanite 6. With eudialyte, ramsayite, and lamprophyllite
	4. Feldspar-hackmanite	7. With eudialyte and ramsayite
	5. Hackmanite-natrolite	8. With steenstrupine
3. Fully differentiated	6. Feldspar-aegirine	9. With eudialyte, lamprophyllite, murmanite, and ramsayite
	7. Feldspar-natrolite	10. With apatite
	8. Hackmanite-natrolite	11. With silicophosphates of rare earths
4. Multiple-replaced	9. Natrolite-microcline	12. With epididymite
	10. Natrolite-microcline	13. With polylithionite
	11. Analcite-albite	14. With epididymite
	12. Ussingite-natrolite	15. With chkalovite

substantially in their mineralogical composition from the enclosing nepheline syenites.

In these pegmatites, minerals such as albite, zeolites, or ussingite, which form in the replacement of minerals of early paragenetic complexes (nepheline, potassium feldspar, sodalite, etc.) in the late stages of pegmatite formation, are of great importance. With the formation of the main minerals of the replacement complexes, there is a concentration of a number of rare-metal minerals, including beryllium and lithium minerals (Table 100).

In the replaced nepheline syenite pegmatites of Lovozero and Khibinsk, all known beryllium minerals of alkalic pegmatites, except meliphanite,[10] were found between 1939 and 1956; also discovered and described were some new minerals (chkalovite, karpinskyite), not known in the pegmatites of other alkalic masses.

The replacement zone which contains beryllium minerals usually occurs in the central part of pegmatite bodies, and is more rarely the intermediate zone between the central natrolitic pegmatite core and the surrounding outer zones (Fig. 49).

The composition of the beryllium-bearing replacement complex is more or less constant. The most important mineral in most places is albite (more rarely late potassium feldspar), which usually develops after microcline or natrolite. In individual cases, ussingite is the main mineral of the replacement complex which contains beryllium minerals. In association with beryllium minerals, there are late potassium feldspar, zeolites (finely crystalline natrolite, chabasite), tainiolite, zircon, neptunite, some rare-earth minerals, hydrargillite, argillaceous minerals of the montmorillonite group, and commonly, the lithium mica, polylithionite. Table 101 and Fig. 49 show the peculiarities of the structure of pegmatites containing beryllium minerals.

The most widely occurring beryllium minerals of alkalic pegmatites of the Lovozero and Khibinsk masses is epididymite, the characteristic accessory mineral of pegmatites of the poikilitic sodalite and nepheline-sodalite syenites.

Three varieties of epididymite are known: finely crystalline to cryptocrystalline, finely micaceous, and spherolitic. The finely crystalline and finely micaceous epididymite occurs usually in large pegmatites of the poikilitic hackmanite syenites, where it forms irregular segregations as much as $15 \times 10 \times 5$ cm in the replacement zone, streaks at the contacts between prismatic natrolite and albite, and streaks in prismatic natrolite of the central zones. The spherolitic variety of epididymite occurs in pegmatites of other petrographic complexes of the Lovozero and Khibinsk

[10] The indication (Kostylova, 1937) that G. P. Chernik has found meliphanite has not been substantiated to date.

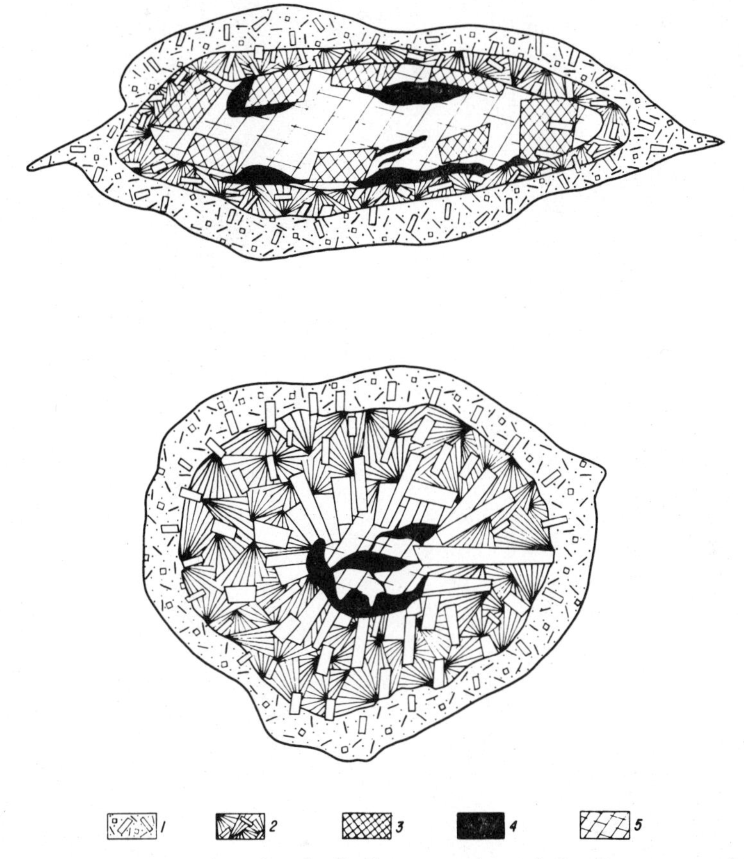

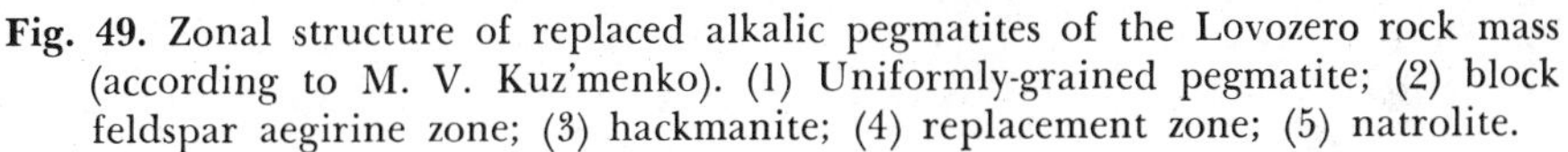

Fig. 49. Zonal structure of replaced alkalic pegmatites of the Lovozero rock mass (according to M. V. Kuz'menko). (1) Uniformly-grained pegmatite; (2) block feldspar aegirine zone; (3) hackmanite; (4) replacement zone; (5) natrolite.

rock masses and forms white radiating or spherolitic aggregates in the albite of the central replacement zones.

A characteristic example of epididymite-containing pegmatites is the pegmatite (studied by M. V. Kuz'menko) on the northeast slope of Mt. Karnasurt (Lovozero). In it there is a noticeable development of albitization phenomena.

The pegmatite occurs in the lujavrite of the first level of the differentiated complex, roughly concordant with the general layering of the rocks. It has the form of a layer and is about 100 m long. The thickness varies from 1 to 2.5 m. The contacts between the pegmatite and enclosing rocks are sharp and have reaction rims consisting of 60 to 90 percent aegirine. The mesocratic lujavrites near the contact with the pegmatite vein are natrolized and albitized. The zone of alteration sometimes attains 1 m in thickness.

Table 101 Mineralogical composition of beryl-bearing alkalic pegmatites of the Lovozero and Khibinsk rock masses

	Hackmanite-natrolite pegmatite (Karnasurt)	Natrolite-albite pegmatite (Karnasurt)	Orthoclase-natrolite pegmatite (Lepkhe-Nel'm)	Orthoclase-analcitic pegmatite (Kuivchorr)	Aegirine-microcline pegmatite (Partomchorr)	Eudialyte-ussingite pegmatite (Punkaruaiv)
Enclosing rock	Occurs at the contact of foyaites and lujavrites with poikilitic sodalitic syenites	Lujavrite	Aegirine lujavrite	Foyaites and ijolite-like poikilitic syenites	Foyaite-like nepheline syenite	Nepheline syenite
Composition of outer zones	Microcline-aegirine with eudialyte, murmanite	(a) Arfvedsonite-microcline-natrolite-aegirine with eudialyte, steenstrupine, nenadkevichite (fine-grained) (b) Natrolite-microcline with aegirine, steenstrupine, nenadkevichite (coarse-grained)	(a) Microcline with eudialyte and sphene (b) Aegirine-orthoclase with nephelinite, eudialyte, etc.	(a) Nepheline-aegirine-eudialyte-microcline with analcite, loparite, zircon, etc. (b) Microcline-aegirine with eudialyte and zircon (c) Orthoclase	(a) Arfvedsonite-microcline-with aegirine (b) Aegirine-microcline with ramsayite and loparite	(a) Eudialyte (b) Aegirine-ussingite (c) Eudialyte-ussingite
Composition of central zone	Hackmanite-natrolite	Natrolite-albite with microcline, hackmanite, epididymite and beryllite	Natrolite	Analcite-albite with epididymite, tainiolite, zircon, etc.	Albite	Ussingite with natrolite and chakalovite
Composition and position in pegmatite of the replacement complex with beryllium minerals	The replacement zone is arranged between the outer and the central zone. It is composed of albite, hackmanite, natrolite, polylithionite, chabasite, and the minerals of the montmorillonite group	The albite replacement complex occurs as irregular pockets and streaks in the central natrolite zone	Beryllium minerals related to cavities in natrolite	Central analcite-albite replacement zone	Beryllium minerals related to cavities in the albite zone	Central ussingite replacement zone

Continued on next page

Continued from preceding page

Table 101 Mineralogical composition of beryl-bearing alkalic pegmatites of the Lovozero and Khibinsk rock masses

Nature of beryllium minerals	Irregular segregations and streaks of epididymite are observed in the replacement zone and in the outer sections of the hackmanite-natrolite zone	Irregular segregations and streaks of finely-crystalline epididymite occur at the contact between natrolite and segregations of albite	Radiating segregations of leucophane occur in the cavities of natrolite druses	Epididymite as accumulations occurs in the analcite-albite zone	Epididymite crystals in association with potassium feldspar and analcite fill the cavities in albite	Irregular segregations of chkalovite are disposed in the outer section of the ussingite zone

The pegmatite body has a symmetrically zonal structure. The following zones are recognized from the periphery to the center.

The *contact zone,* 1 to 10 cm thick, is composed of finely acicular dark-green aegirine (40 to 90 percent), microcline (5 to 10 percent), and natrolite (5 to 20 percent); at places it contains a large proportion of eudialyte.

After the contact zone is the *zone of fine-grained pegmatite,* composed of aegirine (30 percent), arfvedsonite (20 percent), microcline (25 percent), and natrolite (25 percent). The accessory minerals are eudialyte, schizolite, mangansteenstrupine, and nenadkevichite. The grain size varies between fractions of a millimeter and 7 mm. The thickness of the zone is 10 to 20 cm. Fine acicular crystals of aegirine and arfvedsonite are included in microcline and also fill the gaps between its tabular crystals. The microcline crystals are replaced, from the periphery inward, with natrolite.

Towards the center, the fine-grained zone is gradually replaced by the zone of *medium-and coarse-grained pegmatite,* composed mainly of microcline, aegirine, arfvedsonite, and natrolite. The characteristic features of this zone are the decrease in the proportion of dark-colored minerals (aegirine, arfvedsonite, eudialyte) and an increase in the proportion of schizolite, mangansteenstrupine, nenadkevichite, and steenstrupine. The size of the microcline crystals gradually increases, reaching 10 × 7 × 5 cm near the central zone. In these areas a large amount of coarse- prismatic natrolite appears; along with hackmanite, it fills the interstices between the microcline crystals and heals any fissures in them. It is this pegmatite zone, especially with its middle part, that contains all of the rare-metal minerals, except the beryllium minerals.

The *central zone,* more than 1 m thick, is pegmatite of large-block structure, consisting of microcline, hackmanite, natrolite, and albite; the last two account for roughly 80 percent of the entire zone. The accessory minerals are epididymite, schizolite, murmanite, sphalerite, and neptunite. Microcline is usually associated with the peripheral parts of the central zone, where it is either in individual crystals as much as 15 × 10 × 5 cm or as monomineralic aggregates as much as 50 × 30 cm in size. Individual parts of the center of the zone are composed almost entirely of hackmanite, whose irregular segregations attain 4 m in diameter. On the surface, hackmanite is to a large extent replaced by a fine-grained aggregate of natrolite and hydrargillite. All of the central part of the zone is composed of natrolite and albite. Natrolite occurs mainly as the crypto-crystalline, chalcedony-like, and opal-like varieties, and to a lesser extent as large prismatic crystals. Albite, as finely crystalline aggregates, forms irregularly shaped segregations from 5–10 to 60–70 cm across in prismatic natrolite, and it also fills fissures in natrolite. Sometimes natrolite is replaced by an aggregate of albite, microcline, and aegirine.

The beryllium minerals, epididymite and beryllite, are related exclusively to the central zone. The finely crystalline epididymite forms segregations of irregular shape as much as 10 × 5 cm and streaks as thick as 3 to 4 cm, associated with the contacts between prismatic natrolite and albite. The epididymite is corroded and partly replaced by albite. Beryllite, which forms by the alteration of epididymite, occurs in small proportions and fills the leached out cavities in the pegmatite.

Eudidymite, leucophanite, and chkalovite are much less common beryllium minerals in the alkalic pegmatites of the Kola Peninsula. Eudidymite is found in the same paragenetic association as epididymite, and is closely related to the albite replacement complex.

One of the eudidymite-containing pegmatite veins of the Khibinsk rock mass, which has been studied by I. P. Tikhonenkov, is a typical example of pegmatites distinguished by the development of replacement phenomena and by a presence of beryllium minerals. The pegmatite that crops out on the slope of Mt. Partomschorr is a steeply dipping vein, 50 m long and 1 to 4 m thick. The enclosing rocks are foyaite-like nepheline syenites. A distinct zonal structure is observed in the thickest (4 m) section of the body. At the contacts is an arfvedsonite-microcline zone (1 to 1.5 m) composed of large crystals of microcline (60 to 80 percent) and arfvedsonite (10 to 15 percent), which produce pegmatoid intergrowths. The rare interstices between these minerals are filled with radiating aegirine. This zone passes into a 0.5 m thick aegirine-microcline zone towards the center. Large crystals of microcline, as much as 40 × 20 × 7 cm in size, account for 50 to 60 percent of the zone. Gaps between the microcline crystals are filled with green radiating aegirine, amounting to 25 to 30 percent of the zone. There is always ramsayite and loparite, and, less frequently, arfvedsonite in the zone.

The central zone of the thickest part of the vein, which contains the beryllium minerals, is composed of 70 to 90 percent of pink albite, in which there are relics of microcline, steenstrupinized nepheline, and aegirine. In the mass of pink albite there are many cavities lined with brown crystals of potassium feldspar and euhedral crystals of white analcite. Eudidymite is rarely detected among them. In the albitized sections of pegmatites, there also occur galena, sphalerite, zircon, ilmenite, schizolite, fluorite, and, commonly quartz.

Eudidymite, in general a rare mineral, is observed in three varieties. The most common variety is in large mica-like tabular colorless segregations of irregular shape, as much as 8 × 5 × 1.5 cm in size. Less common are euhedral tabular eudidymite crystals of pseudo-hexagonal habit. Crystals of this variety are always scattered in radiating pink albite. Their color is pinkish-yellow, and they are as much as 0.5 × 0.2 cm. The latest generation of eudidymite consists of white and light gray color, closely associated with fine-grained quartz.

It should be noted that segregations of eudidymite were detected in the

Lovozero mass and also in the nepheline-free albite veins, along with narsarsukite and quartz (Shilin and Semenov, 1957).

Very typical is the paragenesis of the very rare beryllium mineral, leucophanite, found in the alkalic pegmatites of the Lovozero mass (Semenov, 1957b). Leucophanite was detected in the orthoclase-natrolite pegmatites, where it forms radiating spherolitic segregations of greenish-white and honey-yellow color in the cavities of natrolite druses in the central natrolite zone of the pegmatite. The sizes of these segregations vary from 1 or 2 mm to 1 cm in diameter.

This zone of leucophanite-bearing pegmatite also contains apatite, tainiolite, irvingite, schizolite, francolite, neptunite, vernadite, and clay minerals of the montmorillonite group.

The pegmatite body occurring on Mt. Punkaruaiv (Lovozero) has a somewhat different paragenesis. In this pegmatite is one of the rarest beryllium minerals, chkalovite. The chkalovite-bearing pegmatite is mainly composed of eudialyte (35 to 40 percent), ussingite (about 25 percent) and aegirine (15 to 20 percent). There also occur in smaller proportions sodalite, microcline, murmanite, schizolite, erikite, neptunite, arfvedsonite, and nepheline. Chkalovite is observed as isolated segregations; in these segregations are belovite, steenstrupine, ramsayite, galena, and spahlerite (Borodin, 1954).

The interrelationship between the paragenetic complexes that compose the pegmatite body enabled L. S. Borodin to isolate the minerals of the primary crystallization of the pegmatite (nepheline, microcline, sodalite, eudialyte, aegirine, and murmanite), and of the replacement complex (natrolite, ussingite, etc.), whose formation was associated with the corresponding disappearance of the primary pegmatite minerals, microcline and sodalite.

Like other beryllium minerals, chkalovite shows a close relationship to the ussingite replacement zone and forms irregular segregations in its outer parts at the contact with the eudialite zone.

It should be noted that the relatively low stability of alkali beryllosilicates characteristic of the nepheline syenite pegmatites gives rise, in the active processes of chemical weathering, to the formation of a number of beryllium minerals (beryllite, helbertrandite) that were detected and described by M. V. Kuz'menko (1954) and E. I. Semenov (1957).

Supergene beryllium mineralization is one of the very characteristic features of beryllium-bearing pegmatites of nepheline syenites.

In summary, the beryllium minerals in pegmatites of nepheline syenites are associated with replacement phenomena which complete the process of pegmatite formation. The leading minerals of the replacement complex here are the alkali, mainly sodium, aluminosilicates (albite, natrolite, ussingite). Moreover, it can be assumed as established that beryllium minerals occur only in the polyzonal bodies of alkalic pegmatites, displaying the most complicated structure, namely, in bodies in which the paragenetic complexes of the replacement stages are widely developed. Here, notwithstanding the sharp difference in paragenesis and composition of beryllium minerals between the groups of alkalic and granitic pegmatites, it is clear that in both types the most important accumulations of minerals are related to the youngest, mainly albite, replacement complexes.

It is difficult to conclude whether this similarity is just superficial or due to deeper causes; anyway, the zonal bodies of alkalic pegmatites, like those of the well-differentiated pegmatites of the granites, show signs of the most intense replacement processes and the most variegated accessories (including rare-metal minerals). Unlike the granitic magma pegmatites, the alkalic pegmatites contain much lower concentrations of beryllium minerals, which, in all deposits of the world, are of mineralogical interest only.

CHAPTER 5

Hydrothermal-Pneumatolytic Beryllium Deposits

The beryllium deposits of hydrothermal-pneumatolytic origin are closely related to greisen and vein deposits of wolframite-molybdenite-quartz and cassiterite-quartz, and with skarn deposits enriched in fluorite, magnetite, and, in a number of places, tungsten, tin, and molybdenum.

All these deposits are associated with acid and ultra-acid granites of medium depth; the greisen and quartz vein beryllium deposits have an association with small intrusions of granites that are somewhat altered by postmagmatic processes (mostly by albitization and greisenization).

Because metasomatism is a major part of the process of forming hydrothermal-pneumatolytic deposits, the paragenesis of beryllium minerals in deposits of this group is controlled by the nature of the enclosing rocks which have been subjected to the action of the mineral-forming emanations and solutions. A detailed analysis of the relationship between the paragenesis of beryllium deposits of hydrothermal-pneumatolytic origin and the composition of the country rocks will be given in the geochemical section; let us note here that the nature of the country rocks is the first distinctive feature, on the basis of which all similar deposits can be subdivided in three distinct groups (Table 90).

In the first group, which occurs in aluminosilicate rocks, it is possible to distinguish, depending on the degree of metasomatism, those deposits that are primarily metasomatic, but with insignificant fissure filling (beryl-bearing greisenized and albitized granites, beryllium-bearing greisens), and vein deposits with slight metasomatism (greisenization) around the veins. All graduations can be found between these two distinct types.

The deposits of the second group, described in the preceding chapter, are near the areas of ultrabasic rocks that have been altered by regional metamorphism; they occur exclusively as fissure deposits. The main factor in the formation of the deposits was metasomatism, which brought about the characteristic form and paragenesis of beryllium-bearing vein bodies of hydrothermal-pneumatolytic origin that occur in ultrabasic rocks.

The deposits of a third group, which occur in carbonate rocks, consist mainly of typically metasomatic deposits; the most common of these are deposits of contact-metasomatic origin. The much rarer quartz and quartz-feldspar veins with beryllium minerals, which occur in isolated cases in limestones, are of slight significance, being a mineralogical rarity rather than an independent type of beryllium deposit.

Hydrothermal-Pneumatolytic Deposits of Beryllium in Aluminosilicate Rocks

Beryl-Bearing Greisenized and Albitized Granites

The greisenized and albitized granites with disseminated crystals of accessory beryl present a new, thus far insufficiently studied type of beryllium concentration, which was discovered by A. A. Beus and A. A. Sitnin in 1956 during the investigation of the distribution of beryllium in the greisen deposits of Transbaikalia (Beus, 1956a).

The granites that contain fine disseminated crystals of beryl usually occur in the apical apophyses of granitic masses, which have an abnormally high (compared with the mean) content of beryllium, and also of tungsten, molybdenum, or tin. Similar apical projections of granitic masses, which crop out in the form of large stock-shaped bodies or domes, are most commonly composed of leucocratic varieties that have been somewhat altered by albitization and greisenization. Tungsten- or tin-bearing quartz veins accompanied by greisens (a number of deposits in eastern Transbaikalia) generally form in the fissures in these dome-shaped rock masses.

In other places, the beryl-bearing facies of the metasomatised granites are found in the endocontact zones of large granitic masses (Upper Altai), and they usually show a spatial relationship to the tectonically disturbed zones.

Besides beryl, the deposits in the greisenized and albitized granites contain the following minerals: fluorite, topaz, wolframite, molybdenite, and rarely cassiterite. The nature of postmagmatic alterations enables one to distinguish between the beryl-bearing granites the (greisenized varieties proper) and granites, in which, apart from greisenization (usually weak), there is a noticeable development of albite. At the same time, in some deposits, the metasomatic processes referred to above are limited to a certain extent and are not accompanied by a fundamental rock change.[1]

Thus, the beryl-bearing granite outwardly resembles ordinary leucocratic muscovite granite. In the individual deposits of this type studied, the increase in the degree of greisenization of the granite as a rule is associated with a decrease in the beryllium content, owing to which the development of beryl in granite precedes the greisenization.

Two groups can be distinguished on the basis of the distribution of beryl in the granites in deposits of the described type:

1. Deposits with uniformly disseminated "accessory" crystals of beryl, whose sizes vary between hundredths or tenths of a millimeter and 3 to 4 mm in diameter (in those with the highest beryl content). The beryl distribution in granite in these deposits shows no apparent relationship to jointing (a number of occurrences in eastern Transbaikalia);
2. Deposits in which the beryl content of granites is controlled by jointing. The beryl content in the beryl-bearing granite usually varies between about 0.005 and 0.04 percent, attaining in the most enriched parts of the granite tenths of 1 percent.

The beryl crystals, disseminated more or less uniformly in the granite, usually have a prismatic form (Fig. 50) they are commonly poorly formed and have uneven faces and rounded edges.

In a number of deposits, microscopic intergrowths of beryl occur with idiomorphic crystals of late albite; relics of an earlier oligoclase also are found in beryl crystals.

The interrelations between beryl and microcline are very peculiar. Grains of microcline-perthite contain the most perfectly formed beryl crystals; but, single, prismatic beryl crystals also transgress the grains of microcline.

From the interrelations observed in polished sections, we see that beryl crystallizes later than microcline-perthite and the early albite-oligoclase, and in a number of places distinctly replaces these feldspars. It is apparently contemporary with albite, although there is not sufficient evidence to draw a clear conclusion. In particular, the interrelations between beryl and albite in intergrowths, in which albite crystals are always idiomorphic with respect to beryl, can be analyzed from various aspects. Similarly, the interrelations with quartz are most indefinite. Because quartz always is present in several generations, there are clear indications of beryl having formed both earlier and later than quartz.

The extention in depth of granites mineralized with beryl varies in

[1] The greisens, which usually occur in the beryl-bearing granites, are related to a later mineralization phase.

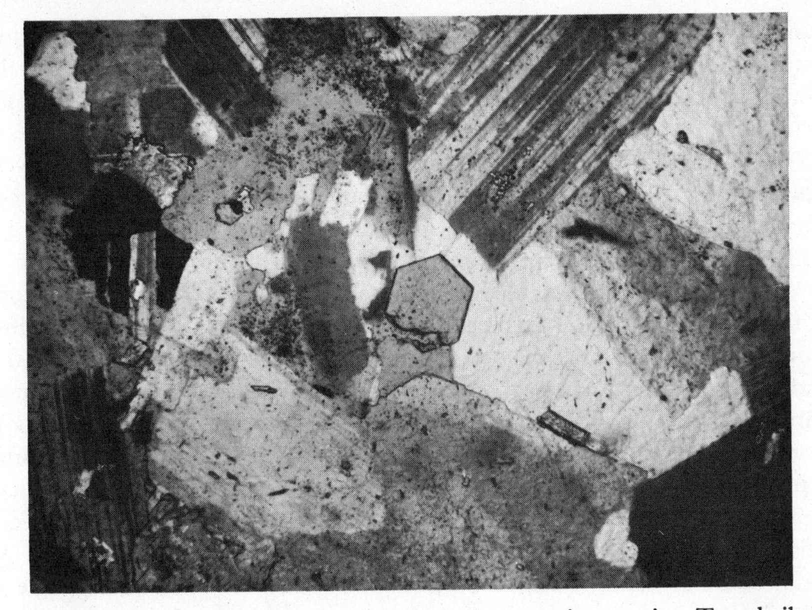

Fig. 50. Prismatic crystals of beryl in albitized muscovite granite, Transbaikalia. Magnification ×20. (Crossed nicols.)

known deposits between 80 and 100 m or more (measured from the apical part of the dome-shaped mass).

A characteristic feature of the beryl-bearing granites of the first group is the relatively uniform distribution of beryl, which varies only where more intensive greisenization is superposed on a weakly greisenized, albitized granite.

There is a much greater heterogeneity in the distribution of beryl in the deposits of the second group, in which the highest beryl concentration are related to small fissures and fracture zones, developed within the granitic mass. The most intensive albitization and greisenization and, in a number of places, the higher content of topaz and fluorite are near the fissures. In these deposits, beryl accumulates in the form of pocket-like aggregates of fairly large crystals in the altered greisenized and albitized granite bordering the fissures.

Thus, the discussed group of deposits virtually forms a transition from albitized and greisenized granite with disseminated beryl crystals to greisen deposits proper, within which the greisen formations are completely definite.

A very characteristic example of beryl-bearing albitized and greisenized granite of the first group is one of the dome-shaped protrusions of the large granitic intrusion of Mesozoic (probably Jurassic) age, which breached Paleozoic rocks in eastern Transbaikalia.

The granites of the main intrusion, which are exposed west of the granite dome, consist mainly of biotite and bimica varieties of various textures (fine- and medium-grained, and porphyritic), Granites of this complex are associated with a number of small tin and tungsten deposits, in which a small amount of beryl is always found.

The beryllium content of the main intrusive granites varies between 5×10^{-4} and 10×10^{-4} percent (the mean value obtained from five combined samples is 8×10^{-4} percent).

The dome of beryl-bearing granites is light-colored muscovite granite whose texture varies from medium-grained in the deep parts of the dome to fine-grained in the parts near its surface. In the uniformly grained granites there are areas of porphyritic and coarse-grained texture that grade into the main mass of granite. In some parts of the granitic mass there are small schlieren-like pegmatite' segregations composed of large crystals of potassium feldspar and quartz (up to 10 cm long). In a number of places, these crystals are cemented with a quartz-feldspar rock of micropegmatitic structure. All granites are more or less greisenized, the degree of greisenization increasing from deep-seated to apical parts until the appearance of greisens, which are associated with the endocontact zone of the apical part of the dome.

The composition of greisenized granites consists of a predominance of quartz (40 to 60 percent), and substantial amounts of albite No. 10-12 ($Ab_{89-90}An_{10-12}$, Ed.) (10 to 20 percent) and muscovite (10 to 15 percent). Microcline (10 to 20 percent) occurs in two generations; only relics of the earlier generation have survived, as much of it is replaced by albite and muscovite. At the same time, the later generation of microcline, which is untwinned and contains fluorite and wolframite inclusions, replaces albite. Both albite and microcline are clearly replaced by muscovite. The latter also forms after biotite, of which small relics are sometimes seen in polished sections.

Accessory minerals occurring in the granites are apatite, sphene, hematite, ore minerals, and monazite. Albitization and greisenization are related to the formation of such minerals as fluorite, topaz, beryl, wolframite, and cassiterite.

Virtually all granites of which the dome is composed are albitized or, as already noted, greisenized. Greisenization, which is most intensively developed in the apical part of the dome, can be traced to a depth of 60 to 80 m and, in individual sections, to more than 100 m.

Besides the development of muscovite, which replaces the feldspars, fluorite, which corrodes microcline and albite, occurs everywhere in the greisenized granites with disseminated wolframite and beryl. However, the external effects of the greisenization of granites are only slightly revealed and most of the rocks are common muscovite granites.

The WO_3 content of the greisenized granites is usually in the tenths of 1 percent; the tungsten concentration increases in places where greisenization is most intense. Wolframite is associated with muscovite and penetrates muscovite and microcline along the cleavages.

The occurrence of accessory beryl crystals in granites was found during the study of beryllium distribution in the deposits. All samples taken from the granites showed a beryllium content of more than 0.003 percent; this greatly exceeds the possible maximum content of disseminated beryllium in acid rocks. In addition, the occurrence of beryl in granites was confirmed by a microscopic investigation of polished sections and crushed samples.

From the total mass of beryllium occurring in granites, 84 percent was present in beryl and 16 percent was disseminated in the rock-forming minerals, mainly in muscovite (Table 102).

Thus the content of beryllium disseminated in the rock-forming minerals of the beryl-bearing greisenized granites (10×10^{-4} percent) was found

Table 102 Beryllium content of the rock-forming minerals of the beryl-containing greisenized granite

Mineral	Be content in 10^{-4}%
Quartz	1
Feldspars (albite, microcline)	6
Muscovite	30
Mean value for the granite (not taking beryl into account)	10

to be close to the mean beryllium content deduced for the muscovite granites (9×10^{-4} percent).

In greisenized granites, beryl occurs either in the form of well-formed prismatic crystals, which are embedded in quartz, or as less regular segregations included in albite. The crystal size varies from hundredths of a millimeter to 0.1–1 mm. The corrosion of beryl is clearly related to muscovite and quartz of the greisen.

The relatively uniform beryllium content of the granites is quite characteristic. At the same time, the distribution of beryllium does not show any obvious relation to the degree of greisenization of the granites (Fig. 51). These facts most probably point to the association of beryllium and tungsten with various stages of the mineralization of the granites.

The greisenized granites of the intrusion dome are transgressed by a series of wolframite-bearing quartz veins with a nearly north strike, and a dip of 45 to 72° west. The veins contain scattered feldspar crystals and irregular fluorite aggregates as much as 3×4 cm. Wolframite is widely distributed as the ore mineral of the veins; much less abundant are scheelite, pyrite, chalcopyrite, bismuthite, and bismutite. It is interesting that beryl, which is virtually absent in the veins that transgress the granites, is a

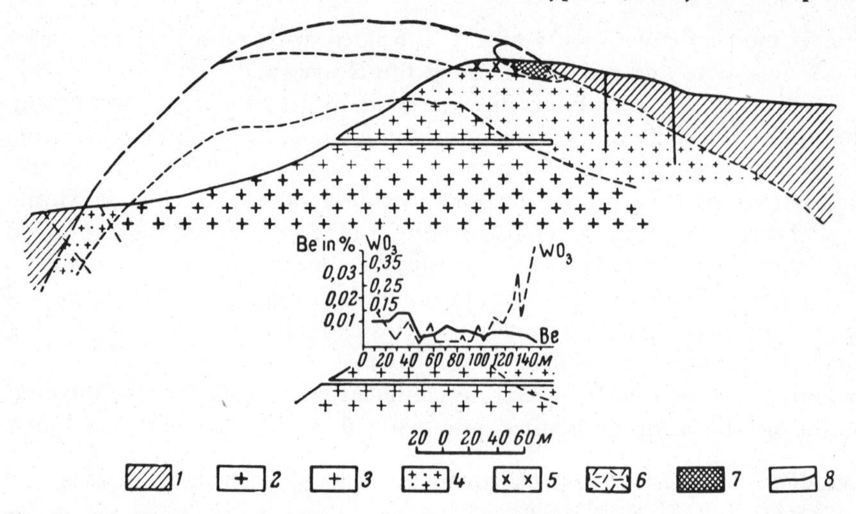

Fig. 51. Distribution of beryllium and tungsten within the dome of albitized and greisenized granites. (1) Metamorphosed shales and sandstones; (2) medium-grained, weakly greisenized granites; (3) fine-grained, greisenized granites; (4) tungsten-bearing, strongly greisenized granites; (5) greisens; (6) banded greisen; (7) quartz stock-shaped body; (8) recent erosional exposure.

typical accessory mineral of the wolframite-quartz veins that occur in the country rocks.

The quartz veins that transgress the granites are accompanied by surrounding muscovite-quartz greisens in intermittent lenses both in the hanging wall and in the footwall of the veins. Also, as a rule, the thickness of the greisen rims varies inversely with the vein thickness, attaining 35 to 40 cm in thin veins and streaks and dropping to a few centimeters in the thicker veins.

The common minerals of the greisen rims are potassium feldspar, albite, and wolframite; the rarer minerals are beryl, chalcopyrite, and scheelite. In the veins in schists, contact rims, as much as 5 cm thick, are mainly muscovite.

Of the minerals composing the veins, only muscovite is the collector of disseminated beryllium (Table 103). Other vein minerals, can be seen from the data given, have a very low beryllium content.

Owing to the importance of the relation of beryllium mineralization to a particular stage of deposit formation, data relating to the behavior of beryllium in the contact zones of the veins are of particular interest as these can be used in an assessment of the presence or absence of beryllium during the formation of the quartz veins and their greisen rims.

The investigation of specially selected samples in a series of sections across the strike of ore veins (Table 104) enables one to draw the following conclusions:

1. In the granites, adjacent to the quartz veins, no addition of beryllium

is observed. In individual places there is even a decrease in beryllium near the contact with the quartz vein, compared with that in greisenized granite away from the vein.

2. At the contact between schists and quartz veins, beryllium is definitely added and the content decreases away from the vein.

A characteristic feature of the deposit is the occurrence, in the apical part of the dome of greisenized granites immediately at the boundary with the schist roof, of a large stock-shaped segregation of quartz surrounded by a zone of banded greisen and a thick mantle of intensively greisenized granites (Fig. 51). In places in the peripheral part of the quartz stock, there are large idiomorphic crystal blocks of feldspar, which led most investigators to erroneously describe this quartz-feldspar body as pegmatite.

A zone of banded greisen surrounds the stock-shaped quartz body and is composed mainly of muscovite and quartz. Beryl is an important constituent of the greisen (up to 1 percent); microcline, albite, fluorite, topaz, wolframite, and scheelite are of lesser importance. Thin quartz streaks lying roughly parallel to the contact of the quartz stock impart to the greisen a banded structure. The beryl crystals as much as 0.8×3 cm are associated with the edge of quartz streaks and are arranged so that their long axes are perpendicular to the streak.

Topaz-muscovite and muscovite greisens occur much more rarely within the apical part of the dome and have no special significance.

Thus, in the dome-shaped granitic mass there is a definite vertical zoning, which is expressed in the development of poorly greisenized and partly albitized granites in the deep levels, then in that of the more intensively greisenized tungsten-bearing granites in the upper horizons and the greisen formations proper in the apical sections at the boundary with the schistose roof.

Analysis of the geological-mineralogical features of the deposit makes it possible to distinguish three basic stages of its formation, each of which

Table 103 Content of disseminated beryllium in quartz vein minerals

Mineral	Number of analyses	Variation of Be content in 10^{-4}%	Mean content of Be in 10^{-4}%
Massive quartz	3	0.5 – 2	1
Potassium feldspar	3	2	2
Quartz-feldspar vein	1	3	—
Feldspar in chalcedonic quartz	1	5	—
Muscovite from massive quartz (vein in granite)	2	30	30
Muscovite from fringe in schists	2	35 – 38	36
Fluorite	2	25 – 30	27

Table 104 Beryllium content in the exocontact zones of wolframite-quartz veins

Characteristic of the sample	Be content in $10^{-4}\%$
Greisen fringe of quartz vein No. 1	
Hanging wall	10
Footwall	7
Granite, greisenized	
Hanging wall (2 m from the vein)	60
Footwall (1 m from the vein)	50
Greisen in quartz	50
Greisen fringe of vein No. 2	
Hanging wall	100
Footwall	90
Granite, greisenized	
10 m from the hanging wall of the vein	90
30 m from the footwall of the vein	90
1–2 m from the vein	100–200
Granite, greisenized	
At the contact of the hanging wall of vein No. 2	100
At the contact of the footwall	90
1 m from the footwall	100
1 m from the hanging wall	100
Metamorphosed shales far from the contact with quartz veins	3
Muscovitized schist near the contact with the beryl-containing quartz vein	20
Metamorphosed shales near the contact with beryl-bearing streaks	20
Metamorphosed shales at 2 m from the contact	10
Chloritized schist at the contact with quartz vein	25
Metamorphosed shales at 1 m from the quartz vein, without beryl	6

is characterized by the specific features of mineral formation and a specific paragenesis of minerals:

1. The first stage–albitization of granites within the dome that forms the apical protrusion of the granitic intrusion.
2. The second stage–greisenization of albitized granites (particularly intensive greisenization below the schistose rocks of the roof); at the end of greisenization, formation of wolframite.
3. The third stage–formation of fissures, which are filled with quartz veins accompanied by greisen rims. The formation of the quartz stock, which presents an agglomeration of vein quartz in the weakened near-contact zone in the apical part of the granite dome, is related to the same stage.

The addition of the main mass of beryllium and the formation of very small beryl crystals uniformly disseminated in the greisenized granites are most probably related to the albitization stage. Otherwise it would be impossible to explain either the absence of any apparent relation between the concentration of beryl and the degree of greisenization of granites, or the difference in the behaviors of beryl and wolframite when disseminated in greisenized granites. There undoubtedly exists a close relationship between wolframite and greisenization.

The addition of beryl occurred on a much smaller scale during formation of the quartz veins and their greisen rims. At the same time, most of the beryllium was concentrated in the apical part of the deposit under the screening cover of the roof rocks; it separated in the solid phase during the formation of the greisen rims that surround the stock-shaped quartz body.

The noticeable decrease of beryllium in the greisenized granites in the deep-seated levels of the dome-shaped granitic mass (compared with feebly greisenized granites of the same levels), and the occurrence of high concentrations of beryllium in greisens of the apical parts of the dome (at the contact with the schistose roof) suggests secondary transportation and redeposition of beryllium during the greisenization of albitized granites that contain disseminated crystals of beryl.

The described deposit is an example of the formation of large-scale beryllium concentrations related to the wide albitization and greisenization of granites within the apical apophyses of the beryllium-bearing granitic intrusions.

Greisen Beryllium Deposits

The greisen beryllium deposits are usually closely related to tungsten-, tin-, or molybdenum-bearing greisen deposits that are developed within acid and ultra-acid granitoid masses. They are usually characterized by a noticeable pneumatolytic alteration of granites with a beryllium content higher than the mean content of the earth's crust (Table 136).

This type of deposit includes deposits in zones of high-temperature post-magmatic leaching, which are the products of predominantly acid fluorine-containing emanations and solutions containing high concentrations of beryllium.

The morphological features of beryllium-bearing greisens are determined by the nature of jointing followed by the ore-bearing solutions that caused the greisenization of the enclosing granites or rocks of similar composition (Vol'fson, 1953). The deposits of the group under discussion are controlled mainly by fine contraction joints formed during the solidification of the parent intrusion. The nature of these joints has determined the predominant development of the stockwork and small vein-like bodies that are very typical of the greisen deposits.

The metasomatic greisen deposits proper (without vein filling) are joined by gradual transitions to the quartz and feldspar-quartz veins with adjacent greisen rims.

Thus, assuming a very conventional subdivision of these very closely related types of deposits, we must consider the predominance of a particular process in separating greisen deposits with insignificant fissure-filling bodies, and quartz veins with subordinate greisen rims.

The mineralogical composition of beryllium-bearing greisens formed during the pneumatolytic-hydrothermal alteration of acid intrusive rocks by fluorine-containing emanations and solutions is usually determined by the ratio of the three main minerals: muscovite (zinnwaldite, siderophyllite), quartz, and topaz.

On the basis of the mineralogical composition, the following most widely occurring varieties of greisen that developed within beryllium deposits can be distinguished:

1. quartz-mica—with incomplete subtraction of alkalis;
2. quartz-topaz and topaz—with the complete subtraction of alkalis and addition of aluminum;
3. quartz—with complete subtraction of alkalis and aluminum;
4. mica—with addition of alkalis and aluminum.

As a result of spatial coincidence of early sodic metasomatism (albitization) and greisenization of the granites, albite-muscovite varieties of greisen develop; later, the peculiar ferrous metasomatism of the granites is associated with relatively rare quartz-hematite greisen deposits containing specific beryllium minerals. When the greisen contains high beryllium concentrations, beryl or muscovite-beryl greisens proper very rarely occur.

All varieties of greisen can be developed within one greisen field.

A large number of stages is characteristic of the formation of greisen beryllium deposits; as a result, the normal metasomatic zoning (Korzhinskii, 1953) becomes complicated by the later stages of the process.

The beryllium mineral most widespread in greisen deposits is beryl, which at times forms accumulations which may have industrial importance. In some greisen deposits, bertrandite is quite common while helvite and danalite are much rarer.

Beryl most frequently shows an association with the quartz-mica type of greisen, in which it occurs in the form of irregular aggregates and intergrowths of crystals that, in a number of places, form virtually monomineralic pockets, short lenses, and streaks. Noticeable beryl concentrations are apparently not characteristic of topaz and quartz-topaz greisens, in which beryllium minerals are usually present only as fissure filling bodies.

Helvite and danalite are associated predominantly with a relatively rare greisen type (quartz-hematite greisen), in which the oxides of iron are important. Both minerals are found in close association with hematite and sulfides, in the forms of small crystals and larger pocket-like accumulations, which at times form a substantial part of the greisen.

Finally, in an overwhelming majority of cases, bertrandite is a secondary mineral found in the hydrothermal alteration of beryl or the helvite-group minerals. Its fine tabular crystals form thin streaks, rosettes, and small pocket-like accumulations in greisens of various types, in which the primary beryllium minerals have been altered.

The Sherlovogorsk granitic mass in eastern Transbaikalia is a typical example of greisen deposits containing accessory beryl and wolframite, which are fairly common but have not been thoroughly investigated geochemically.

The rock mass is composed of granite porphyries and porphyritic granites of Jurassic age, which intrude Devonian sandy shales along their boundary with large decomposed lower Carboniferous plagio-granite intrusions.

The younger granites have produced a noticeable contact metamorphism of both the older intrusions and the surrounding shales and sandstones. In the exocontact zone of the intrusion, the shales and sandstones have been transformed into a thick zone of dark, dense hornfels.

The nature of occurrence of the altered rocks indicates that the Sherlovaya Mountain mass is the apical apophysis of a large intrusion of younger granites not exposed by erosion.

The Sherlovaya Mountain intrusions have been known since 1829 (Kulibin, 1829). From 1918, the greisen formations of the complex were repeatedly studied by many geologists (Tetyaev, 1918; Boldyrev and Lui, 1929; Kholmov, 1929; Levitskii, 1933, 1939) who gave a fairly complete description of their geological-petrographical features and mineralogical composition.

Here is a brief description of the geological structures of the complex, particularly stressing the occurrence and paragenesis of beryllium in rocks and vein bodies.

In the granitoids of the Sherlovaya Mountain mass, distinguished on the basis of their structural features, are granite-porphyries, porphyritic and uniformly-grained granites, and gradual transitions between them. Leucocratic aplite veins occur in small numbers. Both the granites and their vein derivatives are of close mineralogical composition. At the same time, the granite-porphyries, compared with the porphyritic granites, present a more acid facies of the intrusive complex, as seen in the chemical analyses of the noted varieties (Tables 107, 108). The rock-forming minerals that compose both structural varieties of granitoids are quartz, anorthoclase, and albite; biotite is rare. The distinct porphyritic structure and the greater abundance of quartz are the main features that distinguish the Sherlovaya Mountain granite-porphyry from other granitoid varieties. The porphyritic granite differs from granite-porphyry by the absence of quartz phenocrysts and by the less perfect idiomorphism of the feldspar phenocrysts.

All granitoids, even those without traces of alteration, are greisenized to a greater or lesser extent. The greisenization of these macroscopically unaltered rocks is expressed by the appearance of separate fluorite grains, by the replacement of biotite with muscovite, by the penetration of thinly-lamellar mica into feldspars, and by the formation of fine cassiterite grains. Along with the partly greisenized granite-porphyries and porphyritic granites, greisen deposits also occur widely throughout the dome-like mass. They are always associated with various systems of fractures developed in the apical part of the complex, and are united by perfectly gradual transitions with the enclosing granitoids.

Detailed study of the poorly exposed surface of the granite dome shows four main systems of fractures which control the occurrence of greisen bodies:

1. steeply dipping (70°) fractures of latitudinal strike (the Millionnaya vein);
2. the steeply dipping (50° to 80°) fractures of northwest (330° to 340°) strike (the Podnebesnaya, Novikovskaya, and Solotoi Otrog offshoot veins);
3. a system of deeply dipping (80°) fractures of meridional strike (the Melekhinskaya vein);
4. a system of gently dipping (20°) fractures of northeast strike (thin veins of Zolotoi Otrog offshoot).

The most interesting and largest greisen bodies of the deposit are associated with the first two fracture systems and have either northwest strike and northeast dip, or latitudinal strike and north dip.

Most greisen bodies are characterized by distinct vein forms with abundant constrictions and bulges. In the conical Obvinskaya and Melekhinskaya hills, there are also greisen formations of considerable areal extent, apparently related to the complex system of intersecting fractures. The length of most greisen bodies is usually rather short (several tens of meters), attaining in only a few cases 150 to 200 m; the thickness ranges up to 0.5–1 m.

Within the exposed part of the rock mass there are a total of ten vein bodies of relatively large size. The vein-like greisen bodies usually consist of thin vein (fracture) filling and of enclosing greisen rims. The thickness of the vein filling varies from a few centimeters to 10–15 cm, more rarely to 30–40 cm in the bulges of large quartz bodies with beryl. The thickness of the greisen zone that fringes the vein bodies varies between 10–30 cm.

The sections of vein filling, found in the central part of the vein-like greisen bodies, are traced as relatively short individual lenses that usually taper out rapidly along both strike and dip. The flank sections of such bodies are sometimes wholly composed of greisen for lengths of several tens of meters.

The aureole of marked alteration of granite-porphyries extends for several meters from the vein filling. There are large aureoles of altered granite around barren fractures without vein filling.

Without repeating the detailed descriptions of the Sherlovaya Mountain greisens, given in the investigations by G. V. Kholmov (1929) and O. D. Levitskii (1939), we mention below the basic factors important to an

Table 105 Mineralogical composition of the Sherlovaya Mountain greisens

	Quartz-mica greisen	Quartz greisen	Topaz and quartz-topaz greisens	Mica (siderophyllite) greisen
Main rock-forming minerals	Quartz, muscovite	Quartz	Topaz, quartz	Quartz, siderophyllite
Accessory minerals	Fluorite, siderophyllite	Topaz, fluorite	Fluorite, siderite	Topaz, fluorite, siderite
Present in small quantities	Topaz	Muscovite	Muscovite, tourmaline	Tourmaline
Other accessory minerals	Cassiterite, beryl	Tourmaline, pyrite, chalcopyrite, molybdenite, arsenopyrite, monazite, cassiterite		

understanding of features of beryllium occurrence in such deposits.

On the basis of mineralogical composition (Table 105), the following four main greisen types, which grade into each other, can be distinguished within the deposit: quartz-mica; quartz; quartz-topaz and topaz; mica (siderophyllitic) with quartz. The most common is quartz-mica greisen.

The fractures that control the greisen body, or the vein (fracture) filling, control the arrangement of the above paragenetic types of greisens in a clearly expressed zoning, which may differ for the various sections of the deposit or even in various parts of the same body (Table 106).

The mineralogical composition of the vein formations of Sherlovoaya Mountain has been studied and described in sufficient detail in the above papers. All investigators tend to assume that it is possible to distinguish in a greisen field three main paragenetic types of fracture fillings that characterize the vein of Sherlovoaya Mountain: quartz-topaz; beryl-quartz; siderophyllite.

Because transitional varieties exist among all these extreme types, such

Table 106 Zonal types of the Sherlovaya Mountain greisen formations

	Type I. With complete subtraction of alkalis and aluminum	Type II. With complete subtraction of alkalis and addition of aluminum	Type III. With incomplete subtraction of alkalis and addition of aluminum
Outer zone	Greisenized granite-porphyry		
	Quartz-mica greisen	Quartz-mica greisen	Quartz-mica greisen
Intermediate zone	Topaz-quartz greisen	Quartz greisen	Quartz (or quartz-topaz) siderophyllite greisen
Inner zone	Quartz greisen	Topaz (quartz-topaz) greisen	Siderophyllite greisen
Nature of vein filling	Quartz + topaz, topaz (or in fissures, joints)	Quartz, quartz + beryl, beryl, quartz + arsenopyrite (or in fissures, joints)	Quartz, quartz + beryl siderophyllite + beryl

a classification is to a certain extent arbitrary. In a number of places, the transition was observed within the same vein.

The most widely occurring type of vein filling is beryl-quartz (Fig. 52).

The typical quartz-topaz veins are, as a rule, not characteristic of Sherlovoaya Mountain. The veins, composed of an aggregate of fine quartz and topaz crystals, usually contain cavities filled with larger, well-formed crystals of the same minerals and can be considered rather as bimineralic axial zones of symmetrically constructed greisen bodies of mica-quartz-topaz composition. The quartz-topaz greisens, which usually surround the quartz veins, may extend, when the vein tapers out, as a vein-like metasomatic body controlled by the fracture.

Slightly more distinctive are veins of siderophyllite or beryl-siderophyllite, which are associated spatially with the Zolotoi offshoot near the contact of the rock mass. The relatively rare siderophyllite veins show gradual transitions to veins with quartz and beryl-quartz fillings. Unlike the predominantly steeply dipping quartz-topaz and beryl-quartz veins, the siderophyllite veins usually have gentle dips.

Thus, the paragenetic features of the Sherlovaya Mountain vein bodies are determined mainly by the combination of four minerals—topaz, quartz, beryl, and siderophyllite. Topaz is to a large extent associated with the metasomatic greisen formations; siderophyllite appears in considerable quantities under the specific conditions of incomplete subtraction of alkalis and the presence of high concentrations of iron observed in the gentle jointing fractures near the contact of the granite. Accessory minerals of the vein bodies are widely occurring arsenopyrite, ferberite, common fluorite, siderite, bismuthinite, and rarer muscovite, native bismuth, molybdenite, pyrite, and chalcopyrite.

The zonal structure of the largest veins (Millionnaya) is emphasized in the diagrammatic outline by A. K. Boldyrev (Fig. 53). In most places the distribution of minerals in the vein bodies is in pockets and very heterogeneous.

As a typomorphic mineral, beryl is mostly associated with beryl-quartz veins; it is less characteristic of the siderophyllite veins and almost absent in the quartz-topaz vein deposits. The mineralogy of beryl in the deposit has been studied in some detail (Boldyrev and Lui, 1929; Kholmov, 1929; Ikornikova, 1939), although the relations between beryl and the accompanying minerals have not been explained satisfactorily.

Beryl forms accumulations in the central part or monomineralic streaks in the beryl-quartz veins. Cavities filled with brownish clayey mass enclosing free crystals of aquamarine, commonly of the best gem quality, occur in the vein bulges with large crystals of green and violet fluorite. In the individual veins, arsenopyrite, in close association with beryl, cements beryl crystals, forming peculiar beryl-arsenopyrite aggregates.

In siderophyllite veins, beryl is usually disseminated as separate crystals

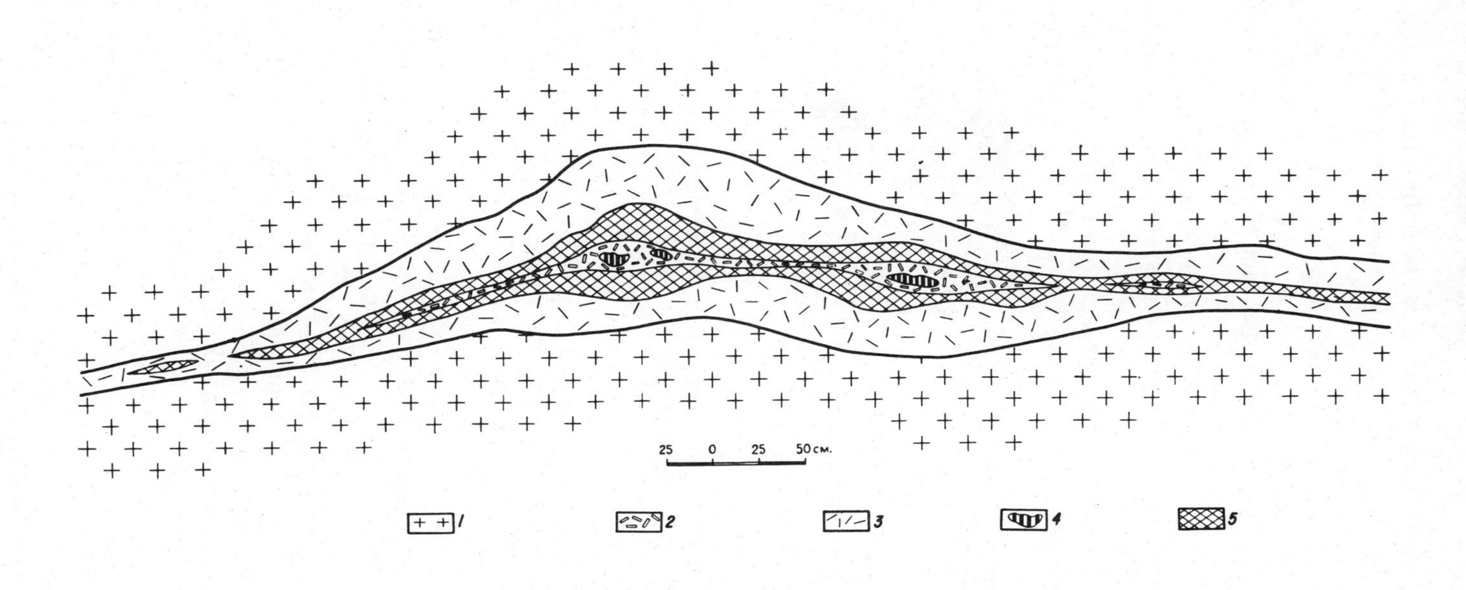

Fig. 52. Structural diagram of greisen body with beryl-quartz vein filling. (1) Feebly greisenized granite-porphyry; (2) quartz-beryl vein filling; (3) muscovite-quartz greisen; (4) beryl crystals in cavities; (5) quartz-topaz, topaz, or quartz greisen.

in a dense siderophyllite aggregate. It is interesting that, in this type of vein enriched in iron, beryl occurs mostly in the form of the wine-yellow variety, heliodor.

Finally, in the quartz-topaz veins, beryl is rare and occurs as fine separate crystals only in cavities and in association with extremely small crystals of ferberite, tourmaline needles, and intergrowths of crystals of various sulfides.

On the basis of interrelations with various minerals, two generations of beryl can be distinguished clearly; these correspond to two separate stages of segregation of this mineral.

The earlier generation of beryl (beryl I) occurs in the form of large (as much as 10 cm along the axis) corroded crystals and crystal relicts, found

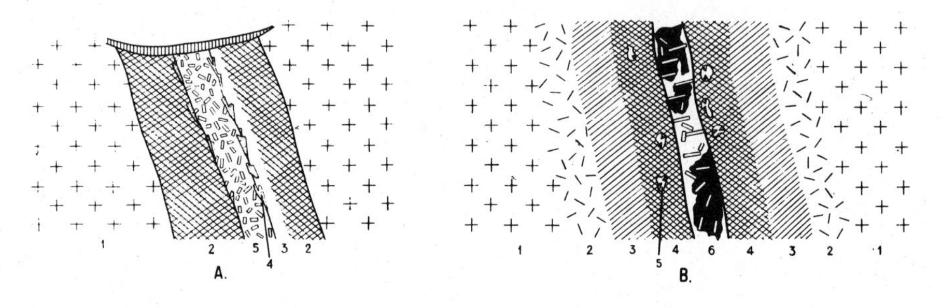

Fig. 53. Structure of beryl-quartz and quartz-arsenopyrite-beryl veins, Sherlovaya Mountain.
A. Millionnaya vein (according to A. K. Boldyrev): (1) granite; (2) greisen; (3) zone of smoky quartz; (4) sections enriched in ferberite, bismutite, and colored stones; (5) beryl.
B. Podnebesnaya vein: (1) greisenized granite; (2) greisenized granite-porphyry; (3) quartz-topaz-muscovite greisen; (4) topaz greisen; (5) beryl crystals; (6) quartz-arsenopyrite-beryl vein filling.

in the quartz-mica greisen and in superimposed topaz (crystal relicts) greisen. Beryl I is usually yellow-green. Its crystals are translucent and strongly fissured, and commonly have the form of corroded relict prisms. On the resorbed surface of beryl I crystals, there are well-formed crystals of topaz and beryl of generation II. The latter occurs as beautifully formed transparent crystals of blue (aquamarine) or golden (heliodor) color, which, in association with quartz and siderophyllite, fill the central fissures of the greisen bodies. It was found that fine beryl II crystals grow on the faces of topaz crystals and also on smoky quartz and beryl I.

The beryl crystals envelop plates of ferberite and intersect some of them. At the same time, milky and pale-smoky quartz fills the free space between the beryl crystals in the quartz-beryl intergrowths that are abundant in the central part of the veins. Arsenopyrite is later than beryl and cements crystals into a beryl-arsenopyrite-quartz filling in the veins.

Turning now to the problem of the distribution of beryllium in the rocks and greisen formations of Sherlovaya Mountain, we shall stress a number of features of the behavior of this element, which must be taken into account in order to characterize correctly the factors that caused the beryl migration and concentration in the deposit.

Because virtually all the rocks of the granite dome are to some degree affected by greisenization, it is very difficult to obtain reliable data about the beryllium content of the granite-prophyries proper or the porphyritic granites.

Four mine specimens affected by greisenization, which were selected after microscopic examination, showed on analysis a low beryllium content (Table 109) that was not as high as the mean value determined for granites.

Although these specimens cannot be considered completely representative of primary rocks of the granite dome, their examination indicates that the concentration of beryl, disseminated in the granites before greisenization, did not exceed the mean values for the rock.

Thus the increased mean content of beryllium, calculated for the Sherlovaya Mountain occurrence from the results of thirty analyses (Table 109), is undoubtedly associated with the addition of beryllium during the greisenization.

The results of studying the distribution of beryllium in various zones of the greisen deposits, which were carried out along the profiles at right angles to the trend of the vein bodies, were quite interesting.

As can be seen from Tables 107 and 108 and from the graphs obtained from these tables (Figs. 54, 55), the content of disseminated beryllium increases from the weakly greisenized granites to those noticeably greisenized, reaching the highest value in the quartz-mica greisens enriched in mica.

Beryl I is in the sections of the quartz-mica greisens, where the beryllium contains up to 80×10^{-4} percent Be; the main minerals of the inner the appearance of beryl in the outer zone of the quartz-mica greisen is fairly rare. Usually the increased beryllium content of greisenized granites and quartz-mica greisens is associated fundamentally with mica, which contains up to 80×10^{-4} percent Be; the main minerals of the inner greisen zones—topaz and quartz—contain virtually no beryllium.

Toward the inner zones of greisen formations composed of quartz-topaz and quartz greisen, the beryllium content drops abruptly, attaining a minimum value at the boundary with the vein filling, in spite of the quartz, quartz-beryl, or beryl filling.

Thus the vein filling, which contains a high beryllium concentration, is separated from the muscovite-quartz greisens and greisenized granites, which contain a considerable quantity of disseminated beryllium, by a mantle of quartz-topaz or quartz greisen, that is virtually free of beryllium.

Because the peculiar features of beryllium migration in greisenization are

Table 107 Analyses along the profile of the Millionnaya vein (in percent)

Physical properties and chemical composition, %	Greisenized granite-porphyry, 40 cm from vein.	Muscovite-topaz-quartz greisen, 10 cm from vein.	Quartz greisen (cavernous) at contact with vein.
Specific gravity	2.61	2.62	2.70
Density by volume	2.54	2.58	2.45
Porosity	2.8	1.5	10
SiO_2	73.85	79.85	90.62
TiO_2	0.10	0.08	0.11
Al_2O_3	12.55	8.38	3.44
Fe_2O_3	1.68	6.55	1.64
FeO	1.15	—	0.30
MnO	0.04	0.02	0.25
MgO	0.20	0.38	0.82
CaO	0.90	0.25	0.40
Na_2O	2.50	1.50	0.20
K_2O	5.24	0.45	0.80
H_2O^+	0.33	1.06	0.32
H_2O^-	0.20	—	0.07
F	0.85	0.70	not detected
BeO	0.0033	0.0016	0.0009
Loss on ignition	—	0.63	0.80
Total	99.59	100.03	99.77

inseparable from the trend of the process, it is of great interest to compare the behavior of beryllium at various stages in the formation of the deposit with the nature of greisenizing solutions and with the behavior of the main rock-forming elements in the mineral deposit.

The formation of the Sherlovaya Mountain deposits was caused by the postmagmatic metasomatic activity of acid fluorine-containing emanations and solutions along the joints in the apical part of the granite dome. So far no signs of postmagmatic alteration of the granites unrelated to the jointing within the deposit, have been noted; thus the question of the possible role of autopneumatolysis remains open.

In the process of formation of the deposit, there are four distinct stages which differ in the nature and composition of the mineral-forming solutions and correspondingly in the paragenesis of the mineral.

1. First stage of greisenization: formation of quartz-muscovite greisen connected with the granite by gradual transition across a thick zone of partly-greisenized granite. The prominent new mineral of the greisenized rock is muscovite. Of minor importance are fluorite and cassiterite. The process of greisenization, starting with the appearance of very small quantities of mica replacing the feldspars, up to the formation of virtually

bimineralic quartz-mica rock, can be traced very clearly on polished sections of samples from along cross sections of the greisen bodies.

The peculiar features of the chemistry of the pervasive alteration of granites, characteristic of the first stage of greisenization, distinguishes it as the stage of incomplete dealkalization. Unlike the outer zone, in which there is only a partial subtraction of alkali cations, the inner zones of greisens usually show more intensive dealkalization, which is usually accompanied by a considerable addition of fluorine.

2. Second stage of greisenization: formation of quartz, quartz-topaz and topaz greisens at the boundary of a fissure or vein filling (stage of complete dealkalization) (Table 106).

Two main types of fracture-zone greisens can be distinguished:

(*a*) mainly quartz (cavernous) type that can be free of topaz;

(*b*) mainly topaz type (usually quartz-topaz).

The principal new mineral of the greisenized rock is topaz.

3. Third stage of greisenization: formation of mica greisen, unaccompanied by a noticeable subtraction of alkalis. In places there is even an addition of potassium and aluminum, compared with the enclosing rock. The deposit of mica greisen at Sherlovaya Mountain is associated with greisen bodies that occur in gently dipping fractures near the contact

Table 108 Analyses along the profile of the Podnebesnaya vein (in percent)

Physical properties and chemical composition, %	Weakly greisenized porphyritic granite, 60 cm from vein.	Topaz-quartz-muscovite greisen, 45 cm from vein.	Topaz-quartz greisen, 20 cm from vein.	Quartz-topaz greisen at contact with vein.
Specific gravity	2.61	3.00	2.80	2.86
Density by volume	–	2.81	2.73	2.72
Porosity	–	6.7	2.6	5.1
SiO_2	66.01	68.45	80.65	71.86
TiO_2	0.12	0.19	0.20	0.10
A_2O_3	16.91	16.08	10.54	24.00
Fe_2O_3	5.77	6.02	3.20	1.60
CaO	1.68	2.16	1.67	0.72
MgO	0.99	0.58	0.44	0.16
K_2O	1.13	1.61	0.98	0.55
Na_2O	2.72	0.39	0.30	—
H_2O	1.32	0.75	0.22	0.39
CO_2	2.37	2.88	0.15	0.20
F	0.54	1.00	0.87	1.66
BeO	0.0017	0.0044	0.0011	0.0005
Total	99.56	100.11	99.22	101.24

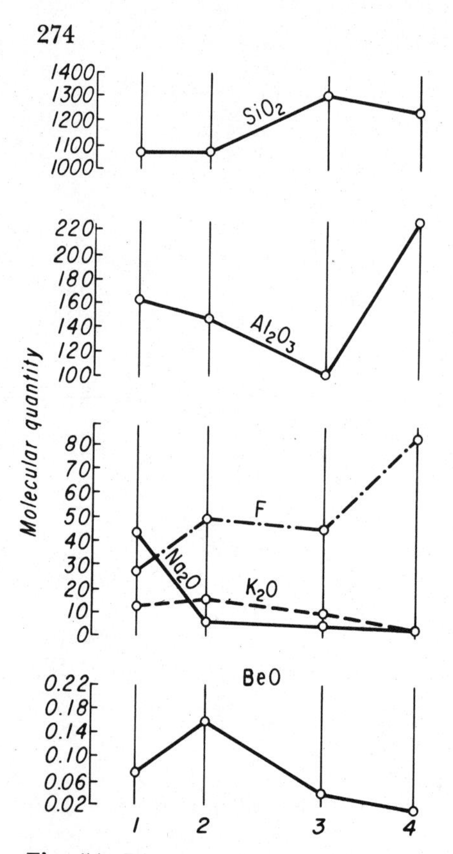

Fig. 54. Diagram of alteration of chemical composition of the greisenization zones of the Podnebesnaya vein. (1) Porphyritic granite, 60 cm from vein; (2) topaz-quartz-muscovite greisen, 45 cm from vein; (3) quartz-topaz greisen, 20 cm from vein; (4) topaz greisen at contact.

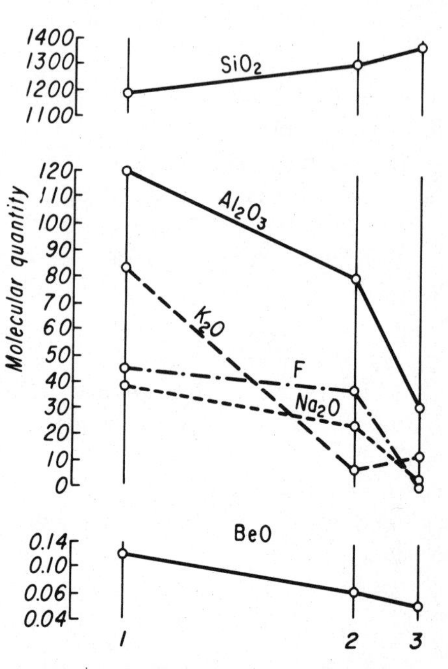

Fig. 55. Diagram of alteration of chemical composition of greisen zones of the Millionnaya vein. (1) Weakly greisenized granite-porphyry, 40 cm from vein; (2) quartz-topaz-muscovite greisen, 10 cm from vein; (3) cavernous quartz greisen at contact.

with the enclosing rocks. Similar deposits may also occur in the upper horizons of the greisen bodies.

4. Fourth stage greisenization: formation of vein fillings of quartz, quartz-topaz, and quartz-beryl. Among the minerals that terminated this stage of mineral formation (Table 105) one should especially note the appearance of carbonates (siderite) and sulfides.

The solutions of the initial front of greisenization, which caused the alteration of granites in the early stages, contained a moderate concentration of fluorine and evidently were saturated with the components of the enclosing rock, with which they attain a certain equilibrium.

The weakly acid fluorine-containing solutions first acted on plagioclase; the sodium was subtracted, while the calcium combined with fluorine to

Table 109 Beryllium distribution in the greisen deposits of Sherlovaya Mountain

	Granite-porphyry	Greisenized granite-porphyry	Quartz-muscovite greisen	Muscovite-topaz-quartz greisen	Quartz-topaz and quartz greisen
Profile through streak at Millionnaya vein	–	–	12/40	6/10	2/contact
Profile through thin beryl streak at Millionnaya vein	–	6/8	13/3	–	2/1
Profile along Podnebesnaya vein (footwall)	–	8/50	65/10	–	1/contact
Profile along Podnebesnaya vein (bulge)	–	6/60	16/45	4/20	2/contact
Mean for the deposit, 10^{-4}%	3 (4 anal.)	8 (2 anal.)	16 (7 anal.)	5 (2 anal.)	2 (8 anal.)
Limits of beryllium content, 10^{-4}%	1–4.7	2.6–15	4.7–65	4–6	1–6

[a] Numerator — beryllium content, 10^{-4}%; denominator — distance from the contact with vein, cm.

form fluorite. The potassium content also decreased (Tables 107, 108; Figs. 54, 55).

The chemical analyses of the samples (Table 109) taken along the profile showed that there was during the first greisenization stage a very limited addition of silica (the chemical analyses plotted on variational diagrams were recalculated allowing for porosity) and a marked addition of beryllium. However, the concentration of the latter in solutions was apparently insignificant; as a result, there was virtually a complete dissemination of beryllium as an isomorphous impurity of muscovite. The solutions also contained small quantities of tin that were precipitated as cassiterite during reaction with the wall rock.

Thus, the formation of the muscovite-quartz greisen of Sherlovaya Mountain can be considered as the hydrolysis of the granite feldspars, accompanied by the complete elimination of sodium, and a partial loss of potassium.

Much greater activity occurred in the emanations and solutions of the second stage of greisenization, which were substantially different in composition.

At present, unequivocal data that would point to the presence or absence of a discontinuity between the two above mentioned stages of mineralization is lacking. Probably the alteration in the composition of the introduced solutions took place gradually during greisenization, and the front of complete dealkalization was directly behind the solution front that formed the early zone of the quartz-mica greisen.

The main feature of the emanations and solutions of the second greisenization stage was the high concentration of fluorine. Unlike the solutions of the first stage, they were not saturated with any of the components of the enclosing rock, except silica, and the alteration of the rocks they produced could be called the process of complete dealkalization.

Under conditions of a sharp increase in fluorine concentration, aluminum, usually a sluggish element, acquired mobility along with other elements. In view of the fact that the front of complete dealkalization was superimposed on the earlier formed quartz-mica greisen, during the second stage of greisenization there was, together with the extensive subtraction of alkalis and aluminum, a loss of such elements as beryllium, which had separated into a solid phase during the first stage of greisenization.

The migration of beryllium (like that of aluminum and other elements) during this period of greisenization can be represented as a diffusion towards the increase in concentration of the solvent (fluorine in solution), that is towards the fracture.

From the mean beryllium content of the quartz-mica greisen and, correspondingly, of the quartz-topaz and quartz greisens, it is not difficult to calculate that during the process of complete dealkalization, which accompanied the formation of the two latter types of greisen, more than 30 g of beryllium[2] were extracted into the fracture from every cubic meter of affected rock.

Thus, during the stage of complete dealkalization the solutions that circulated along fractures were enriched in alkalis, aluminum, and beryllium, which were extracted from the surrounding enclosing rocks.

During continuous neutralization and gradual fall of temperature when the solution moved up to the higher level, the increase in concentration of the somewhat immobile aluminum in the acid fluorine-containing solution resulted in a fairly rapid precipitation of aluminum in the surrounding fractures as topaz.

The formation of topaz, which removes from the mineral forming solutions considerable quantities of fluorine, ought, in turn, to result in a noticeable decrease in the acidity of the solution. The highly active fluorine is replaced, as the transporter of cations in the solutions, by the weaker (and previously suppressed) carbonic acid (the stage of carbonate formation). Under conditions of abruptly lowered acidity of the solutions, the mobility of beryllium is considerably lowered and it is combined with aluminum and separates as a solid phase in the form of beryl, which fills the central part of the fracture veins. The absence of fluorine-containing

[2] About 1 kg of beryl can be formed from 30 g of beryllium.

minerals in association with beryl (the main mass of topaz separated out before beryl) indicates that the stage of crystallization of beryl precedes the removal from solutions of fluorine—an element which contributes most actively to the migration of beryllium.

The process is somewhat different in the upper level of the greisen zones, and in the gently dipping joints of the endocontacts of the granitic mass. In these areas the formation of inner zones of the greisen bodies was caused by solutions highly saturated with potassium, aluminum, and iron, which were added from the lower level. Under these conditions, the dominant new mineral of the greisen, which combined potassium, aluminum, and most of the fluorine, was mica (in this case siderophyllite). Mica accumulated in the mica-rich greisen, whose formation was due to a lowering of the migration capacity of potassium and aluminum under conditions of the continuously falling temperature and the parallel decrease of acidity of the mineral-forming solutions. The formation of the mica greisen terminated with the deposition of vein quartz, in which beryl II was concentrated in a number of places.

Thus, in the greisen formations of the Sherlovaya Mountain complex, there are two fairly distinct stages of beryl concentrations. The addition of beryl is clearly related to the action of emanations and solutions of the initial front of greisenization, which were to a certain extent saturated with potassium and other elements of the enclosing rocks, on the areas surrounding the fracture zones. However, the maximum beryl concentration, indicated by the formation of accumulations of beryllium minerals, occurs only in the final formative stages of the metasomatic greisens during the process of dealkalization and segregation of beryllium (disseminated in the initial stage of greisenization) in fractures.

The characteristic features of the concentration of beryllium in the formation of the greisens of the Sherlovaya Mountain deposit explain the following:

1. small extent of beryl mineralization;
2. association of beryl with non-persistent fractures, which rapidly taper out in length and in depth;
3. almost complete absence of beryllium minerals and of disseminated beryllium in the quartz-topaz and quartz greisens surrounding the fractures.

It is assumed that the addition of considerable quantities of beryllium during the formation stage of the quartz-muscovite greisen would result in the formation of accumulations of beryllium minerals in the outer quartz-muscovite zone of greisen bodies.

Examples of this kind are fairly common, in particular among the greisen deposits of central Kazakhstan.

One of the characteristic deposits of this group occurs in the endocontact zone between a Varisan granitic mass and the Caledonian granite gneisses which intrude metamorphosed strata composed of phyllite, schists, quartzites, and preCambrian porphyries. The greisen bodies occur within a narrow tectonic zone, 20 to 60 m in thickness, and 1000 to 1500 m in length, and have the form of steeply dipping lenses. The latter have a length varying from 5–7 to 400 m and a thickness varying from 2–5 cm to 10 m. On the basis of their composition, the greisens are subdivided into quartz-muscovite, muscovite, and quartz greisens, depending on the amount of dealkalization of the fracture walls. The characteristic minerals of the greisen formations are quartz, muscovite, fluorite, beryl, wolframite, hematite, and magnetite; rarer minerals are cassiterite, molybdenite, zircon, topaz, monazite, and some sulfides.

The higher concentrations of beryl are associated with quartz-muscovite and muscovite greisens. In the quartz-muscovite greisens, beryl forms very irregularly distributed small pockets and lenses from 3 cm in diameter to 5×15 cm. Apart from the pocket-like accumulations, beryl is in monomineralic streaks, 1 to 1.5 cm thick and as much as 5 m long. Such streaks are especially characteristic of muscovite types of greisen, where they are associated with the central parts of muscovite segregations. Wolframite is associated with beryl in these greisens.

A study of the distribution and paragenesis of beryl in greisen formations makes it possible to relate the addition of beryllium to the stage of formation of quartz-muscovite and especially muscovite greisen. The beryllium concentration in the greisenizing solutions apparently was sufficiently high to considerably exceed the isomorphous capacity of muscovite; this brought about the formation of beryllium minerals proper in the greisens.

Examples of beryl-bearing greisen formations in which the stage of early sodium metasomatism (which precedes greisenization) was of substantial significance, are those of the Altai (China). The greisens occur within small dome-shaped rock masses of biotite and bimica porphyritic granites whose relation to the main pegmatitic intrusive of the Mongolian Altai has so far remained unexplained. The spread of greisen deposits is controlled by systems of intersecting fractures that are most probably contractional in origin. The fractures, which can be distinctly traced along a thin tourmaline seam, are accompanied by zones of muscovite-quartz-albite greisen that carry numerous beryl concentrations (Fig. 56).

The composition of the greisen deposits is primarily determined by quartz and albite, which characterize the earliest stage of the replacement of granite around fractures. The greisenization proper, which is manifested by the formation of muscovite and of secondary topaz and fluorite after albite, is superposed on the already albitized granites. Molybdenite and bismuthite are present with beryl in the greisens, as is common in similar formations.

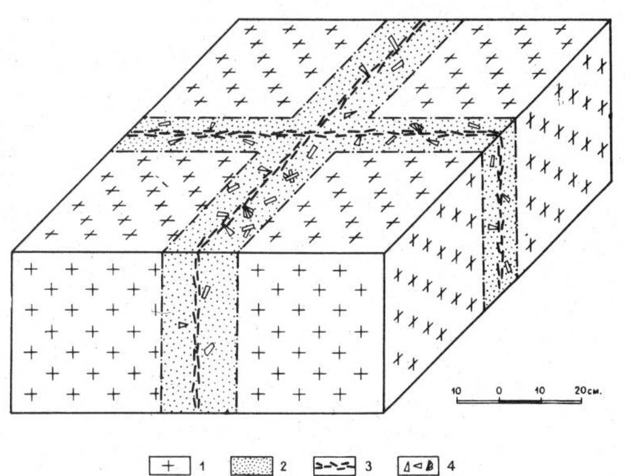

Fig. 56. Beryl-bearing albitized and greisenized zones, controlled by jointing in granites, Altai (according to T. F. Boiko). (1) Medium-grained porphyritic biotite granite; (2) albitized and greisinized granite; (3) tourmaline seam along the fracture; (4) beryl crystals.

The beryl crystals in the altered granites have mostly an irregular, less commonly a prismatic, form and contain numerous relict inclusions of the minerals of the unaltered granite. Intergrowths of beryl crystals (resembling star-like growths) penetrate into the albitized and greisenized granite from the fractures together with coniform clusters of beryl crystals oriented with their pyramidal ends toward the fracture which, in some cases, is filled with a thin tourmaline streak (tourmaline seam). The dimensions of beryl crystals related to the zones of altered granite attain 2 $\times$ 3 cm. although most of the disseminated crystals do not exceed 0.5 $\times$ 1 cm. The partial replacement of beryl in the greisen with muscovite is widespread, and points to the fact that beryl formed relatively early, before the greisenization. The beryl crystallization is probably related to the stage of early sodium metasomatism (albitization) of the granite, which has affected a large part of the deposit.

As an example of the fairly rare greisen deposits which contain helvite, we can cite the greisens occurring in the endocontact zone of one of the late Variscan granitic masses of Kazakhstan, which intrude effusive rocks of Lower Devonian age. The granitic mass is mainly composed of coarse- and fine-grained porphyritic granites having a small content of dark-colored minerals.

The greisen bodies which are separated by 150 to 200 m, are as much as 150 m long and have an apparent thickness of as much as 20 m; they are gently dipping layers controlled by the contraction fractures in the granites. Based on the mineralogical composition, quartz-mica–hematite and mica-quartz greisens are distinguished. The former contain helvite, whereas the latter contain higher beryl concentrations. The helvite-bearing greisens have a peculiar zonal structure: the outer part of the greisen body is composed of quartz-mica greisen, 15 to 20 cm thick, followed by quartz-hematite greisen, in which are accumulations of nearly monomineralic hematite as well as irregular crystals and pocket-like segregations of helvite. The individual helvite crystals do not exceed 2 to 3 mm across, are light-brownish, greenish, or yellowish and are octahedral. The composition of the mineral is determined by the abundance of the genthelvite molecule (16 to 30 percent) (Table 19, analyses 12, 15). Besides helvite, danalite and bertrandite also occur in the greisen as rare crystals. Accessory minerals in the greisen are fluorite, garnet, and opal. Less common are tourmaline and magnetite. Helvite is not uniformly distributed in the greisen body: some parts contain 60 to 80 percent helvite; others have almost completely none. Bertrandite is present as very fine lamellae and radiating accumulations which form at the expense of helvite, as a result of substitution by late hydrothermal solutions.

Helvite easily decomposes on the surface and is converted to yellow-brown, ochre-like formations; this suggests the possibility of an intensive supergene migration of beryllium in the described types of deposits.

Deposits of Beryllium in Feldspar-Quartz and Quartz Veins

Deposits of beryllium in feldspar-quartz and quartz veins have many features in common with the greisen deposits referred to above. Many vein deposits of this group are accompanied by enclosing greisens that also contain beryllium minerals. However, the alteration and reworking of the enclosing rocks in this group of fracture-filling bodies are much less than in deposits of the greisen type.

The structural features of beryllium deposits in feldspar-quartz and quartz veins have a number of specific features. The classification suggested by F. V. Vol'fson (1953) distinguishes the following basic types:

1. veins in contraction fractures in granitoids;
2. steeply dipping veins in faults;
3. veins in tectonic shear zones.

The first type of vein formation related to contraction fractures is usually represented by thin streaks rapidly tapering out in depth, which in a number of places form typical stockwork zones. In individual deposits, the beryl concentration in the streaks is fairly high, although the overall values of deposits are usually insignificant.

The second type, steeply dipping veins in faults, is very widespread in ore fields of beryl-bearing deposits. Although of rather limited length and depth, they may form widespread ore districts containing a large number of vein deposits. This makes is possible in several places to profitably mine rare metals from deposits of this structural type.

The third type of vein deposit, associated with shear zones, is accompanied by surrounding greisens and characterized by a great persistence in strike and dip. Vein formations in shear fractures are known to extend 1000 m and more in length. This structural type is the most promising for industrial use (Beus, 1956).

Table 110 Main paragenetic associations of vein-type hydrothermal-pheumatolytic beryllium deposits

Type of vein filling	Minerals			
	Main vein	Ore (widespread)	Vein (subsidiary)	Ore (subordinate)
Quartz-feldspar	Quartz, feldspar	Wolframite, beryl	Muscovite, topaz, fluorite	Scheelite, sulfides
Hematite-quartz-feldspar, hematite-quartz	Quartz, feldspar	Hematite, wolframite, helvite-danalite, beryl	Biotite, topaz, fluorite	Scheelite, sulfides, magnetite
Wolframite-quartz and beryl-wolframite-quartz	Quartz	Wolframite, beryl	Potassium feldspar, topaz, fluorite, muscovite	Cassiterite, molybdenite, bismuthinite, helvite, pyrite, chalco-pyrite
Cassiterite-quartz	Quartz	Cassiterite, beryl	Potassium feldspar, topaz, fluorite, muscovite	Cassiterite, molybdenite, bismuthinite, helvite, pyrite, chalco-pyrite
Molybdenite-quartz	Quartz	Molybdenite, beryl	Muscovite, topaz, fluorite	Cassiterite, wolframite, bismuth, bismutite, sulfides
Scheelite-quartz	Quartz	Scheelite	Fluorite	Beryl, bismuth, pyrite
Topaz-quartz	Quartz, topaz	Wolframite, beryl	Muscovite, fluorite	Cassiterite, rutile
Muscovite-quartz	Quartz, muscovite	Beryl	Fluorite, topaz, bertrandite	Wolframite, molybdenite
Beryl-muscovite	Muscovite, beryl	Beryl	Quartz, fluorite, topaz, tourmaline, bertrandite	Wolframite
Fluorite-biotite	Biotite, fluorite	Beryl	Oligoclase, orthoclase, sericite	Pyrite

The peculiar paragenetic features of beryllium deposits in feldspar-quartz and quartz veins are very characteristic and are determined in most types by the dominating role of quartz, together with potassium feldspar (less frequently albite), muscovite, fluorite, topaz, and beryl. The relative importance of these minerals in individual deposits varies; this makes it possible to determine the basic paragenetic groups of beryllium deposits in hydrothermal-pneumatolytic veins (Table 110).

Of all the genetic types of beryl-bearing veins, the most common are quartz-feldspar and quartz with beryl and wolframite, and the quartz type with beryl and molybdenite. High beryllium concentrations are also noted in the rarer topaz-quartz and beryl-muscovite veins.

Let us consider some characteristic features of the most common types of beryllium-bearing veins.

Typical of the high-temperature quartz veins with greisen rims and beryllium minerals are the tungsten-bearing veins of one of the characteristic granitic rock masses of central Kazakhstan, studied by F. V. Chukhrov and L. P. Ermilova.

The stock-shaped granitic intrusion is a typical small intrusion in the volcanic rocks of Paleozoic age near a large tectonic fault. The rock mass is composed of ultra-acid biotite granites of alaskite type. The medium-grained porphyritic varieties are the dominant granite type; of lesser importance are fine-grained granites and granite porphyries that mainly comprise the central part of the rock complex.

Within the granitic complex and, to a lesser extent, among the surrounding effusive rocks, high-temperature quartz and quartz-feldspar veins accompanied by greisen rims and lower-temperature vein deposits are widespread.

Based on the nature of the component minerals and the pervasive alteration of the enclosing rocks, the following vein types can be distinguished:

1. molybdenite-quartz (and quartz-feldspar) veins with greisen rims;
2. high-temperature wolframite-quartz (and quartz-feldspar) veins with greisen rims;
3. medium-temperature wolframite-quartz veins;
4. low-temperature fluorite and quartz veins.

The beryllium minerals within any ore district are associated with high-temperature wolframite-quartz veins, 0.2 to 0.5 m thick; the veins found at the exocontact of the granitic mass in the enclosing volcanic rocks are most enriched in beryl. All veins are accompanied by greisen rims. The thickness of the surrounding greisens bears no apparent relation to the thickness of the vein filling and averages 0.5 m.

Mica-quartz and mica-quartz-topaz greisens can be distinguished on the basis of composition. The latter comprise the inner part of the greisen rims at the boundary with the quartz vein, passing into mica-quartz towards the enclosing granites. The transition from mica-quartz-topaz greisen through mica-quartz greisen to granite is gradual. In places albitized rock is found where a transition to granite occurs; then there is a transitional zone of mica-plagioclase greisen. In veins occurring in the volcanic rocks at their contact with the granitic complex, the nature of the alterations around the veins is somewhat different. In particular, the quartz porphyries at their contact with veins containing wolframite and beryllium minerals, are lighter colored and enriched in mica. Such areas do not contain topaz.

The main mineral of the veins is coarsely crystalline, almost compact quartz, which forms smoky crystals, some nearly black, in cavities. Abundant vein minerals are topaz, muscovite, potassium feldspar, fluorite, beryl, helvite, siderite, rhodochrosite, and dickite. The most widely occurring ore mineral is wolframite, commonly associated with cassiterite, molybdenite, pyrite, chalcopyrite, cosalite, native bismuth, sphalerite, galena, and some other sulfides.

The above-mentioned gangue and ore minerals are irregularly distributed in veins. Such widely occurring minerals as topaz and potassium feldspar may be segregated in individual sections of the veins and not in others. In several places the distribution in veins of the common minerals shows a peculiar horizontal zoning which is expressed by a certain spatial separation of topaz, micas, and potassium feldspar along the strike of the veins.

In the high-temperature wolframite-quartz veins, the beryllium minerals are beryl, helvite, and bertrandite; the most common is beryl, which occurs as elongated thin prismatic crystals with color varying from bluish to greenish-white. The largest crystals attain 5 to 6 cm along the *c*-axis. Radiating intergrowths characteristic of this generation of beryl are fairly common.

The distribution of beryl in veins is closely related to their structure and mineralogical composition. Beryl segregations adjacent to vein selvedges are most characteristic, but in some parts of the veins, the accumulations of beryl are associated with the central part. Where this happens, the sections adjacent to selvedges are composed of topaz and microcline.

The interrelationships between beryl and topaz in veins, noted by F. V. Chukhrov and L. P. Ermilova, are of some interest. These two minerals are not really antipathetic, but in many places where one of them is found in considerable accumulations, the other is either absent or forms rare individual crystals. Especially characteristic of this phenomenon is vein No. 1, in which there is a marked zonal distribution of the most common vein minerals, including beryl. In the northwest part of the vein, which is enriched in potassium feldspar and where beryl forms noticeable accumulations, topaz occurs only in single crystals. At the same time, the northeast and central parts of the vein, where topaz occurs in significant quantity, are impoverished in beryl. Beryl is usually associated with muscovite, potassium feldspar, wolframite, cassiterite, molybdenite, bismuth sulfides, and pyrite. In the last stages of mineral formation there was an intensive replacement of beryl by green sericite, even forming sericite pseudomorphs after beryl crystals. Less commonly, there is replacement of beryl by an argillaceous mineral of halloysite type.

Helvite, occurring as greenish, yellow-green, and yellowish-brown crystals, is usually in close association with sulfides and carbonates. Distinct corrosion and replacement of helvite with carbonates, especially rhodochrosite, is accompanied by the formation of bertrandite and late sulfides.

Along fractures, in the helvite crystals, there are commonly segregations of sulfides and streaks of rhodochrosite with bertrandite, which replace helvite. Helvite segregations in rhodochrosite are, as a rule, severely corroded and are accompanied by bertrandite and masses of sulfides.

Bertrandite, which is fairly widespread in the veins of the deposit, is a secondary beryllium mineral closely related to the carbonate replacement complex. The association of bertrandite with rhodochrosite is most characteristic. The bertrandite-rhodochrosite streaks transgress accumulations of sericite and siderite, and usually are isolated in helvite. When they are isolated in helvite, there are helvite relics in rhodochrosite among the crystals and radiating intergrowths of bertrandite. Fine prismatic crystals of bertrandite are less common in association with gilbertite in drusy cavities, where they grow on crystals of quartz.

It is possible to roughly distinguish three stages of mineralization in the formation of the deposit. The earliest is characterized by the important role of fluorine, the second of sulfur, and the third of carbonic acid. Specific beryllium minerals are related to each of the stages.

The study of paragentic associations in the wolframite-quartz veins indicates that the crystallization of beryl followed the separation of topaz at the end of the first phase. As sulfur concentration in the mineral-forming solution increased, beryl was replaced by helvite. In the stage of carbonate metasomatism, the dissolution of the early beryllium minerals, mainly helvite, occurred. At the same time, beryllium combined as beryllium hydrosilicate, forming bertrandite.

From the deposit described above, it is possible to trace the transition, characteristic of many hydrothermal-pneumatolytic beryllium deposits, from high-temperature parageneses of the early stages of mineralization of quite different parageneses peculiar to the low-temperature hydrothermal deposits. Correspondingly, the forms of beryllium concentration change. This depends entirely on the conditions of mineral formation and the composition of the mineral-forming solutions.

An example of beryl-wolframite deposits, which are characterized by the absence of greisen rims along the contacts of quartz veins, occurs in a small dome-shaped granitic mass in eastern Siberia. This granitic mass is composed mainly of porphyritic bimica granites. In these are a minor proportion of fine-grained muscovite granites, and the rocks of the vein-related intrusive series, which are represented by muscovite granites and granite-alpites.

The beryllium content of granites of the rock mass increases slightly from the bimica porphyritic granites (3 to 5×10^{-4} percent Be) to the fine-grained muscovite granites (6 to 7×10^{-4} percent Be); however, the highest concentration is in the veined albitized granites (up to 32×10^{-4} percent Be). It should be noted that the Paleozoic schists that enclose the granitic mass have a beryllium content close to that found in the main mass of porphyritic granites (3 to 5×10^{-4} percent Be.)

The quartz veins which fill shear fractures in the granites have a northwest trend and can be traced for as much as 500 m. The thickness of various veins ranges from 4 to 65 cm. In all veins there is finely crystalline beryl in varying proportions; wolframite is less abundant. Besides widely occurring beryl and rarer wolframite, some feldspar, fluorite, scheelite, arsenopyrite, pyrite, and scorodite also occur in quartz veins. After quartz, beryl is the most widespread mineral, occurring as crystals with well-developed faces and in solid granular masses, which form peculiar fringes in these parts of the vein adjacent to the selvedges. It is characteristic that thinner veins and vein apophyses have a higher beryl concentration (Fig. 57) which, in veins 4 to 5 cm thick, constitutes 75 to 80 percent of the vein mass. The color of the beryl is greenish-yellow, or pale-yellow to colorless. The crystal size does not exceed 3 to 4 $\times$ 0.3 to 0.5 cm, attaining in some cases 10 $\times$ 2 cm. Very small individual crystals penetrate into granite to a distance of 5 cm from the contact, and develop metasomatically in the microcline of the granite. A higher beryllium concentration (up to 50×10^{-4} percent Be) occurs in muscovite, whose fine lamellae are disseminated in large quantities near the contact. It should be noted that more than 5 cm away from the contact (the beryllium concentration suddenly falls, approaching its content in the unaltered granite (Fig. 57).

Thus the main mass of beryl in quartz veins of the deposit is segregated at the contact between the vein and the granite and is most probably the product of the early stage of interaction of the ore-forming hydrothermal solutions with the enclosing rocks. The rare separate beryl crystals noted in solid quartz or in small geodes, indicate beryllium impoverishment in the central part of the quartz veins during their final stage of formation.

The high-temperature quartz veins in granites, with helvite-danalite minerals have a very characteristic paragenesis. The geological features of these deposits are close to those previously discussed of wolframite-quartz deposits that contain beryl.

The deposits of the group under discussion stand apart geochemically from the general series because of the presence of high concentration of iron, zinc, manganese, and sulfur. For instance, the typomorphic minerals of the quartz and feldspar-quartz veins containing helvite and danalite are hematite and some sulfides. The vein formations are generally accompanied by hematite-quartz greisens, also containing helvite and danalite.

Typical examples are some helvite-containing veins developed in the endocontact zone of the granitic mass (central Kazakhstan) which has already been mentioned during the description of the helvite-bearing quartz-hematite greisens. The quartz veins that fill shear fractures in granites are traced for a distance of as much as 450 m, their thickness ranging from 1 to 50 cm. The veins are accompanied by mica-quartz and hematite-quartz rims. The widespread minerals of the quartz veins are feldspar, hematite, biotite, danalite, helvite, beryl, topaz, fluorite, muscovite, wolframite, garnet, and bertrandite; common also are sulfides of iron, copper, and zinc; less common are allanite, zircon, rutile, sphene, and native bismuth. The helvite in the vein is usually of pocket form, the individual pocket-like accumulations of helvite attaining 20 cm across. Helvite is brownish or yellowish, and its largest crystals attain 6 cm across. The disseminated phenocrysts (small crystals) of helvite are observed in the greisen surrounding the veins. It should be noted that within the same

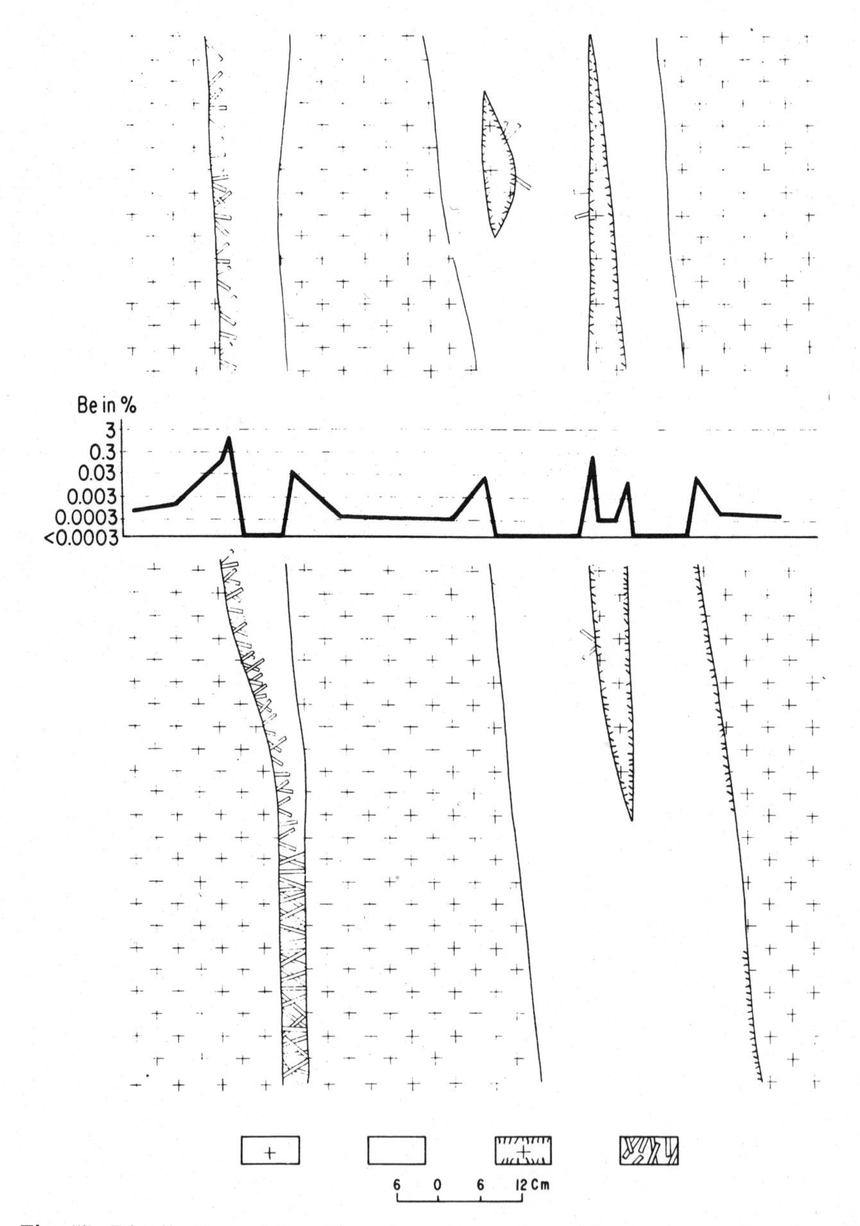

Fig. 57. Distribution of beryllium in quartz veins with poorly developed greisen zones, eastern Siberia. (1) Bimica granite; (2) quartz; (3) mica greisen in granite; (4) beryl crystals.

vein district there are also the usual wolframite-quartz veins with beryl, which differ from the helvite-containing veins by the absence of higher concentrations of iron and sulfur.

Hydrothermal-Pneumatolytic Deposits of Beryllium in Carbonate Rocks

Fluoritic Metasomatic Deposits in Limestones

Fluoritic metasomatic deposits in limestones are a fairly rare type of beryllium deposits related to the activity of postmagmatic acid emanations and solutions which penetrated carbonate rocks.

The deposits of this type, recently studied in detail by I. N. Govorov and M. G. Rub, are usually near intrusive masses of granitoid rocks, which have a high content of fluorine and other rare and disseminated elements. Greisenization occurs at places within these masses and at their contact with the aluminosilicate rocks.

The deposits consist of thick vein-like, pipe-like, or more complex metasomatic bodies, mainly of fluoritic composition, related to tectonic disturbances and shatter zones in limestones. Within these zones, a fluoritic replacement occurs not only in limestones, but also in epigenetic formations occurring among them (e.g., skarns, quartz bodies, etc.).

The mineralogical composition of the deposits is predominated by fluorite and micas, including the lithium mica from the margarite group. Along with the main minerals, the following also occur in the mica-flourite aggregate: tourmaline, less commonly microcline, apatite, quartz, sellaite, scapolite (relics), cassiterite, pyrite, arsenopyrite, and zircon.

In the predominantly fluoritic deposits formed by replacement of limestones, the beryllium minerals are represented almost exclusively by phenacite. Small grains of phenacite (fractions of 1 m) are disseminated in the mica-fluorite aggregate, producing intergrowths with fluorite and tourmaline. Less common are radiating and sheaf-like growths of acicular rod-shaped crystals measuring several millimeters. There is also a concentration of phenacite in thin fluorite streaks that transgress the metasomatic bodies. In the thinnest streaks, phenacite occurs in a larger proportion than fluorite and is usually closely associated with apatite. The nature of beryllium minerals in metasomatic deposits formed by replacement of scapolitic skarn bodies in limestones is different. Such deposits usually contain a considerable increase in micas and the presence of chrysoberyl, whose formation took place by local enrichment of the mineral-forming solutions in aluminum, derived from the replaced skarns rich in alumina. The third beryllium mineral occurring in fluoritic deposits of this type is euclase, which is associated with parts of metasomatic bodies, formed as a result of the replacement of vein quartz.

A number of characteristic features connect this type of beryllium-bearing mica-fluorite deposits in limestones with contact-metasomatic beryllium deposits of the skarn type (see below). Yet the geological situation and mineralogical composition warrant a separate genetic classification for the latter.

Contact-Metasomatic (Skarn) Beryllium Deposits

These contact-metasomatic beryllium deposits are developed at the contact between beryllium-bearing granites and limestones. They occur relatively widely and are known in many regions of the world. There is a definite relationship between the skarn beryllium deposits and the tungsten- or tin-bearing intrusive complexes which contain higher concentrations of beryllium and fluorine.

The nature of beryllium-bearing granites in this type of deposit is virtually analogous to the parent granites of beryllium greisen deposits. Very characteristic of the granites are an alaskite habit, the increased alkali content, and the presence of products from earlier stages of postmagmatic alteration of granitoid rocks (muscovite, fluorite, and topaz). Their fluorine content attains tenths of 1 percent, and the beryllium content varies within limits analogous to those encountered in granites of greisen-type deposits, usually being one and a half to four times as great as the mean percentage deduced for the granites.

Deposits of this type occur as a rule within the tungsten- or tin-bearing provinces similar to the greisen and quartz-vein beryllium deposits, and in most fluorine-enriched skarn deposits, the higher beryllium concentrations usually occur simultaneously with tungsten or tin. A number of granitic masses are known (Central Asia and other regions), with which are associated both greisen (or vein) beryl-bearing deposits (in the areas of contact with aluminum-rich silicate rocks) and skarns containing beryllium minerals (in areas of contact with carbonate rocks).

Analysis of all data makes it possible to point out a number of characteristic textural and paragenetic features of beryllium-bearing skarns. All such deposits are normal reaction skarns with a superimposed metasomatic complex of minerals that are products of the activity of fluorine-containing postmagmatic solutions of the acidic stage of metasomatism.

The most typical rock-forming minerals of beryllium-bearing skarns in the majority of known deposits are fluorite and magnetite, although the presence of small quantities of beryllium minerals is also sometimes noted in other types of skarns that contain fluorite and magnetite as only accessory components of the mineral complex.

On the basis of mineralogical composition, the following types of beryllium-bearing skarns are distinguished:

1. Mainly magnetite
   - fluorite-magnetite
   - mica-magnetite
   - fluorite-vesuvianite-magnetite
   - vesuvianite-magnetite
   - pyroxene-vesuvianite-magnetite
   - fluorite-feldspar-magnetite
   - garnet-fluorite-magnetite
2. Mainly fluorite
   - magnetite-fluorite
   - mica-fluorite
   - mica-epidote-fluorite
   - vesuvianite-fluorite
3. Other rarer varieties
   - epidote-garnet
   - fluorite-garnet
   - fluorite-feldspar
   - vesuvianite
   - pyroxene
   - spinel

Among the beryllium minerals proper that form the higher concentrations in skarns, the most characteristic are helvite, danalite, chrysoberyl, and phenacite. Occasionally, beryl and some other beryllium minerals form in such deposits. The characteristic feature of beryllium-bearing skarns is the fine granularity of the associated beryllium minerals, which, as a rule, makes their identification difficult without the use of optical or special chemical methods of determination. Another characteristic feature is the presence of several (including relict) generations of the most widely occurring minerals; this points to a multi-stage formation of complex deposits of this type.

It has been noted already (Chapter 3) that the skarn formations contain an accumulation of beryllium as an isomorphous impurity in a number of common skarn minerals (vesuvianite, micas, etc.). The main collector of disseminated beryllium in deposits of the analyzed group is vesuvianite, which contains as a rule about 1 percent or more beryllium oxide.

A very characteristic, though not essential, textural feature of beryllium-bearing skarns is a thin-banded structure caused by the stratified arrangement of the main rock-forming skarn minerals: magnetite on the one hand, and fluorite with associated silicates on the other. The bands enriched in magnetite are black, unlike the interbedded layers composed of fluorite and silicate minerals of lighter colors. The layers are usually wavy, at times quite corregated, and this gives to the rock a very characteristic thin-laminated form. Beryllium minerals are usually concentrated in the light-colored streaks, but many times very fine inclusions of these minerals are found in magnetite.

Typical examples of beryllium-bearing skarn formations include the Iron Mountain deposit, New Mexico, U.S.A., and a number of deposits in various parts of the Soviet Union.

The region of the Iron Mountain deposit is composed of a thick bed of limestones and shales, complexly transgressed by necks, flat sheets, and dikes of rhyolite, porphyritic rhyolite, and aplite-like granite, probably of Miocene age (Jahns, 1955). The sedimentary rocks that enclose the intrusive complex are considerably changed as a result of intensive contact metasomatism. The contact changes of enclosing rocks are shown in the conversion of shales to hornfels and in the recrystalization of limestones. The latter are largely transformed to skarn near contacts with volcanic rocks.

In the deposit are two skarn varieties, easily discernible by their mineralogical composition and texture, which are massive and banded (Fig. 58). The most widely occurring massive variety occurs usually in the form of large stratified bodies, which occur conformably with the stratification of the enclosing rocks, usually stopping directly at the contact with the volcanic rocks.

The banded skarns form thick lenses and pipe-like thinner stratified bodies, which usually occur in massive skarns. Wherever banded and massive skarn varieties are found together, the latter occurs usually between the banded skarn and the nearest contact of the intrusive body. The boundaries between the two skarn varieties and the enclosing rocks are sharp, but at a distance of several tens of centimeters both varieties are gradually substituted by country rocks.

The massive skarn variety is a magnetite-andradite rock varying from black to greenish and brownish and having a small content of fluorite (not exceeding 4 percent). Sometimes the rock contains small proportions of hedenbergite, hematite, apatite, diopside, quartz, feldspar, vesuvianite, etc. No beryllium minerals have been found in this rock.

Much more interesting is another skarn variety composed mainly of a magnetite-fluorite rock, poor in garnet, which has a peculiar banded texture. The rock consists usually of thin (0.05 to 3 mm, averaging 0.2 mm), complexly corrugated layers differing in mineralogical composition and color. The layers of magnetite and closely related hematite alternate with thinner layers composed of fluorite and silicate minerals. Unlike the former variety, the banded skarn contains a noticeably higher beryllium content. Two varieties of beryllium-bearing banded skarn can be distinguished; they differ mainly in the mineralogical composition of the magnetite-free layers.

The dark variety, rich in beryllium, is composed of thin, wavy magnetite

---

→

Fig. 28. Diagrammatic geological map and profiles of the Iron Mountain deposit (according to Jahns). (1) Aplite and fine-grained granite of Tertiary period; (2) coarse-grained recrystallized limestone; (3) quartz-pyroxene-clinozoisitic granulite; (4) massive magnetite-andraditic skarn; (5) banded fluorite-magnetitic skarn; (6) angles of dip, strike.

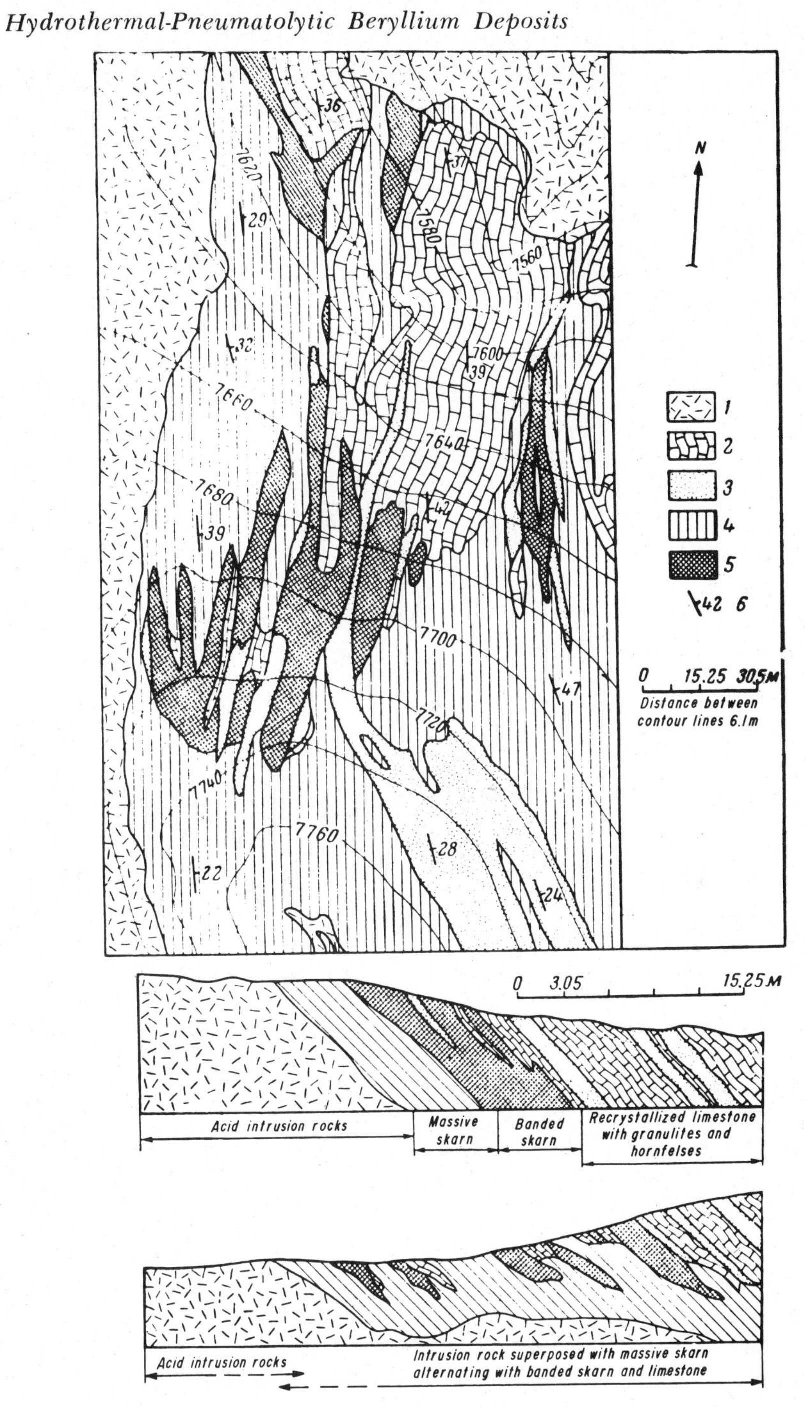
N
1
2
3
4
5
42 6
0 15.25 30.5M
Distance between contour lines 6.1m
7560
7580
7600
7620
7640
7660
7680
7700
7720
7740
7760
0 3.05 15.25M
Acid intrusion rocks
Massive skarn
Banded skarn
Recrystallized limestone with granulites and hornfelses
Acid intrusion rocks
Intrusion rock superposed with massive skarn alternating with banded skarn and limestone

layers, 0.2 to 10 mm thick, and of interbedded, even thinner laminated aggregates of fluorite, helvite, and in places, quartz. Irregular inclusions of adularia occur in the less distinctly laminated sections of the rock. It is characteristic that garnet is absent in the skarn variety enriched in magnetite. In this rock helvite is a very common mineral, occurring in a fairly considerable quantity (Table 111).

The other, more typical and more widespread variety of banded skarn contains less magnetite and consequently has a lighter color. The light-colored minerals here are fluorite, green biotite, and chlorite, and the pink and yellowish-green beryllium-bearing vesuvianite. Of less importance are helvite and danalite, which are hardly distinguishable from the grossularite occurring in the rock.

Table 111 Mineralogical composition of skarns of the Iron Mountain deposit (in percent)

Minerals	Fluorite-magnetite skarns	Fluorite-vesuvianite magnetite skarns
Magnetite	28—68	23—82
Fluorite	16—37	5—33
Helvite	2—24	trace—3
Vesuvianite	0	0—37
Biotite and chlorite	0—4	4—28
Adularia	0—9	0—2
Quartz	0—4	0—4
Alteration products (limonite-kaolinite, etc.)	2—11	2—17
Garnet	0	0—7
Hematite	0	trace—7
Diopside	0	0—1
Clinozoisite	0	0—2
Sulfides	0	0—trace

Data in Table 111 give an idea of the mineralogical composition of the beryllium-bearing skarn formations of Iron Mountain, both for fluorite-magnetite and fluorite-vesuvianite skarn varieties containing helvite and danalite.

The sharp drop in helvite content with increasing amounts of silicates (particularly vesuvianite) in the rock is very characteristic.

According to Jahns (1944), the formation of beryllium-bearing skarns is the result of a multi-stage process of the metamorphic and metasomatic transformation of sedimentary rocks, related genetically to the contact effect of emanations and solutions when the acid intrusive was established. The formation of the massive skarn with its relatively simple mineralogical composition is explained by the activity of iron-enriched, postmagmatic emanations of the earliest stage of contact metasomatism, which, in later stages, contemporary with the formation of banded skarns, were substituted by acid beryllium-enriched solutions. It is a characteristic feature of the banded skarn that its formation was preceded by folding and crushing of the earlier formed contact rocks.

As an example of beryllium-bearing contact-metasomatic formations having a more complex mineralogical composition and a more varied beryllium mineralization, we consider one of the mineralogically and geochemically interesting fields of Kazakhstan.

The region of this skarn district is composed of metamorphosed and effusive rocks of Middle and Upper Devonian age, which have been compressed into steep folds of northwest trend and, in the southern part of the area, have been intruded by Variscan alaskite granites.

The metamorphosed rocks consist of hornfelsized sandstones, shales, conglomerates, acid and basic extrusives, and lenses of metamorphosed limestone, opal-chalcedony and silicified rocks, and skarns. The complex of sedimentary metamorphic rocks in parts of the deposits has a fairly constant westnorthwest, almost latitudinal strike with a monoclinal dip towards the northeast at an angle of 65 to 85°.

The zone of beryllium-bearing skarnized rocks, about 100 m broad, has been traced for roughly 5 to 6 km in the westnorthwest direction; it is conformable with the general strike of the sedimentary-metamorphic rocks, and presents a series of conformably arranged lens-shaped bodies with sharp or gradational contacts. The skarnized zone is associated entirely with a thick zone, which coincides with the strike of the sedimentary-metamorphic stratum.

A. M. Zasedatelev, who studied in detail the skarn formations of this region, distinguishes six main skarn types having a number of specific paragenetic features of the constituent minerals:

1. mica-fluorite-magnetite with chrysoberyl
2. mica-fluorite-magnetite with feldspar and topaz
3. mica-fluorite with beryl and phenacite
4. garnet-fluorite-magnetite with vesuvianite and epidote
5. fluorite-feldspar with helvite
6. fluorite-garnet with vesuvianite.

The varieties of beryllium-bearing rocks are in some places joined by gradual transitions, while in others they are rather sharply separated.

In external appearance the beryllium-containing skarns are fine-grained rocks, (individual minerals vary between tenths and hundredths of a mm) with a characteristic banded texture caused by the alteration of capriciously curving light and dark bands differing in mineralogical composition and varying in thickness (from hundredths of a mm to 1–2 cm). The thickest bands consist in places of a series of thinner bands. A characteristic feature of the rocks described is the presence of geode-like cavities filled with the same minerals of which the given skarn is composed. Relics of the earlier garnet and vesuvianite-garnet skarns, which point to a multi-stage skarn formation, are very typical (Georgievskaya, 1955).

The highest beryllium concentrations are characteristically in the mica-fluorite-magnetite skarns with chrysoberyl, and slightly smaller concentrations are in the fluorite-feldspar and garnet-fluorite-magnetite skarns.

The increased beryllium concentrations in the beryl-bearing rocks are due mainly to chrysoberyl, also to beryllium-bearing vesuvianite, beryl, helvite, phenacite, and to a lesser extent, bavenite and bertrandite. Some beryllium is disseminated as an impurity in other minerals, particularly in magnetite, maghemite, hematite, (hundredths and tenths of 1 percent),[3] mica, garnet, epidote (thousandths of 1 percent), and in some other minerals.

The most widely occurring beryllium mineral of the skarn zone is chrysoberyl, associated with light mica-fluorite bands of the mica-fluorite-magnetite skarns. Chrysoberyl forms tabular and irregular yellowish-gray and greenish-yellow segregations, usually closely intergrown with lamellar aggregates of muschketowite and greenish ferromuscovite. The chrysoberyl plates may attain dimensions of a few millimeters across and as much as 0.1 mm thick, but most frequently they are 0.05 to 0.1 mm long and a few hundredths of a millimeter thick. The tabular crystals are flattened along the *c*-axis. Trillings are found at times.

Chrysoberyl almost always contains a large amount of finely dispersed other minerals, the most common of which are fluorite, magnetite, muscovite, iron oxide hydrates, and sometimes pyrite. At times magnetite and chrysoberyl form intergrowths giving rise to micrographic structures. Skeletal crystals of chrysoberyl are common and filled with fluorite, mica, or muschketowite. Unlike phenacite and helvite, apparently chrysoberyl does not occur in the drusy cavities. When muscovite is present and when the quantity of magnetite and hematite (muschketowite) decreases, beryl appears in the rocks instead of chrysoberyl.

Beryl is the characteristic mineral of the mica-fluorite skarns; it is also common in the slightly altered garnet-fluorite-magnetite skarns with vesuvianite epidote. It is noted much more rarely in fluorite-feldspar skarns, in sections enriched in muscovite.

Beryl is in both the main mass of the mica-fluorite skarns and in druses and streaks. In the main skarn mass its occurrence is relatively uniform and in the form of fine, short-columnar, white, colorless, yellowish, and green-bluish crystals up to a few tenths of a millimeter in length. Beryl crystals may be corroded by fluorite and sericite mica. In druses the beryl crystals have an elongated prismatic form and attain a few millimeters in length; they are associated with the dark-violet fluorite, sulfides, topaz, phenacite,

[3] The investigation of the insoluble residue, after magnetite and hematite had been treated with acids, showed that they contained microscopic inclusions of beryllium minerals, particularly of chrysoberyl.

and helvite. In optical properties the beryl from the drusy formations does not differ from the beryl in the main skarn mass.

Phenacite is less widespread than chrysoberyl and beryl. It usually occurs in mica-fluorite skarns, or, less commonly, in fluorite-garnet and garnet-fluorite-magnetite skarns; in the latter two, it is only in druses and streaks.

The largest specimens in druses are short-columnar, almost isometric crystals, up to 1 mm across. It is usually associated with fluorite, micas, hydromicas, and sulfides. Its association with feldspar is less characteristic.

A. M. Zasedatelev notes the formation of an idiomorphic helvite crystal inside a phenacite crystal; this points to the later formation of phenacite. Phenacite in mica-fluorite skarns is intensively corroded by fluorite and mica.

Helvite is a fairly widely occurring mineral of beryllium-bearing skarns, but it forms its largest accumulations in the granular fluorite-feldspar skarn.

Based on color there are four helvite varieties: smoky, brownish, honey-yellow, and green, the most common being the brownish and honey-yellow varieties.

The brownish helvite is found mainly in fluorite-feldspar skarns that contain a large proportion of magnetite, hematite, and garnet, and the greenish-yellow variety is in fluorite-feldspar skarns, consisting almost completely of fluorite and feldspar (fluorite constitutes 60 to 70 percent of the rock).

Helvite is rare in the other skarn types and is usually associated with those parts enriched in feldspar (mainly albite and, to a lesser extent, orthoclase).

Bertrandite is found primarily in banded mica-fluorite skarns containing small proportions of magnetite, maghemite, and hematite in association with greenish-grey muscovite and hydromicas. The sheaf-like aggregates of tabular bertrandite are usually observed in parts of mica pseudomorphs after chrysoberyl. Most probably, bertrandite forms as a result of the replacement of chrysoberyl with muscovite.

Vesuvianite is a widespread mineral of the skarnitized zone; it is particularly abundant in banded garnet-fluorite-magnetite, dense garnet-vesuvianite, and granular fluorite-garnet skarns, of which it constitutes 40 to 50 percent.

Chemical analyses show that vesuvianite contains up to 50 percent BeO.

Below is a brief description of the different varieties of beryllium-bearing skarns found within the skarn field.

The skarns most widespread in the area are fluorite-garnet skarns with vesuvianite. Skarns of this type usually have a relatively coarse-grained texture, sometimes a banded structure. They are composed mainly of fluorite and garnet (grossularite and, less commonly, andradite). Sometimes hematite (muschketowite), vesuvianite, feldspar (orthoclase, albite), clay minerals, and sulfides (sphalerite, chalcopyrite, galena, molybdenite, etc.)

are present in quite considerable quantities. Quartz, opal, chalcedony, and calcite are noted in small quantities.

The beryllium concentration in skarns is low (hundredths of 1 percent) and is associated with beryllium-bearing vesuvianite, and also with helvite and phenacite which, however, occur very rarely.

The mica-fluorite-magnetite skarns present several varieties with gradual transitions between them. The most widely occurring, and the most interesting from the point of view of beryllium content, are the mica-fluorite-magnetite skarns with chrysoberyl. These are fine-grained black (with bluish and greenish shades) rocks with thin-banded structure, whose mineralogical composition can be diagnosed only under a microscope. The main mass of the rock consists of fluorite and magnetite with maghemite and hematite. Of subordinate significance are ferromuscovite, accumulations of opal-chalcedony, and argillaceous masses composed of montmorillonite, nontronite, halloysite, hydromicas, and a small quantity of chlorite. There are euhedral crystals or thin streaks of sulfides (pyrite, less commonly sphalerite, chalcopyrite, galena, chalcocite, and covellite), and masses of chrysoberyl aggregates. Epidote, clinozoisite, jarosite, tourmaline (dravite and schorl), garnet, vesuvianite, feldspars (orthoclase, rarer albite), topaz, green spinel, gypsum, calcite, aragonite, allanite, scheelite, helvite, phenacite, and diaspore are rarer.

The fine lamination of the rock is caused by the alternation of bands of varying mineralogical composition. The dark bands are mainly composed of magnetite, maghemite, and hematite, and the light bands of fluorite, mica, and chrysoberyl.

A characteristic feature of the rocks is the presence of spherical and lens-shaped geode-like cavities in which violet fluorite, hydrated iron oxides, and opal develop in druses. In the cavities are small quantities of muscovite, hematite, muschketowite, calcite, black tourmaline, and bertrandite.

The beryllium content of the rocks described is mainly related to the presence of chrysoberyl. Other beryllium minerals (bertrandite, phenacite, and helvite) and the admixture of beryllium in magnetite and hematite (about 0.025 percent Be), attributable to the micro dissemination of beryllium minerals, have no substantial significance.

An increase in the proportions of garnet, vesuvianite, feldspar, and topaz in the rock or a considerable reduction in magnetite indicate a gradation to other skarn varieties, which are usually connected by a gradual transition.

The mica-fluorite-magnetite skarns with feldspar are characterized by a coarser and more distinct lamination. The fundamental composition of the rock is determined by the presence of magnetite and feldspar, mainly orthoclase. The content of mica, represented by greenish ferromuscovite, varies within wide limits to its complete absence. A large proportion of mica (above 25 to 30 percent) is accompanied by the appearance of topaz and by a reduction in feldspar, which indicates a transition to mica-fluorite-magnetite skarns with topaz.

The rock contains insignificant proportions of quartz, sulfides (pyrite, chalcopyrite, sphalerite, and molybdenite), and clay minerals (montmorillonite, micas), and chlorite. The beryllium content of this skarn type is due to an admixture of beryllium in magnetite attributable to finely disseminated inclusions of beryllium minerals and to small quantities of chrysoberyl and helvite.

Less widespread than these two skarn varieties are the mica-fluorite-magnetite skarns with topaz, which have a granular or laminated structure. The main minerals of the rock are ferromuscovite, fluorite, magnetite, hematite, and topaz (as much as 5 to 10 percent). Feldspar, sulfides, hydromicas, chlorite, and apatite are less common. Fluorite, micas, and topaz are noted in cavities. In many properties these rocks are intermediate between the above-described skarn varieties with chrysoberyl and with feldspar. Their beryllium content is due to the presence of chrysoberyl and, partly, magnetite with micro-inclusions of beryllium minerals.

The mica-fluorite skarns with beryl and phenacite are usually laminated, sometimes granular, light or dark rocks; they are composed mainly of muscovite, sericite, and fluorite. Sometimes magnetite, hematite, muschketowite, sulfides, and feldspars (orthoclase and albite) are present in notable quantities. Of much lesser significance are biotite, jarosite, epidote, quartz, beryl, phenacite, apatite, chrysoberyl, bertrandite, helvite, chlorite, zeolites, scapolite, topaz, green spinel, and garnet. Compared with other rocks, they have abundant geodes with drusy fillings of fluorite, mica, and sulfides.

When the proportion of magnetite and hematite (muschketowite) is increased, ferromuscovite and chrysoberyl appear in the skarn. When feldspar is abundant, the rocks pass into fluorite-feldspar aggregates with helvite or beryl. The most widely occurring beryllium minerals of this type of skarn are beryl and phenacite; of lesser importance are bertrandite and helvite.

The garnet-fluorite-magnetite rocks with vesuvianite are dark-gray and of magnetite and fluorite with light bands composed of fluorite and have a laminated structure, caused by alteration of dark bands composed vesuvianite.

The content of the main minerals indicated above varies within wide limits. There are small quantities of montmorillonite, hydromicas, chlorite, and halloysite; also feldspars (orthoclase, albite), sulfides, epidote, calcite, malachite, azurite, opal, chalcedony, and quartz. Bertrandite, beryl, phenacite, helvite, zeolites, and green spinel are rare.

The geode-like cavities are filled with garnet, fluorite, less commonly with epidote, feldspars, hydromicas, and sulfides. Transgressive streaks in the rock are composed of garnet, fluorite, more rarely sulfides, vesuvianite, epidote, feldspars etc. In some streaks of fluorite and feldspar, there are beryl, phenacite, and helvite.

The beryllium content of this skarn type is determined mainly by the presence of vesuvianite, which contains an isomorphous beryllium impurity.

Relatively rare in the deposit are garnet-fluorite-magnetite skarns with epidote, which differ from the skarn types referred to above by the presence of considerable quantities (10 to 20 percent and more) of epidote and feldspars. In the streaks and druses are beryl, less commonly phenacite, helvite, and bavenite, usually accompanied by dark fluorite. Druses and streaks contain small proportions of epidote, feldspar (orthoclase, albite), and sulfides. In some places there is a large quantity of muscovite with epidote; this indicates a certain relationship to skarns of the mica-fluorite-magnetitic type. The beryllium content of garnet-fluorite-magnetite skarns with epidote is caused mainly by the presence of beryllium-containing vesuvianite and beryl (in streaks and druses). It is possible that helvite and bavenite locally have some significance.

The occurrence of the fluorite-feldspar skarns is also relatively limited; they are connected by gradual transitions with skarns of mica-fluorite type. They have an irregularly grained texture and weak lamination. Besides the main rock-forming minerals (fluorite and feldspar), there occur, in varying proportions, garnet, magnetite with hematite and muschketowite, montmorillonite, muscovite, helvite, quartz, sulfides, opal, chalcedony, zeolites, apatite, beryl, wulfenite, calcite, malachite, azurite, and chrysocolla.

The geodes and streaks are filled with drusy coarsely crystalline aggregates of feldspar (orthoclase), fluorite, quartz, and helvite. In the base of the druses there are usually feldspar, helvite, and fluorite, while in the center milk-white quartz and helvite are common.

The beryllium content is almost entirely due to the presence of helvite.

The interrelations between minerals in various types of beryllium-bearing skarns, and the presence of numerous relics of the early contact-reaction vesuvianite-garnet and garnet skarns make it possible to relate the formation of beryllium-bearing rocks to the final stage of formation of the contact-metasomatic deposit, which corresponds to that of the post-magmatic acid metasomatism (Korzhinskii, 1953).

It should be noted that the beryllium-bearing contact-metasomatic deposits briefly described in this section, have been so far little studied, and many problems relating to their origin have not yet been solved. This refers to the distribution and genesis in such deposits of beryllium minerals whose crystallization, according to available data, took place in various stages of formation of the metasomatic complexes. However, the insufficiently studied age relations of various beryllium minerals present in skarns make it possible to conclude that chrysoberyl crystalized earlier than beryl, helvite, and phenacite. Where the last three appear together with chrysoberyl, they occur in streaks or geode-like cavities and represent the later stage of formation of the metasomatic rock.

The problem of the causes of banding, which is characteristic of these formations, has apparently been solved most successfully by O. G. Georgievskaya (1955), who explained their formation as due to the rhythmic precipitation of minerals from the fluorine-containing replacement solutions, according to the principle "concentrational" diffusion. However, in Georgievskaya's treatment of the origin of banding in the fluorite-magnetite metasomatic rocks, the important role of pH change in the skarn-forming solutions has not been taken into account. This problem will be studied in more detail when we discuss the geochemical features of beryllium in processes of contact-metasomatism.

The constant paragenesis of structural-textural features of contact-metasomatic beryllium deposits in various parts of the world completely justify their separation as a distinctly individual genetic type.

CHAPTER 6

Hydrothermal Beryllium Deposits

Unlike the high-temperature hydrothermal-pneumatolytic deposits, whose beryllium content has attracted the attention of investigators for many years, the meso- and epithermal formations, which in many places contain noticeable accumulations of beryllium minerals, have been very insufficiently studied.

It can now be shown by the example of a whole series of greisen deposits that the appearance of high concentrations of beryllium in the formation of these deposits is not limited to the high-temperature mineralization. The formation of beryllium minerals in these deposits takes place at various stages, including the last, low-temperature mineralization phase. For many deposits of the type under consideration, the final low-temperature stages of their formation had a substantial carbonate character, shown by both the phenomena of carbonate metasomatism and the appearance of numerous calcite, rhodochrosite, siderite, and other carbonate streaks.

Weak signs of the carbonate mineralization stage were noted above in the final stages of the formation of greisen deposits. This stage is much more distinctly shown in individual greisen deposits characterized by a wide development of carbonate veins and streaks in which beryl and helvite are noted in places. In some calcite streaks, fine crystals of thinly prismatic blue beryl occur in considerable quantity and are detected in the insoluble residue following the decomposition of carbonate with an acid (Smol'yaninov, 1940).

Elsewhere there are even greater beryllium concentrations in deposits that are the products of activity of hydrothermal carbonate solutions. However, the current information of individual known deposits of this type does not show in sufficient detail the features of their paragenesis and formation.

The most interesting of these deposits, Muso, Columbia, was known in ancient times and was mined by the local population for emeralds a long time before America's discovery (Oppenheim, 1948). The enclosing rocks of the deposit are black crystalline limestones of Cretaceous age, alternating with coaly-clay shales. These rocks are deformed into steep folds, and are disturbed and transgressed in various directions by numerous veins and streaks filled with calcite, aragonite, or cerium-bearing dolomite. Along with the carbonate veins there are albite veins and streaks, and albitization of the enclosing rocks is noticeably developed.

The emerald-bearing veins, composed of white calcite and gray cerium-bearing dolomite, occur towards the upper (the so-called "productive") horizon of the schist-limestone strata.

The beryl of the Muso deposit is emerald-green, varying from dark green to almost white. Many dark-colored crystals contain inclusions of carbonaceous matter. The crystal habit is hexagonal, prismatic; the crystal length is usually equal to the side of the basal pinacoid. Their dimensions usually do not exceed 2 to 3 cm.

In association with emerald (beryl) are calcite and dolomite, pyrite, quartz, parisite, apatite, fluorite, albite, and, less commonly, barite. Emerald is rare in the enclosing rocks near mineralized fractures, both in shales and limestones.

The paragenetic features of the vein formation of the deposit classify it as typically hydrothermal. Attempts at designating the emerald-bearing Muso veins as a special pegmatite type (Pyatnitskii, 1932, 1934), or finding a close relation between the beryl-bearing formations and pegmatites, lack any serious foundation.

Based on conditions of mineral formation, the little studied emerald deposit in Brazil (Bom Jesus dos Meiras) is apparently similar to the Muso region deposits. It is related to mineralized fractural zones in lower Paleozoic dolomitic marbles overlying preCambrian gneisses (Pyatnitskii, 1932a, 1932b).

The emerald-bearing fractures are filled with talc and contain geodes filled with quartz and calcite crystals. In association with the latter, there are emerald crystals, which, in many places, are growing into calcite. Emerald is also associated with tourmaline, topaz, and monazite, which are present in geodes. Garnet, hematite, mica, and chalcedony are found in the mineral complex that replaces dolomite.

Another type of hydrothermal beryllium deposit, occurrences of which have become increasingly numerous each year, is in various sulfide deposits (including sulfide-cassiterite) with helvite-danalite mineralization (Hewett, 1937). The minerals of the helvite-danalite groups in these deposits are undoubtedly of late character, and are arranged in cavities among metasomatic, polymetallic ores, or transgress such ores along narrow fractures. In some sulfidic polymetallic deposits (e.g., the Grandview deposit, New Mexico, U.S.A.) helvite is closely associated with fluorite; it either grows on fluorite crystals, which are found in cavities, or forms intergrowths with them (Weissenborn, 1948). However, in other deposits of analogous type there is not the usual paragenetic relationship between beryllium and fluorine minerals. One such polymetallic deposit in the Middle East occurs in the zone of contact between middle Paleozoic limestones and an intrusion of upper Paleozoic syenites. S. T. Badalov (1956), who found beryllium minerals in this deposit, notes helvite in the following types of vein formations that transgress the polymetallic ore bodies of metasomatic origin:

1. in polymetallic veins and streaks
2. in calcite-amethyst veins
3. in quartz-pyrite veins
4. in "talcized" fractured zones
5. in quartz-chalcedony formations with pyrites.

In all of the above vein formations, helvite is a large mineral related to the final low-temperature hydrothermal stages.

Besides helvite and danalite, phenacite is fairly common in the hydrothermal sulfide formations (Pough, 1936); individual deposits are known to contain beryl and herderite, although these minerals are most probably related to the earlier stages that preceded the sulfide formation (Cornwall, England). In some of these deposits, topaz and fluorite occur (Cornwall, etc.) indicating the usual beryllium-fluorine paragenesis. In other deposits, fluorine minerals are apparently absent; this absence points to the fact that the beryllium-fluorine paragenesis is not essential in hydrothermal conditions (Table 112).

In this respect, the paragenesis of beryllium minerals in Alpine type veins is very demonstrative. Although Alpine veins containing beryllium minerals are very rare and little studied, available data indicates that the beryllium minerals are of fairly late formation. The euclase, phenacite, milarite, and bavenite crystals found in Alpine veins usually grow on the faces of quartz or feldspar crystals. In a number of places their close paragenesis with chlorite was noted, the chlorite shales often enclosed phenacite or euclase crystals (Pough, 1936). It should be noted that because we have

Table 112 Paragenesis of beryllium minerals in hydrothermal sulfide deposits

Deposit	Minerals	Association of vein and ore minerals
Grandview, New Mexico, U.S.A.	Helvite	Fluorite, sphalerite, galena
Uzbekistan, USSR	Helvite	Calcite, quartz, pyrite, sphalerite, galena
Butte, Montana	Helvite	Rhodonite, rhodochrosite, quartz, sulfides
Cornwall, England	Beryl, herderite, phenacite (in the sequence of separation)	Quartz, sphalerite, cassiterite, arsenopyrite, topaz, molybdenite, apatite, fluorite
Fremont, France	Phenacite (short-prismatic crystals)	Magnetite, hematite, siderite, manganite, barite, topaz, pyrite, tetrahedrite, chalcopyrite, galena, sphalerite, antimonite, bismuth
Sao Miguel, Brazil	Phenacite	Tourmaline, pyrite, gold, chlorite
Durango, Mexico	Phenacite	Martite (after magnetite), apatite, sulfides
Henneberg, Thuringia	Milarite, bavenite	Calcite, barite, fluorite, chalcopyrite

no data on any simultaneous occurrence of various beryllium minerals in Alpine veins, it is impossible at present to say anything definite about their relationship.

PART III
Geochemistry of Beryllium

CHAPTER 7

Beryllium in the Universe

Beryllium is a scarce element in the universe, although information of its occurrence is very limited.

The main cause of beryllium scarcity is usually thought to be the instability of the nucleus of the natural beryllium isotope. However, in general, it is not correct to present the cosmic history of beryllium as a nondirectional process of constant progressive decay of its atoms.

As a result of various nuclear reactions that take place in the universe; the decay of the beryllium atoms is accompanied by the parallel, continuous production of its various isotopes, accompanying the reactions of fission of atoms of many elements.[1]

It is known that beryllium (like lithium and boron) is exceptionally rare in stars; this as already noted (Chapter 1), is usually related to the facility with which its nuclei decay during the fundamental emission period of a star's life. However, the great scarcity of beryllium in stars cannot serve as a basis for assuming its absence in the interstellar gaseous and dust-like material that constitutes about one-half of the entire substance of the Milky Way.

[1] In this connection, one must note the indication (Daiton, Fowler, Kent, 1954) of the presence in cosmic radiation of a considerable quantity of beryllium nuclei (along with Li and B), whose origin has not yet been explained.

The beryllium content of meteorites, which reflects to a certain degree its occurrence in the universe, was studied by V. Goldschmidt and C. Peters (1932). Their figures confirm in general the cosmic scarcity of this element (Table 113). However, the beryllium content of some stony meteorites is very close to its mean content in the accessible upper part of the lithosphere.

The investigation of the occurrence of beryllium in the sun (Greenstein and Tandberg-Hanssen, 1954) showed a rough correspondence to terrestrial values and to beryllium in meteorites. The ratios Be/H $= 10^{-10}$, Be/Li $= 8$, and Be/Ca $= 6 \times 10^{-5}$, calculated by these investigators, point to the fact that in the sun, beryllium is more widespread than lithium,

Table 113 Beryllium content of meteorites

Nature of analyzed material	Location	Be content in 10^{-4}%
Meteoric iron	From various regions	0
Olivine from pallasite	Kansas	0
Chondrites	From various regions	3.6
Sesquioxides from chondrite	Pultusk, Poland	3.6
Eucrites	From various regions	3
Moldavites (10 analyses)	From various regions	3.6–36

whereas the earth's crust the ratio Be/Li $= 5 \times 10^{-2}$. The scarcity of lithium, with respect to beryllium, in the sun is explained by the existence, in the solar envelope, of a layer in which beryllium is relatively stable, whereas lithium is rapidly destroyed by thermonuclear reactions. It is also possible to find other explanations based on the ready reproductibility of beryllium nuclei during the fission of atoms of other elements in thermonuclear reactions.

The continuous genesis of beryllium atoms as a result of nuclear reactions is feebly evident also within the terrestrial atmosphere, where some atmophilic elements (e.g., gold and oxygen) are split by cosmic rays. The result of such a fission is, in particular, the formation of radioactive beryllium isotopes Be^7 and Be^{10}, whose half-lives are 53 days and 2.7×10^6 years, respectively.

The radioactive Be^7 was found in the residue, separated from rainwater and snow (Arnold and Al-Salih, 1955). Investigations are also being carried out on the separation of the radioactive isotope Be^{10} (which can be utilized as a peculiar geological chronometer) from rainwater, seawater, and marine precipitates (Peters, 1955).

Generalization of available fragmentary data on the cosmochemistry of beryllium indicates that its occurrence in the universe is the manifestation of a certain equilibrium between continuous nuclear processes of decay and generation of beryllium atoms.

CHAPTER 8

Beryllium in the Magmatic Process

In the geochemical processes taking place in the earth's crust, beryllium behaves as a typical lithophilic element. This is born out by its distribution in various rocks of the lithosphere.

V. M. Goldschmidt and C. Peters (1932) were the first investigators to study systematically the distribution of beryllium in rocks of the terrestrial crust. The investigation was carried out by means of the spectrographic method, which enabled 0.001 percent BeO (3.6×10^{-4} percent Be) to be determined in the sample. Mostly individual samples and, to a lesser extent, average samples of various rocks were analyzed.

According to V. M. Goldschmidt and C. Peters, the mean beryllium content of granites is 3.6×10^{-4} percent, of nepheline syenites, 36×10^{-4} percent. They found that the overall mean beryllium content of the earth's crust is 1.8×10^{-4} percent (0.0005 percent BeO).

Between 1943 and 1952, Sandell (Sandell and Goldich, 1943; Sandell, 1952), using their fluorescence (morin) method of chemical analyses of silicate rocks for beryllium, investigated sixteen average samples prepared from mixtures of various rocks, and a number of specimens of rocks and minerals (Table 114).

After preliminary chemical treatment of the sample, the fluorescence method enables 0.2×10^{-4} percent Be to be detected in a weighed batch

Table 114 Beryllium content of rocks (according to Sandell)

Rock	Number of mixed samples	Location	Be content in $10^{-4}\%$
Ultrabasic rocks	6	Newfoundland	0.25
Anorthosite	3	United States	0.5
Basalt	2	United States	0.9
Diabase	2	United States	1.3
Medium rocks	24	Antarctica, Newfoundland, India, Africa, United States	0.8–0.9
Diorites	7	United States	1.6
Granites	16	Canada, United States	2.4
Granites and other acid rocks	14	Canada, United States	2.7
Granites	20	Canada, United States	3.0
Granites	9	Africa	3.3
Granites	5	Llano, Texas	5.5
Mean mixture of granites	–	–	3
Syenites	6	United States	2.2
Phonolites	4	Africa	7

of 0.1 g; this considerably increases the accuracy of the investigation.

The overall mean beryllium content of the earth's crust, as calculated by Sandell (2×10^{-4} percent Be), was found to be very close to the data found by Goldschmidt and Peters.

To study the beryllium content and reveal the regularities of its distribution in rocks and minerals, the author examined in 1953–1955 mean samples and typical specimens in various intrusion complexes from various regions of the Soviet Union.[1]

More than five hundred samples were investigated. The improved fluorescence (morin) method (Beus and Fedorchuk, 1955) and the quantitative spectrographic method (Beus and Sazhina, 1956) were used; in the analysis of some samples, both methods were used for cross-checking.[2] There is good agreement between the results of the chemical and spectrographic analyses. The results of these investigations are listed in Table 115-117 and in Fig. 59.

These results showed a considerable difference among beryllium contents of rocks in various regions of the USSR; this difference corresponded with the metallogenetic features of the geochemical provinces lying within the respective regions. The mean figures obtained are naturally not final,

[1] The specimens of the Petrographic Museum of the IGEM of the Academy of Sciences of the USSR were also used.

[2] Chemical analyses of samples for this research were carried out by S. N. Fedorchuk, and all quantitative spectrographic determinations were carried out by L. I. Sazhina.

Table 115 Beryllium content of ultrabasic, basic and intermediate rocks in the USSR

Rock	Number of samples	Location	Limits of Be content in $10^{-4}\%$	Mean Be content in $10^{-4}\%$
Dunites, pyroxenites	15	Urals, Karelia	<0.2	<0.2
Labradorites, gabbro-norites	9	Ukraine, Urals	<0.2	<0.2
Gabbro	10 Mixture	Sinkiang, Urals, Ukraine, Far East	–	0.3
Pegmatoid gabbro	2 Mixture	Urals (Talov complex)	–	1.6
Basalts	10	Transcaucasia, eastern Siberia, Kazakhstan, Far East	less than 0.2–2.5	0.3
Diorites and gabbro-diorites	10	Urals, Central Asia, Altai Kazakhstan, Far East	1–3	1.8

Table 116 Beryllium content in acid rocks of the USSR and China (Sinkiang)

Rock	Number of samples	Location	Limits of Be content in $10^{-4}\%$	Mean Be content in $10^{-4}\%$
Biotite granites (rapakivi, etc.)	10	Karelia	2–4	2.3
Biotite and hornblende granites	14[a]	Ukraine	2–6	3.5
Biotite and bimica granites	10	Caucasus	2–7	3.5
Biotite granites	15	Tuva	1–6	3.6
Biotite and bimica granites	20	Urals	2–14	3.8
Biotite, bimica and muscovitic granites	45	Mongolian Altai, China	2–14	4.5
Biotite, bimica and muscovitic granites	20[a]	Primor'e (Far East Littoral Province)	2–10	5.6
Biotite, bimica and muscovitic granites	13[a]	Upper Altai	2–25	5.6
Biotite, bimica and muscovitic granites	15[a]	Central Kazakhstan	2–11	6.4
Biotite, bimica and muscovitic granites	84[a]	Eastern Transbaikalia	2–16	7
Mean value for biotite and hornblende granites (Fig. 59)	130	From various regions of the USSR and China (Sinkiang)	1–13	4
Mean value for bimica and muscovite granites (Fig. 59)	40	From various regions of the USSR and China (Sinkiang)	2–17	9
Mean value for granites in the USSR	200	From various regions of the USSR	1–32	5
Acid effusive rocks	20[b]	Caucasus, Crimea		6

[a] Combined samples for various complexes or rock masses

[b] Mixture of specimens

Table 117 Beryllium content of alkalic rocks in the USSR

Rock	Number of samples	Location	Limits of Be content in $10^{-4}\%$	Mean Be content in $10^{-4}\%$
Mariupolites	5	Mariupol alkalic rocks	3–7	5
Miaskites	6	Il'men alkalic rocks	3–10	5
Miaskites	[a]	Vishnevaya Gora alkalic rocks	–	2
Biotite syenites	[a]	Vishnevaya Gora alkalic rocks	–	4
Aegirine-augite syenites	[a]	Vishnevaya Gora alkalic rocks	–	6
Syenites	10	From various regions of the USSR	2–14	7
Nepheline syenites	4	Botogol' rock mass	2–3	2
Nepheline syenites	4	Turkestan range	3–5	4
Nepheline syenites	a	Khibiny rock mass	–	7
Khibinites	2[a]	Khibiny rock mass	6–8	7
Urtites	[a]	Khibiny rock mass	–	5
Foyaites	[a]	Khibiny rock mass	–	6
Ristschorrites	[a]	Khibiny rock mass	–	6
Poikilitic nepheline syenites	[a]	Lovozero rock mass	–	10
Foyaites	4[a]	Lovozero rock mass	10–20	15
Malignites	[a]	Lovozero rock mass	–	4
Loparitic juvites	[a]	Lovozero rock mass	–	5
Juvites	[a]	Lovozero rock mass	–	16
Lujavrites				
Normal and hornblende	4[a]	Lovozero rock mass	5–13	8
Eudialytic	3[a]	Lovozero rock mass	8–24	15
Loparitic	[a]	Lovozero rock mass	–	5
Melanocratic	[a]	Lovozero rock mass	–	13
Urtites	[a]	Lovozero rock mass	–	9
Loparitic urtites	[a]	Lovozero rock mass	–	20
Ijolite-urtites	[a]	Lovozero rock mass	–	12

[a] Mean combined samples from various complexes. For the Khibinsk rock mass, L.S. Borodin's samples were used, for the Lovozero rock mass those of E.M. Es'kova.

but they point objectively to concrete geochemical provinces. There are provinces distinctly impoverished in beryllium (Karelia, Ukraine), and provinces enriched with it (Primor'e, upper Altai, central Kazakhstan, eastern Transbaikalia). From the available data, it is interesting to note that regions where beryl-bearing pegmatite districts are developed occupy a somewhat transitional position, their beryllium content being either the same as, or slightly exceeding, the mean overall content found in granites (Beus, 1956c). The analyses in Tables 118-122 give the content of beryllium in various complexes of magmatic rocks of the Ukrainian crystalline mass, eastern Transbaikalia, and the pegmatite province of the Mongolian Altai.

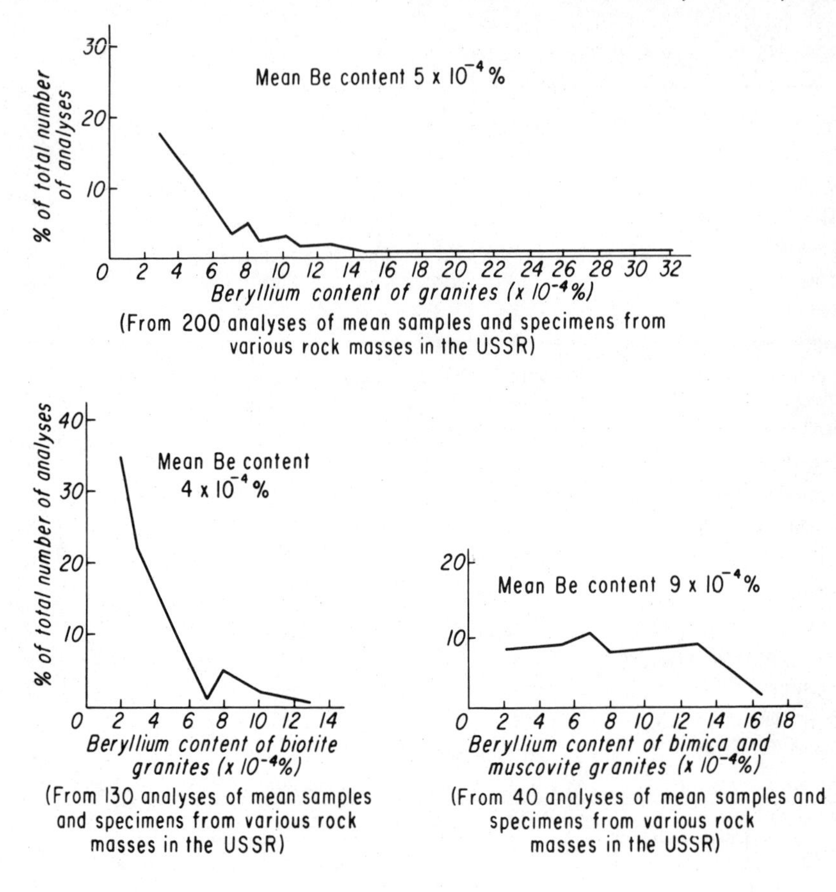

Fig. 59. Beryllium content of granites in the USSR.

Table 118 Mean beryllium content of the main masses of alkalic rocks in the USSR

Rock masses	10^{-4}%
Mariupol'	6
Il'men	5
Vishnevaya Gora [a]	4
Botogol'	2
Khibiny [b]	6
Lovozero [a]	12

[a] From samples of E.S. Es'kova

[b] From results of L.S. Borodin

Table 119 Mean beryllium content of granites associated with pegmatite fields (in 10^{-4}%)

Location	Number of samples	Mean beryllium content
Pegmatite province of Mongolian Altai	45	4.5
Kalbin pegmatite province	14	6
Pegmatite field of Turkestan range	15	5
Pegmatite-bearing granites of Transbaikalia (the Talachin and Sakhanai complexes and Borshchevka Borshchevka ridge)	39	4

The discrepancies between the mean beryllium content of acid and, particularly, alkalic rocks that was calculated for the USSR, and the data of V. M. Goldschmidt and Sandell (Table 114) can be explained by the specific nature of pegmatite provinces developed in the USSR and by the relatively small number of specimens that were examined earlier. In particular, it appears that the mean beryllium content of nepheline

Table 120 Beryllium content of granitoid rocks in the Ukraine

Rocks	Number of samples	Location	Mean Be content in 10^{-4}%
Korosten' red biotite granite	4	Korosten' region	6
Kirovograd-Zhitomir biotite granite	3	Region of river Korchik	2
Coarse-grained biotite granite (Kapustyansk)	2	Kiev province	2
Coarse-grained biotite granite	3	Korsun'-Shevchenkovsk district	4
Charnockite granite	2	Podolia	2
Charnockite granite	1	Area near Azov Sea, region of Old Crimea	3
Biotite granite	2	Ingul'ts district	3
Red Dnieper-Tok granite	3	Krivorozh'e	3
Red Tok granite	2	Krivorozh'e	4
Gray plagioclase granite (Saksagan)	4	Saksagan'	5
Red augite granite	2	Area near Azov Sea, region of Old Crimea	9
Porphyritic biotite granite	1	Oktyabr'skii rock mass	2
Leucocratic granite	1	Oktyabr'skii rock mass	2
Dnieper-Sluch gneiss	6	River Korchik	3
Mean for all granites of the Ukraine	36		3.5

Table 121 Beryllium content of rocks in the pegmatite province of the Mongolian Altai

Rock	Number of samples	Location	Limits of Be content in 10^{-4}%	Mean Be content in 10^{-4}%
Biotite granite	3	Karasu	4	4
Porphyritic and gneissose biotite granites	5	Koktogai	2–4	3
Porphyritic and gneissose biotite granites	6	Kozhurty	1–3	2.3
Porphyritic and gneissose biotite granites	2	Kichkine-Khusty	3–4	3.5
Mean for biotite granites	16		1–4	3.2
Muscovite and bimica granites	3	Chunkur-Dzhailyau	7–8	7
Bimica granites	8	Khusty	mixture of 8 samples	6
Bimica granites	14	Kozhurty	mixture of 14 samples	14
Mean for bimica and muscovite granites	25		6–14	9
Vein muscovite granite	1	Kozhurty	17	–
Aplite-like granite	1	Koktogai	2	–
Aplite-like granite (vein)	1	Kozhurty	3	–
Granite-aplite	1	Kichkine-Khusty	5	–
Mean for granites (allowing for occurrence)	45			4.5
Metamorphosed schists in the roof of the intrusion	20	From various areas	1–8	4

syenites, based on Goldschmidt's data, is much to high, owing to the lack of systematic sampling.

It can be seen from Table 118 that, even in the most intensively mineralized alkalic complex of the USSR (the Lovozero complex), the mean beryllium content determined as a result of the investigation of a large number of combined average samples of the alkalic rocks of which the complex is composed, was found to be only 3 times as great as the overall beryllium content of biotite granites and only 1.4 times as great as the overall content of the muscovite and bimica granites of the USSR. The data on the beryllium content of alkalic rocks in the USSR agree well with the results of L. L. Shilin's (1957) investigations.

Turning now to the problem of beryllium distribution among the minerals of granitoid rocks, we should note that 60 to 80 percent of the beryllium is associated here with the feldspars which form most of the rock. The highest beryllium concentrations are characteristic of muscovite

Table 122 Beryllium content of Mesozoic granitoid rocks and schists of Transbaikalia

Rock	Number of samples	Location	Limits of Be content in $10^{-4}\%$	Mean Be content in $10^{-4}\%$
Granodiorite	1	Upper Telengui	–	2
Biotite granite	5	Borshchevochnyi ridge	3–6	5
Biotite granite	22	Talachin rock mass	3–6	4
Biotite granite	12	Sakhanai rock mass	3–8	4
Porphyritic biotite granite	2	Khangilai-Shily ridge	5–10	8
Biotite granite	4	Kangin district	3–7	5
Biotite granite	1	Aldakachan rock mass	–	8
Biotite granite	2	Area of Shumilov deposit	5–8	6
Gneisose biotite granite	2	Imalkin rock mass	mean sample	6
Biotite granite	1	Adun-Cholon ridge	–	14
Biotite granite	1	Ust'-Chiron	–	4
Bimica granite	1	Area of Molodezhnoe deposit	–	5
Muscovite granite	5	Area of Onon deposit	7–16	10
Bimica granite	1	Area of Kedrov deposit	–	13
Bimica granite	4	Urda-Taptanai rock mass	3–7	5
Muscovite granite	2	Khangilai-Shily ridge	mean sample	5
Muscovite granite	1	Kil'kinda ridge	–	10
Granite-porphyry	15	Sherlovaya Gora	5–20	12
Granite-porphyry	1	Motogorskaya crest	–	10
Leucocratic granite	1	Cherskogo ridge	–	3
Vein granite-aplite	1	Urda-Taptanai rock mass	–	32
Mean of 20 granites (except the preceding)	84		–	7
Metamorphosed schists	20	From various areas	2–6	3.8

and, to a lesser extent, of the dark-colored minerals of the granite, as clearly shown in Tables 123-124.

The results obtained by the author on the distribution of beryllium in the granite minerals agree with those of Sandell's (1952) investigations on two specimens of acid rocks from the United States (Table 125), although in the investigated quartz monzonite, the highest beryllium concentration is characteristic of plagioclase. A similar finding was noted in the porphyritic biotite granites of the Borshchevochnyi Ridge (eastern Transbaikalia), in which up to 80 percent beryllium is contained in oligoclase-albite, which contains on average 10×10^{-4} percent Be.

As in granites where the main mass of disseminated beryllium is associated with feldspar, in alkalic rocks beryllium is mainly contained in nepheline and feldspars, which contain 2 to 20 $\times$ 10^{-4} percent Be. It should be stressed here that the more complicated nature of the beryllium distribution in alkalic rocks, compared with granitoid rocks, is most probably caused by the different conditions of formation of various types of alkalic rocks. Thus, for example, an appreciable beryllium accumulation was noted in the late potassium feldspar of ristschorrites, formed metasmatically (Table 126). At the same time, the primary potassium feldspar of the khibinites does not have, as far as can be seen from the analyses, a higher beryllium content. In individual cases the highest beryllium concentrations among the minerals of alkalic rocks are in the accessory dark-colored minerals (aegirine—as much as 25 $\times$ 10^{-4} percent Be; arfvedsonite—as much as 30 $\times$ 10^{-4} percent Be).

The regularities of beryllium distribution in minerals of various types of alkalic rocks deserve further study. Attention should be given to a comparison of the beryllium content in minerals of various stages of formation of alkalic rocks, including minerals formed during metasomatism, which is clearly shown in many alkalic masses of the USSR.

Concluding the discussion of the occurrence of beryllium in magmatic rocks of the earth's crust, we should note that, as shown by the given data, beryllium is accumulated neither in ultrabasic nor in basic magmas; its proportion in these magmas is usually much smaller than its overall mean proportion in the earth's crust. Some accumulation of beryllium, only slightly in excess of its overall average, is observed in granites, particularly in their muscovite-containing facies, which have been to a lesser or

Table 123 Distribution of beryllium in minerals of granites

Rock and its component minerals	Location	Be content in 10^{-4}%
Coarse-grained biotite granite	Eastern Transbaikalia	2
Plagioclase		5
Microcline		1
Quartz		<0.2
Biotite		10
Porphyraitic biotite granite	Central Transbaikalia	8
Feldspar		7
Quartz		0.2
Dark-colored minerals (biotite, hornblende)		32
Muscovite granite	Urals	14
Feldspar (mainly plagioclase)		10
Quartz		0.2
Muscovite		50
Mean value for 10 samples of biotite, bimica, and muscovite granites	Transbaikalia and Ukraine	4
Quartz		0.2
Feldspar		3.5
Muscovite, biotite, and hornblende		16

greater extent affected by autopneumatolysis, and in alkalic rocks.

Thus the geochemical history of beryllium in the earth's crust is principally associated with the history of acid and alkalic magmas, which contain about 95 percent of the total amount of beryllium atoms in the lithosphere. The behavior of beryllium during the process of crystallization

Table 124 Distribution of beryllium in minerals of the genetically linked series of granitoid rocks of the Durulguev mass, eastern Transbaikalia (according to N.E. Zalashkova)

Mineral	Mineral content of rock in %	Be content of mineral in 10^{-4}%	Be proportion found in mineral in %
Granodiorite			
Feldspar[a]	53	8	85
Quartz	31	trace	–
Biotite	9	trace	–
Hornblende	7	8	15
Mean value for the rock		5	
Porphyritic biotite granite			
Feldspar	63	6	88
Quartz	30	1	7
Biotite	7	3	5
Mean value for the rock		6	
Coarse-grained biotite-muscovite granite			
Feldspar	58	14	72
Quartz	32	not determ.	–
Biotite	1	15	1
Muscovite	9	34	27
Mean value for the rock		12	
Coarse-grained albitized muscovite granite[b]			
Feldspar	56	20	68
Quartz	34	1	2
Muscovite	10	49	30
Mean value for the rock		49	
Coarse-grained greisenized muscovite granite			
Feldspar	46	16	62
Quartz	41	1	4
Muscovite	13	31	34
Mean value for the rock		13	

[a] Feldspars (albite-oligoclase, albite, microcline) are not subdivided, owing to their fine-grained habit or fine intergrowth between microcline and albite in most granites.

[b] The quantity of beryllium in the rock-forming minerals is not balanced by its overall amount in the rock, owing to the presence of accessory beryl.

Table 125 Beryllium content of acidic rocks and constituent minerals in the United States (according to Sandell)

Rock type and constituent minerals	Location	Be content in 10^{-4}%
Quartz monzonite	Rockville, Minnesota	2
Microcline		1
Plagioclase		4
Quartz		0.35
Biotite		0.5
Granite	Devil's Slide, New Hampshire	3.3
Amphibole		26

of acid and alkalic magmas is determined by the geochemical specificity of the different types of magmatic processes.

When analyzing the normal trend of crystallization of the granite melt, we should take into account a fact important to the fate of beryllium disseminated in granitic magma, namely, that titanium and rare earths contained in the acid melt are usually precipitated during the relatively early stages of granite crystallization as ilmenite and monazite.

The negligible average beryllium content in the granitic melt excludes the possibility of formation of individual beryllium minerals in the magmatic stage; at the same time the absence, during the fundamental stages of granite formation, of higher concentrations of free high-valency cations that would be able to compensate for the entry of beryllium into the crystal lattice of silicates, makes difficult, and sharply limits, the capture of beryllium by the rock-forming granite minerals.

Thus, the limited dissemination of beryllium in the products of the main crystallization phase of granitic magma naturally leads to its accumulation in the products of the final stages of crystallization.

Particularly sudden, erratic enrichment in beryllium of late magmatic products apparently occurs in the crystallization of the quartz of granite,

Table 126 Beryllium content of minerals of khibinites and ristschorrites of the Khibiny complex (in 10^{-4}%)[a]

Minerals	Rocks	
	Khibinite	ristschorrite
Nepheline	10	8
Potassium feldspar	2.6	19
Aegirine	5.8	4
Mean content of the rock		10

[a] From the results of an investigation of combined mean samples of the comples, carried out by L.S. Borodin

which normally does not accept beryllium into its lattice (Table 23).

This process is most probably associated with the origin of melts, emanations, and solutions, enriched in beryllium to different degrees during the late stages of the formation of granite. The diversity of these formations is determined by laws governing the development of the magmatic hearth and its geochemical specificity.

Traces of the activity of the late magmatic liquids are found in the widespread muscovitization and greisenization of the granites, when muscovite containing thousandths of 1 percent of beryllium is formed in the granite during its autopneumatolytic or pneumatolytic alteration; thus the overall average beryllium content of bimica and muscovite granites is increased more than twofold, compared with the common biotite and other granites unaffected by muscovitization. The activity of these melts, emanations, and solutions, however, is shown most clearly in the formation of various genetic types of postmagmatic beryllium deposits, the largest of which contain thousands of tons of this element.

Generalization of the analytical results makes it possible to estimate the highest possible value of the average content of beryllium, which is present as isomorphous impurity in the rock-forming and accessory granite minerals, as 15 to 20 $\times 10^{-4}$ percent.[3] This amount of disseminated beryllium in granites, so different from the normal amount, is always related to their postmagmatic alteration (muscovitization, etc.). A somewhat higher degree of dissemination of beryllium is sometimes observed also in granites with a higher content of rare earths, especially in allanite-bearing granites. It should be noted that accessory gadolinite was observed in granites enriched in rare earths of the yttrium group.

While dwelling on the crystallization of alkalic magmas, we must stress the following factors that determine the fate of beryllium in the alkalic process:

1. the overall high average content of rare earths (especially of the cerium group), zirconium, and titanium;
2. the protracted participation of a number of high-valency cations in processes of mineral formation;
3. increased alkalinity of the medium, which determines the possibility of the presence of the complex $BeO_4{}^{6-}$.

These factors facilitate the isomorphous capture of beryllium in the crystallization of the rock-forming and accessory minerals of alkalic rocks by preventing the concentration of beryllium. Indeed, in view of the relatively high overall average beryllium content of alkalic rocks, the concentration of beryllium in postmagmatic processes related to alkalic magma is not characteristic. As already mentioned, however, a number

[3] The higher beryllium content of granite points as a rule to the presence of discreet beryllium minerals.

of minerals of alkalic rocks have a higher content of beryllium, which occurs as an isomorphous admixture. Notwithstanding the much higher beryllium content, compared with the average overall content of the lithosphere, the isomorphous dissemination is the most typical characteristic of beryllium in alkalic rocks.

The formation of beryllium concentrations in alkalic rocks can be anticipated, owing to the redistribution of beryllium in areas of widespread albitization of alkalic rocks, which have a high content of disseminated beryllium.

CHAPTER 9

Beryllium in the Pegmatitic Process

Beryllium in the "Pure-Line" Granitic Pegmatites

The geochemical history of beryllium in the pegmatitic process serves as a clear example of the postmagmatic concentration of a disseminated element, occurring in the original melt in the proportion of ten-thousandths of 1 percent. The leading factor that determines the concentration of beryllium in pegmatites is the differentiation of crystallization, which is of particular importance in the early stages of pegmatite formation (Vlasov, 1956a). In the late stages of pegmatite formation the concentration of beryllium is enhanced by the emanation process, which in the replacement stage appears to be the main factor in the concentration of beryllium.

There is no need to consider in detail the ideas of the author or the origin of pegmatites, as these have been discussed and substantiated in a number of publications (Beus, 1948a, 1948b, 1951, 1953b, 1954, 1956).

The basic foundations of the theory of crystallization by stages from the pegmatite melt, which are defined and developed in the above-mentioned papers, can be summarized as follows:

1. Pegmatites form as a result of crystallization by stages from the pegmatite melt, which is a derivative of the late stage of the normal granite melt, enriched to a certain extent in volatile constituents.

2. The crystallization of the melt takes place in a relatively closed system. This, however, does not exclude the possibility of the escape of a part of the components (including the volatiles) or of their entering from deep levels, depending on tectonic conditions.

3. The replacement phenomena, characteristic of pegmatites, are considered to be a result of interaction between the paragenetic complexes of primary crystallization and the emanations (later the solution) which, in a relatively closed system, separate out of the pegmatite melt-solution during its crystallization at various levels. This by no means denies the possibiiity of the vertical movement of replacing emanations and solutions within the pegmatite intrusive.

Table 127 shows a diagram of the origin of zones in granite pegmatites (Beus, 1954), which illustrates the propositions referred to above.

In our analysis of these aspects of the origin of granitic pegmatites, we will study the behavior of beryllium at various stages of pegmatite formation in order to detect, on the basis of concrete facts, the peculiarities of its migration and concentration under various conditions.

From the behavior of beryllium in the initial stages of pegmatite formation, we may conclude that, as a rule, there is no enrichment in beryllium in the early paragenetic complexes (zones) of which the pegmatite deposits are composed, and that these zones sometimes have even a lower beryllium content than the parent pegmatite-bearing granites (Table 128). The latter is naturally related to the fact that the early parageneses of pegmatites contain no minerals which would be able to take into their lattice any noticeable quantities of beryllium. The mean beryllium content obtained from ten samples from various areas of the graphic zone of beryl-bearing pegmatites, which consist of microcline-perthite and quartz, is 3×10^{-4} percent. This is roughly only two-thirds of the beryllium content characteristic of pegmatitic granites.

Thus, together with the separation of the zones at the beginning of crystallization, which capture only a very limited number of beryllium ions, and with the increase in the content of volatile components, the concentration of beryllium in the residual part of the pegmatite melt-solution also increases.

The extent of concentration depends on a number of factors—the geological position, form, and features of formation of each pegmatitic intrusion, which unites in space a system of pegmatite bodies from their roots to the apical sections.

It is known that, in the main rare-metal pegmatite provinces, more than 80 percent of the pegmatite formations (calculated with respect to mass) consist of the nondifferentiated and poorly differentiated pegmatites of granitic, graphic, or apographic structure, which do not contain any rare-metal (or beryllium) minerals (Beus, 1954). Considering that, during

Table 127 Diagram of the origin of zones in granitic pegmatites (group of microcline and albite pegmatites)

Stage	Medium	Composition	Process	Result	Zone
1st stage – epimagmatic	Eutectic melt in which H_2O, Cl, F, rare elements (Be etc.) are dissolved in quantities not affecting the course of crystallization	$(K,Na)[AlSi_2O_8]_2,SiO_2$	→ solid phase	Zone of graphic and coarse-grained pegmatite	a
2nd stage – pneumatomagmatic	Melt solution saturated with volatile	$K[AlSi_3O_8]$	→ solid phase	Zone of block microcline	b
		$q(Na,K)_2O.pSiO_2.sH_2O$; H_2O mNa_2On (BeO etc.). $b(Cl,F.OH,CO_3)$	Solid phase →	Beryl, spodumene, etc.	
	Supercritical solution	H_2O; $q(Na,K)_2O.pSiO_2$; $mNa_2O.n$(BeO etc.). $1(Cl,F,OH,CO_3)$	Replacement → of zones a and b	Formation of replacement perthites. At the end of the stage formation of muscovite replacement zone	
3rd stage – hydrothermal pneumatolytic	Solid phase	$q(Na,K)_2O.pSiO_2.sH_2O$	hydrolysis → solid phase	Zone of block quartz	c
	Supercritical, then hydrothermal solution	$H_2O(Na,K)OH,(Na,K)(Cl,F)$ $mNa_2O.n$(BeO etc.). $1(Cl,F,OH,CO_3)$	Replacement → of zones a,b,c.	Formation of replacement zones: albitic, greisen, lepidolitic. Crystallization of alkalic beryls, tantalo-niobates	

crystallization of these paragenetic complexes, only a part of beryllium in the disseminated state occurring in the original melt undergoes capture, we must note that, even if the beryllium concentrations in the pegmatite melt and in the parent granite melts are the same, higher beryllium concentrations may be expected in the later stages of pegmatite formation. Thus, in the initial period of evolution of the pegmatitic process, the peculiarities of formation of the early paragenetic complexes of pegmatites, combined with the limited capability of beryllium to enter isomorphously the rock-forming minerals of these complexes, are the main factors that determine its concentration.

As the pegmatitic process develops, following the formation of the zones of graphic and medium-grained pegmatite, and as the large monomineralic

Table 128 Beryllium content of some granites and associated early pegmatite zones

Location	Be content of granites, in 10^{-4} %	Be content of the zone of graphic pegmatite, in 10^{-4}%	Be content of block microcline-perthite, in 10^{-4}%
Ukraine	2	<0.5	1
Altai	4	3	4
Transbaikalia	4	7	2
Transbaikalia	5	3	2
Altai	7	4	5

blocks of microcline-perthite separate out, beryllium concentrates in the residual parts of pegmatite melt-solution, enriched in volatile components.

Finally, at a certain time, which usually coincides with the end of formation of the monomineralic microcline-perthite blocks, crystallization of the main beryllium mineral (beryl in granitic pegmatites) begins, under the conditions of strong supersaturation with silicon and accumulations of sodium and the volatile components. Beryl continues to form during the stage of pneumatolytic-hydrothermal replacements, until the formation of the last lepidolite replacement complex of the pegmatites and greisen.

The earliest beryllium deposition, represented by alkali-free beryl that crystallized in the block quartz of the central block zone of pegmatite formations in which replacement processes were not noticeably developed has no apparent connection with replacement phenomena. These beautifully formed prismatic beryl crystals most probably form in relatively free conditions prior to the crystallization of block quartz; this is borne out in particular by the numerous instances of intersection and cementing of large crystals of prismatic beryl with block quartz.

The usual association of beryl crystals of this generation with the edge of feldspar and of the later block quartz indicates that the major crystallization of beryl in these sections was the result of reaction between late silicate solutions and feldspars at the boundary of the two media. The development in these places of high-temperature dealkalization in a number of examples is confirmed by the close association between the early alkali-free beryl and the quartz-muscovite replacement complex, segregations of which are associated with the boundary between the quartz core and surrounding feldspar zones.

The main mass of beryl in pegmatites, consisting of the alkalic varieties, shows a close relationship to albitization and crystallized during the replacement of microcline by beryllium-containing sodic solutions, which separated as a result of the crystallization of the residual batches of silica in the pegmatite melt-solution and formed the zone of block quartz (Beus, 1954; Beus and Zalashkova, 1956).

The separated sodic-containing solution replaces parts of the pegmatite around the block-quartz zone being formed and gives rise to the characteristic beryl-bearing albite and muscovite-albite aureoles around the quartz core. The solutions also partly penetrate along fractures into the sections near the selvedge and, migrating along the weakened contact zones of the pegmatite into upper horizons, form endocontact albite replacement zones that contain sodium and sodium-lithium beryls.

In this period of pegmatite formation (the pneumatomagmatic and pneumatohydrothermal stages), the mode of migration and concentration of beryllium is determined by its close relationship to the behavior of volatile components of the pegmatite melt-solution. This relationship is shown clearly in the formation of the highest concentration of beryllium minerals in the apical parts of pegmatite bodies, in domes, and at various "barriers" characteristic of some pegmatite bodies, which have a complicated shape or include large xenoliths of the enclosing rocks. The function of these volatile components may be illustrated by the uniformity of distribution of beryllium in all beryl-bearing pegmatite fields and separate pegmatites in which replacement processes have been somewhat developed.

Thus, depending of the degree of development of replacement caused by the regular change in concentration of volatile compounds in various stages of the process (Vlasov, 1952; Beus, 1951, 1954) the evolution of the pegmatite results in a separation of the beryllium in the pegmatite melt-solution.

Under conditions of a limited development of replacement, part of the beryllium crystallizes directly from the residual silicate solution and forms the zone of block quartz (alkali-free beryl varieties). Another much greater part is captured by sodium-containing emanations and solutions which separate out in the crystallization of the residual portion of the pegmatite melt-solution and, migrating into various sections of the pegmatite body, precipitate in the solid phase in the replacement process in the form of alkali beryl varieties.

Now, what are the possible migration forms of beryllium in the pegmatitic process?

The solution of this complex and interesting problem can be found only by a detailed analysis of the paragenesis of beryllium minerals of pegmatites that takes into account the nature and properties of the mobile beryllium compounds. The special role of the multi-phase inclusions occurring in beryllium minerals must also be considered, because the composition of these inclusions is so far the only criterion that permits one to form an objective judgment of the importance, in the pegmatitic process, of a number of volatile components. These play a leading part in the composition of the anionic part of volatile and readily soluble compounds of many rare elements, including beryllium, that can be assumed to migrate in the pegmatitic process. The few investigations of the composition of liquid-gaseous inclusions in beryls (Ermakov, 1950; Cameron *et al.,* 1953) and the wide occurrence in beryls of various generations of primary micro-inclusions of chlorides and fluorides of alkali metals, fluorite, and carbon dioxide, allow one to conclude that, besides the OH group, such anions as Cl^{1-}, F^{1-}, CO_3^{2-}, HCO_3^{1-} also actively participate in the beryllium transfer during the formation of pegmatites.

Under conditions of a relatively high concentration of alkalis (mainly sodium), which is characteristic of this period of pegmatite formation, and in the presence of halogen (chlorine or fluorine) and carbon dioxide, which are active extracting and mineralizing agents, the transfer of beryllium took place most probably in the form of mobile complex compounds such as chloroberyllates, fluoroberyllates, and carbonate-beryllates of alkali metals, which migrated in the pegmatite formation process in supercritical (later in aqueous) solutions into the central parts of pegmatite bodies and into the upper levels of the pegmatite injection.

Thus, when beryllium is transferred in the form of mobile complex halogenic or carbonate compounds with alkali metals, the precipitation of beryllium in the solid phase in the form of beryllium minerals can be visualized as a complex process of decomposition of mobile beryllium compounds and of its binding in the form of poorly soluble beryllium-aluminum metasilicate. Depending on the type of compounds, this process should be accompanied by the continuous separation of the soluble halogen compounds of alkalis or of carbon dioxide, the major part of which is evacuated or combined in other minerals. Only a negligible proportion is captured by the growing crystal in the form of inclusions; this conclusively points to the importance of halogen compounds and carbonates in the beryllium-transfer and beryl-forming process.

Such a solution to the problem of the mechanism of beryl crystallization, which apparently can be applied to a number of other rare-metal minerals, indicates that beryl may be formed both by free crystallization from the residual portions of the pegmatite melt-solution, which form the zone of block quartz, and within the solid medium by the replacement of feldspar by beryllium-containing emanations and solutions.

Thus, if we start from the paragenetic association characteristic of sodium and sodium-lithium beryl, the scheme of formation of this generation in the process of the replacement of microcline can be represented in general as follows:

$$\underset{\text{microcline}}{K[AlSi_3O_8]} + \underset{\text{sodium beryllium-containing solution}}{H_2O + NaBeX_3{}^{1}} \longrightarrow$$

$$\underset{\text{albite}}{Na[AlSi_3O_8]} + \underset{\text{muscovite}}{KAl_2[AlSi_3O_{10}](OH)} + \underset{\text{quartz}}{SiO_2} + \underset{\text{beryl}}{Al_2Be_3[Si_6O_{18}]}$$

$$+ \underset{\text{solution}}{H_2O} + \underset{\text{loss of alkali halides and carbonates}}{(K,Na)X}$$

Both in free crystallization and in the process of replacement, crystal growth is determined by the gradual decomposition of the complex mobile beryllium compounds that takes place as a result of the change of the physico-chemical state of the system at various stages of pegmatite formation. At the same time, the smallest proportions of gaseous-liquid inclusions captured during the growth process may be expected to occur in crystals that form by slow, quiet crystallization from gaseous-aqueous solutions in relatively free conditions ensuring the easy removal of the gaseous and liquid decomposition products.

The hypothesis is substantiated by the absence or relatively small amount of gaseous-liquid inclusions in transparent beryl crystals from the quartz cores and cavities of pegmatites. Beryl crystals formed by rapid crystallization or grown in a solid medium, which hampers the evacuation of reaction products, are usually full of gaseous-liquid inclusions that commonly contain the solid phase.

Very little is known about the factors that determine the probability of decomposition of the complex beryllium compounds. Of particular importance, apparently, is the change in the acidity-alkalinity conditions of the solution towards higher pH values, which always occurs during sodium metasomatism. A very important moment in the evolution of the pegmatite melt-solution also is the appearance of the liquid H_2O phase, which readily causes the hydrolysis of substances unstable in the presence of water, such as chloroberyllates, etc. It can be assumed that the transfer of beryllium in the form of such easily hydrolyzable complex compounds, which occur along with more stable complexes, can take place under supercritical conditions, as observed in the early stages of pegmatite formation (the pneumatomagmatic stage and the initial periods of the pneumatohydrothermal stage).

Owing to the decomposition of unstable complex beryllium compounds in the late stages, the function of the more stable complexes (e.g., fluoroberyllates, carbonate-beryllates) increases. Thus, as the evolution of the

[1] X—anions-ligands: F^{1-}, Cl^{1-}, $HCO_3{}^{1-}$, etc.

pegmatitic process progresses, the nature of the compounds in whose form the transfer of beryllium is effected, may change.

Differences in the stability and reactivity of the complex beryllium compounds, which may be assumed to be present in the pegmatitic process, are most probably one of the causes of the protracted participation of beryllium in this process. This possibility offers an explanation of differences in the composition of the gaseous-liquid inclusions, characteristic of various generations of beryl, and in particular of the predominance of fluorides in beryl related to the early stages of albitization, and of the predominance of carbonic acid in the late beryls that crystallize in cavities. One can also explain the usual absence of industrial accumulations of beryl in pegmatitic intrusive complexes containing an abundance of fluorine in the pegmatite-formation process. In the presence of greater fluorine concentrations, beryllium is last in the pegmatitic process as fluoroberyllates or fluorides, and takes part in pneumatolytic and hydrothermal processes. As a rule, high fluorine concentrations in beryl-bearing pegmatites are not noted, and the fluorine-containing minerals, such as topaz or fluorite, are rare in these pegmatites or occur in negligible quantities. The paragenesis of beryl with topaz and fluorite is observed only in cavities of miarolitic pegmatites, but the amount of beryl formed in these conditions is very small.

With the crystallization of alkali beryls in later periods of the replacement stage, recrystallization and partial dissolution of alkali-free or sodium beryl takes place by the action of solutions enriched in lithium and cesium. Such phenomena are accompanied by the redeposition of beryllium in the form of sodium-lithium or lithium-cesium beryl, characteristic of the cleavelandite and lepidolite replacement complexes.

Another precipitating agent of beryllium, which has passed into solution as a result of the dissolution of beryl under the action of late sodic solutions in this final period of pegmatite formation, is phosphorus. It forms with beryllium a number of minerals stable under the usual hydrothermal conditions (herderite, beryllonite, moraesite, etc.), which crystallize in small cavities within albite.

When the late hydrothermal solutions, already impoverished in alkalis, act on beryl, individual crystals of it are partly or, more rarely, wholly recrystallized with the formation of peculiar pseudomorphs of secondary beryllium minerals. The most common products of such transformation are bertrandite, and, less commonly, phenacite, which forms in paragenesis with the potassium mica that absorbs aluminum. In the event of a deficiency of potassium, bertrandite and euclase are formed together (Strand, 1953). The addition of calcium, which, in a number of cases is characteristic of the final stages of the pegmatite process (Ginzburg, 1955a), results in the formation of pseudomorphs of bavenite or bavenite plus bertrandite (when calcium is deficient) after beryl.

It should be noted that the late-hydrothermal alteration of beryl occurs,

Table 129 Disseminated beryllium content of minerals and mineral complexes of the "pure-line" granitic pegmatites (in 10^{-4} percent)

Mineral or rock	Number of samples from various areas	Pegmatites containing no rare-metal minerals (Ukraine)	Pegmatites containing beryllium minerals		Pegmatites containing rare-metal minerals but no beryllium minerals
			Limits	Mean	
Graphic pegmatite	16	1 — 2	3 — 7	—	1 — 20
Medium-grained pegmatite with tourmaline and garnet	6	1 — 3	—	—	—
Block microcline-perthite	30	1 — 3	5 — 36	8	12 — 20
Block oligoclase	5	—	—	—	10 — 36
Block quartz	9	1	0.5 — 4	2	1
Albite	30	—	4 — 61	18	—
Muscovite	30	1	20 — 108	56	40
Lepidolite	10	—	16 — 126	50	—
Black tourmaline	4	—	13 — 36	—	—
Multichromed tourmaline	2	—	20 — 36	—	—
Garnet	3	—	6 — 20	—	—
Spodumene	5	—	5 — 72	10	—
Apatite	1	—	18	—	—
Cyrtolite	2	—	—	—	56 — 210
Monazite	1	—	—	—	28
Allanite	4	—	—	—	124 — 685

in general, rather rarely. Such processes as the kaolinization of beryl, accompanied by the loss of beryllium, are also observed in some deposits. The author fully agrees with Kerr (1946), who studied this question in detail and demonstrated the small probability of an exogenous origin of the kaolinization of beryl, which is chemically a very stable mineral with respect to the agents of hypergenesis.

Turning to the question of the relation between disseminated and concentrated beryllium in pegmatites, we should note that, in the replacement stage, the process of dissemination of beryllium is somewhat intensified, owing to the capture of a part of its ions in the lattices of the rock-forming minerals of the replacement complexes. The main collectors of disseminated beryllium are naturally albite and micas (Table 129). However, in the beryllium-bearing pegmatites the total mass of disseminated beryllium is much smaller than that concentrated as beryllium minerals as can be seen from the numerical data given in Table 99, the coefficient of beryllium concentration $k/(k + p) \times 100$ (where k is the beryllium content in beryllium minerals, and p the content of disseminated beryllium), as a rule, does not fall below 90 percent in pegmatites containing 0.2 percent or more beryl. The variation in the limits of the content of disseminated beryllium in pegmatites in general is not great. Thus, for example, when comparing pegmatite deposits in which the total beryllium content varies by a factor of 7 (Tables 94–99), we see that the content of disseminated beryllium in these formations varies only by the factor of 2 (Fig. 60). Summarizing the data relating to disseminated beryllium in beryllium-bearing pegmatites, we must conclude that the limits of its dissemination in pegmatite formations do not exceed those in granites and sometimes are even less.

Thus, in such pegmatites, the important geochemical factor that governs the concentration of beryllium as beryllium minerals proper (even when

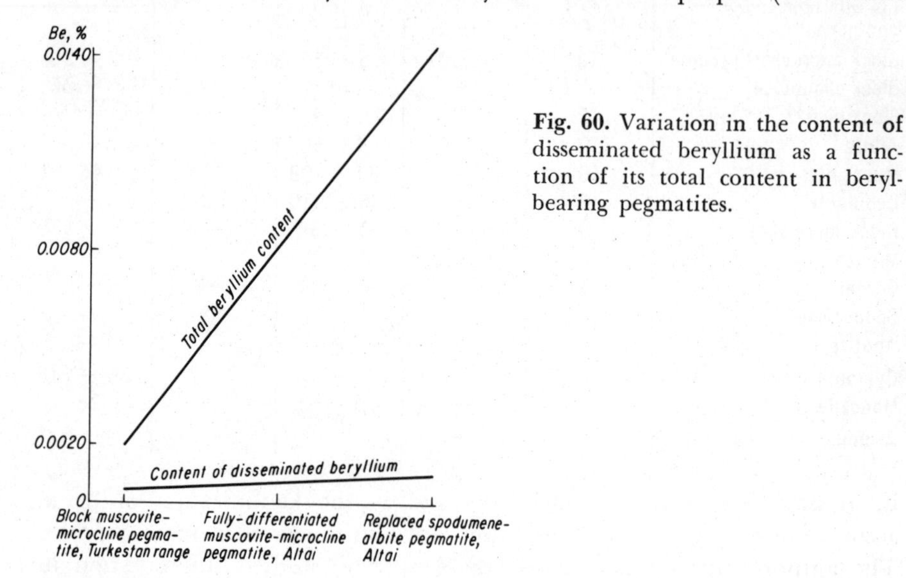

Fig. 60. Variation in the content of disseminated beryllium as a function of its total content in beryl-bearing pegmatites.

its content is relatively low) is the extremely low degree of its dissemination, caused in particular by the unimportance of a number of elements that would be able to compensate with energy for the entry of beryllium into silicate lattices.

Somewhat different is the behavior of beryllium in varieties of granitic pegmatites that contain higher concentrations of rare earths, niobium, tantalum, and titanium. A considerable proportion of beryllium is disseminated under these conditions, entering as an isomorphous admixture into feldspars, allanite, cyrtolite, and the yttrium-earths in metamict tantalo-niobates (fergusonite, yttro-tantalite, etc.). In particular, relatively high beryllium concentrations are found in a number of minerals (including oligoclase and microcline) from the block zones of pegmatites of the Baltic Shield, containing noticeable proportions of yttrium-earths in tantalo-niobates (Table 129). The analysis of feldspars for rare earths confirmed the presence of yttrium in oligoclase, and of lanthanum in microcline. Despite the higher mean beryllium content in these pegmatites, beryllium minerals are absent.

Given favorable conditions (presence of iron and absence of boron) and high beryllium concentrations, gadolinite is formed in the rare-earth pegmatites. It is natural that under these conditions the formation of beryl is hampered, and deposits simultaneously containing high concentrations of gadolinite and beryl or of rare-earth tantalo-niobates and beryl are extremely rare. Despite the very different nature of beryllium minerals, determined by the active part played by iron and the rare earths during mineral formation, beryllium migration during the formation of gadolinite-containing pegmatites apparently differs but little in principle from the above-mentioned features of beryllium migration in normal (pure-line, Ed.) beryl-bearing pegmatites.[2] The relationship between the highest beryllium concentration and albitization, which indicates the common forms of beryllium transfer in these seemingly different types of pegmatite deposits, is clearly shown.

Brief mention should be made of the behavior of beryllium in pegmatites whose formation was accompanied by assimilation of the enclosing rocks; it has exerted an important influence on the chemistry of the pegmatitic process. Thus, for example, the nature of beryllium mineralization changes abruptly in pegmatite formations characterized by an appreciable reaction between the pegmatite melt and enclosing rocks enriched in alumina. As a result of this reaction, an excess of Al_2O_3 is introduced during the pegmatite formation (aluminous contamination;) at the same time an energetic migration of potassium from the pegmatite into the enclosing rocks resulted in the formation of characteristic exocontact aureoles of the altered enclosing rocks enriched in mica or in feldspar.

The disturbance of the aluminum-alkali relation usually found in pegmatites results in the appearance of a certain aluminum excess in the process of mineral formation; this excess cannot be bound by alkalis and calcium in the composition of feldspars or micas, and separates as a solid in the form of aluminum silicates, and later of aluminum phosphates.

The formation of beryl with the ratio Be:Al = 3:2 is difficult in the presence of an excess of aluminum and under conditions of alkali deficiency. In such pegmatites beryllium combines during the process of muscovitization with aluminum in the form of chrysoberyl (ratio Be:Al = 1:2), which separates out in the stage of formation of the quartz-muscovite replacement complex, or somewhat later.

Besides the primary enrichment in aluminum, the formation of chrysoberyl in muscovite-oligoclase pegmatites may be caused by the albitization of oligoclase, the absorption of silicon, and the separation of excess alu-

[2] Crystallization of beryl and gadolinite point to the analogous conditions, in particular, the development of skeletal forms of crystals formed in the process of replacement of microcline, and other features of their mineralogy.

minum, which in this case definitely binds the beryllium in the form of chrysoberyl.

Thus, when analyzing the factors that determine the transfer of beryllium in the pegmatitic process, we should pay special attention to the important role of sodic emanations and solutions which, in the presence of volatile mineralizing agents (chlorine, fluorine, carbonic acid) are the carriers of a number of rare elements, including beryllium. Of great importance are such properties of beryllium as its capability to form a number of readily migrating complex compounds. Depending on their type, these compounds have a diverse degree of stability and can be transported in the acid and weakly alkaline mediums in supercritical or hydrothermal solutions.

This can explain the continuous paragenesis of beryllium in deposits, with such rare elements as niobium, tantalum, and zirconium, which show in granitic pegmatites a constant relationship to the activity of replacing sodic emanations and solutions.

Like beryllium, niobium, tantalum, and zirconium are also complex-formers, and the complex compounds of these elements are also the most probable forms of their transport in mineral-forming solutions. The possible similarity between the properties of the complex compounds of the above-mentioned rare metals and those of some complex beryllates determines their common paths of migration and the similar conditions of decomposition when the physico-chemical conditions of the system undergo a change. This is most probably the main cause of the paragenetic link between beryllium, tantalum, niobium, and zirconium in the rare-earth pegmatites.

Reverting to the general problem of the distribution of beryllium in pegmatites, it is clear that chrysoberyl, phenacite, gadolinite, and other beryllium minerals account for a negligible amount of the total beryllium balance of granitic pegmatites; this balance is determined by the sum of beryllium atoms combined in beryl and disseminated in the lattices of the rock-forming minerals of the pegmatites.

The diversity of beryllium content characteristic of the various pegmatite formations and regions creates certain difficulties in the calculation of the mean beryllium clarke in pegmatites. Thus, it is necessary to take into account here the following:

1. the different content of disseminated beryllium in pegmatites of the rare-earth and nonrare-earth provinces;
2. the different content of disseminated beryllium and of beryllium concentrated in beryllium minerals in pegmatites of various types;
3. the quantitative relationships between pegmatite groups with different beryllium concentrations, and between pegmatites containing beryllium minerals and those containing none.

The results of study of the distribution of beryllium in pegmatites, and the analysis of data on relations between various pegmatite types within the most characteristic rare-earth pegmatite fields, indicate the mean beryllium clarke by weight is 20×10^{-4} percent (Table 130).

The obtained data make it possible to correct the beryllium clarke in

Table 130 Beryllium content of various groups of granitic pegmatites

Pegmatite groups	Limits of beryllium content (in 10^{-4}%)	Coefficient of beryllium concentration $K = -\frac{k}{k+p}100$
Pegmatites containing no rare-metal minerals (not albitized)	2 — 10	0
Block pegmatites containing rare-metal minerals (not containing beryllium minerals)	10 — 25	0
Pegmatites containing 0.01 — 0.1% beryllium	10 — 57	40 — 80%
Pegmatites containing 0.2 — 0.5% beryllium	100 — 250	80 — 95%
Mean for pegmatites	20	

pegmatites, derived previously by A. E. Fersman (1940), as 0.05 percent. This high clarke can be applied only to the very rare pegmatite formations that contain not less than 1 percent beryl.

Beryllium in Pegmatites and Pneumatolites of the Crossing Line

There is disagreement among investigators about the origin of the so-called beryllium-bearing "crossing line" (or "desilicated", Ed.) pegmatites.

Most widely accepted is the well known hypothesis of desilication (Du Toit, 1919, 1928; Fersman, 1925c; Pyatnitskii, 1929, 1932a, 1932b, 1934; Vlasov, 1936a, 1938a), whose adherents claim that the mica-plagioclase and mica veins in ultrabasic rocks are the products of reaction between the pegmatite melt enriched in volatile components and the enclosing ferruginous-magnesia rocks poor in silica.

There are far fewer adherents to the hypothesis that explains the formation of the altered aureoles of plagioclase bodies by the action of late hydrothermal solutions that are unrelated to the crystallization of the vein series and that originated in depth from the granite of a basic magma source (Larsen, 1928; Lodochnikov, 1935, etc.).

Finally, another point of view has recently become somewhat accepted. Adherents, while admitting that the phenomena of reaction between post-magmatic emanations and solutions and the enclosing rocks have a determining significance in the formation of deposits of this type, consider that veins of the "crossing line" are analogous not to pegmatites, but to pneumatolytic-hydrothermal formations of quartz-feldspar and quartz-greisen vein types.

The genesis of the mica-plagioclase and micaceous beryllium-bearing veins, which we separate conventionally as "crossing line" pegmatites, will not be discussed, because it is a separate and very large subject. However, to understand the geochemistry of beryllium in these deposits, it is expedient to touch upon some genetic problems, approaching their possible solution by analysis of the fundamental geochemical features of these very interesting deposits.

There is no doubt at present about the genetic relationship between beryllium-bearing "crossing line" pegmatites and granitic intrusions, in whose contact aureole these deposits occur. This relationship is clearly shown by the rare-metal associations of the parent granites, such as the Murzinskii granitic intrusion, within which widely occur facies and phases of pegmatites with accessory beryl mineralization, while the beryllium content in the muscovite granites of the endocontact zone attains 14×10^{-4} percent, which is nearly three times that of the normal beryllium content of granites.

Also there are few reasons to deny the close genetic relationship between quartz-plagioclase vein deposits and their surrounding rims; this relationship is shown very clearly by the identity of the rare-metal mineralization in these sections of one particular vein complex, which totally differ in their mode of formation.

However, we must note that, from the geochemical aspect, the formation of the reaction zones around veins have not been studied sufficiently despite a number of special papers (Fersman, 1925c, 1940; Vlasov, 1936a, 1938a,). This is due to the absence of a detailed investigation on the behavior of the rock-forming elements of the reaction zones around the veins, based on a sufficient number of systematically chosen average samples of the various zones. Although the "crossing line" pegmatites have been studied for a fairly long time, until recently all geochemical conclusions were based on random analyses of specimens from individual zones that did not give their average composition.

From the survey and comparison of the analyses, we may conclude that, in the transformation of the enclosing ultrabasic rocks, the migration of potassium, aluminum, silicon, and fluorine into these rocks is very clearly exhibited in the endocontact zone of quartz-plagioclase vein bodies (Fig. 61). Here the role of potassium is limited by the boundaries of the first reaction rim composed of phlogopite and biotite, whereas aluminum plays an important role also in the formation of the chlorite zone. More complex is the problem of the part played by silica, the unknown amount of quartz present in the individual sections of the reaction complex, has to be taken into account.

In the first biotite-phlogopite reaction zone, the amount of SiO_2 (not allowing for free quartz) is even less than in the original rock; this points to the fact that the formation of this zone virtually requires no addition of silica. A higher (compared with the original serpentinite) SiO_2 content is observed only in the actinolite and talc zones. The chlorite zone has a sharply reduced silica content. Thus, in the alteration of ultrabasic rocks around the veins, a redistribution of SiO_2 has taken place in the altered zone simultaneously with the probable addition of silica. This redistribu-

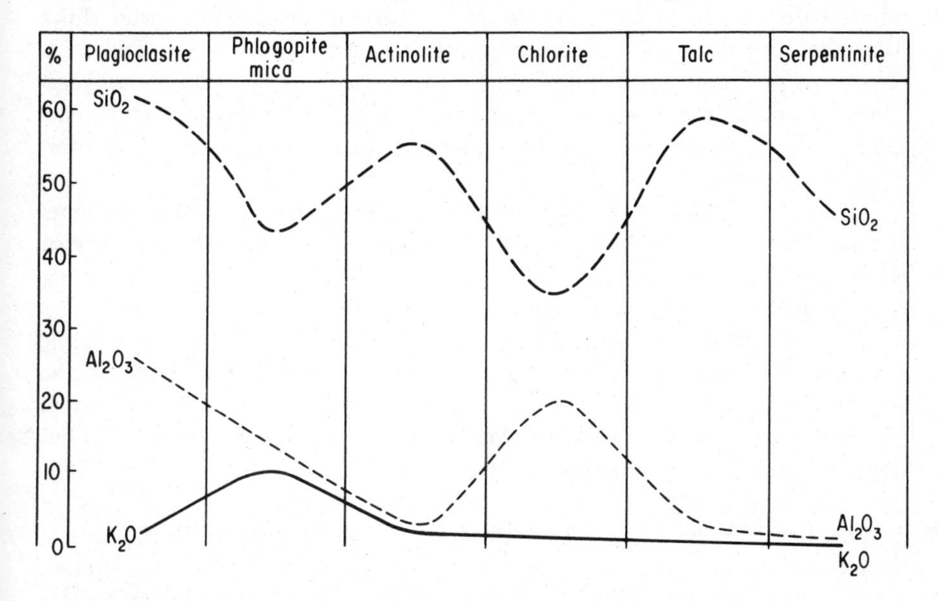

Fig. 61. Diagram showing variation of SiO_2, Al_2O_3, and K_2O contents in reaction zones of the crossing-line pegmatites and pneumatolites (according to A. E. Fersman and K. A. Vlasov).

tion has resulted in the formation of complexes of various acidity, both enriched or impoverished in silica (compared with the enclosing rocks).[3]

Without dwelling in detail on the possible formation of reaction zones (as the above literature deals with this subject) let us note the important role of the most active mineralizing agent (fluorine) in the formation of the reaction complex. The geochemical role of fluorine in the reaction between postmagmatic emanations and solutions and ultrabasic rocks was first stressed by K. A. Vlasov (1938a), who convincingly demonstrated the significance of fluorine as a catalyst that accelerates and facilitates the alteration of enclosing rocks by acid emanations and solutions separating out during the formation of the quartz-feldspar veins.

[3] In connection with the complexity of SiO_2 distribution in the reaction complex, one has to carry out (to substantiate the desilication theory) an additional study of SiO_2 distribution in various zones by investigating representative samples taken from all parts of the complex.

The presence of high fluorine concentrations is one of the most characteristic features of the "crossing-line" pegmatites. Undoubtedly—and one must agree here with Vlasov—it was the participation of a large amount of fluorine during the formation of the vein complex that caused thick reaction rims around veins and the unique form of deposits of the beryllium-bearing "crossing-line" pegmatites.

On analyzing data relating to the geology, mineralogy, and geochemistry of deposits of this type, we must agree with the investigators who think that the formation of beryllium-bearing mica-quartz-plagioclase and mica veins is a protracted and complex process of reactions between the segregations of granitic magma, considerably enriched in volatile components (including fluorine), and the enclosing ultrabasic rocks partly metamorphosed to serpentinites.

The fundamental peculiarity of this process is the loss, into the zones around the veins, of alkalis, aluminum, silicon, fluorine, and a number of secondary components, which are characteristic of the mineral-forming solutions that form the vein bodies.

However, have we a basis for drawing a complete analogy between the source of emanations and solutions, which have a leading function in the formation of beryllium-bearing "crossing line" pegmatites, and the normal pegmatite melt from which, at various stages of its evolution, these or other types of rare-metal pegmatites are formed? It is the author's opinion that we lack such a basis.

The beryllium-bearing vein formations of the "crossing line" show a much greater similarity to quartz-feldspar and quartz veins with greisen rims, which are usually considered to be pneumatolytic-hydrothermal formations, geochemically very different from pegmatites.

Table 131 summarizes the fundamental geochemical features of vein formations of the "crossing line", also of normal ("pure line," Ed.) pegmatites and pneumatolytic veins, which allow conclusions to be drawn on their similarities and differences.

A. E. Fersman and P. P. Pyatnitskii, and K. A. Vlasov, who developed the theory of desilication of the pegmatite melt on its reactions with ultrabasic rocks, noted many times that here we must deal with a residual part of the pegmatite melt, which is considerably enriched in volatile components, and, in this sense, forms a transition to pneumatolites. On the basis of the leading function of volatile components, they explain the intense alteration of the enclosing rocks, which in general is not characteristic of the common pegmatites, including the replaced granitic pegmatites in ultrabasic rocks. A. E. Fersman and P. P. Pyatnitskii have used the concept "pegmatite" very broadly; thus they are able to unite formations with the pegmatitic process, that the author is unable to relate to pegmatites at present, owing to their geological-mineralogical, and genetic peculiarities.

Suffice it to say that P. P. Pyatnitskii (1932a, 1932b) separates into a

Table 131 Distribution of some elements in "pure-line" pegmatites, "crossing-line" pegmatites, and pneumatolites

Elements	Rare-metal granitic pegmatites	Beryllium-bearing "crossing-line" pegmatites	Quartz-feldspar, quartz-muscovite, quartz-fluorite veins
Potassium	One of the main elements	Of great importance in the formation of micaceous reaction rims of vein bodies	Rock-forming element in quartz-feldspar and quartz-muscovite veins. In pure quartz and quartz-fluorite veins—of little importance
Fluorine	Does not form noticeable concentrations, usually being present as impurity in micas, etc.	Highly characteristic element. Forms high concentrations (large accumulations of fluorite)	Highly characteristic element. In a number of places forms noticeable concentrations
Lithium	Highly characteristic element	A typical element	Little characteristic element
Tantalum and niobium	Highly characteristic element	Not characteristic	Not characteristic
Molybdenum	Not characteristic	Highly characteristic element	Characteristic element
Tungsten	Not characteristic	In some deposits a characteristic element	Highly characteristic element
Beryllium	Concentrations in excess of 0.02% Be per vein are rare	Concentrations in excess of 0.02% Be per vein are common	Concentrations in excess of 0.02% Be per vein are common

"hydrothermal pegmatite type" even the typically hydrothermal carbonate veins containing emerald, although these deposits, as will be shown below, bear no relationship to pegmatites.

His separation of "pneumatolytic pegmatites" is also conventional, because it is known that pneumatolytic or pneumato-hydrothermal formations (including greisens, quartz-feldspar, and quartz-mica veins) differ substantially from pegmatites by a number of geological and mineralogical-geochemical features, apart from the mode of formation (Ginzburg and Gorzhevskii, 1957).

It is obvious from table 131 that the beryllium-bearing "crossing-line" pegmatites differ, geochemically, a great deal from pegmatites in general. This is shown first by the fact that during their formation, fluorine, which has a very limited function in rare-metal pegmatites, is very important. Similarly, the "crossing-line" pegmatites contain negligible amounts of such elements (beryllium satellites) as lithium, tantalum, and niobium, which are typomorphic for rare-metal pegmatites. Molybdenum (Urals, Transvaal, Puuna) and tungsten (Puuna), elements not characteristic of pegmatites, are typomorphic of "crossing-line" varieties. All features that distinguish the "crossing-line" pegmatites from pegmatites proper bring them closer to pneumatolytic-hydrothermal formations.

It is natural that available data are insufficient for completely rejecting theories of the possible formation of deposits of "crossing-line" beryllium-bearing pegmatites involving reaction between the pegmatite melt proper and the ultrabasic rocks, but there is no doubt that certain processes, in general not characteristic of pegmatites, play a dominant part in their formation.

The final solution of this problem should be based on a detailed geochemical investigation of deposits. Such an investigation has not yet been carried out.

The features of beryllium geochemistry in pegmatites and pneumatolytes of the "crossing line" are completely determined by the vein formation and composition, which are very interesting from scientific and economic aspects. One of the most characteristic geochemical features of the analyzed group of deposits is the presence of high beryllium concentrations, which are not characteristic of normal beryllium-bearing pegmatites. However, such beryllium concentrations are, as will be shown below, common in pneumatolytic-hydrothermal formations.

Attempts have been made at explaining the beryllium concentrations in deposits of this type (which are abnormally high for pegmatites) by a regular accumulation of beryllium during the reaction between the pegmatite melt and the enclosing ultra-basic rocks (Vlasov, 1936a, 1938a). According to the adherents of this hypothesis, during reaction with the ultrabasic rocks, a large part of the pegmatite melt is used up in the formation of reaction rims of pegmatite veins, whereas beryllium, apparently not entering into the lattices of the minerals then being formed, concentrates in the residual part of desilicated pegmatites composing the cores of the veins.

Such an explanation could only arise in earlier years by a complete absence of data on the beryllium content of minerals in the reaction rims of the "crossing-line" veins.

We now know that, unlike the "pure-line" granitic pegmatites, the geochemical features of "crossing-line" pegmatites and pneumatolites govern the wide dissemination of beryllium as an impurity in rock-forming and accessory minerals of the beryllium-bearing vein deposits (Beus, 1953a, 1953b, 1955). The factors that promote this process and facilitate the capture of beryllium by silicate lattices are these:

1. A high concentration of fluorine, which, aids in the active migration of beryllium and the replacement in silicates (especially in micas) of $AlO_4{}^{5-}$ with $BeO_3(F,OH)^{5-}$ and of $SiO_4{}^{4-}$ with $BeO_2(F,OH)_2{}^{4-}$, until the formation of brittle beryllium micas of the margarite group.

Table 132 Content of disseminated beryllium in minerals of the "crossing-line" pegmatites, pneumatolites, and their reaction rims

Description of mineral or rock	Number of samples	Limits of Be content in $10^{-4}\%$	Mean Be content in $10^{-4}\%$
Albite	1	25	–
Medium plagioclase	19	18–223	106
Muscovite from beryl-bearing vein	1	90	–
Quartz from beryl-bearing vein	1	1	–
Margarite	5	4300–6700	5100
Fluorite	3	1–25	–
Actinolite from actinolite schist, 1.5 m from the contact with beryl-bearing vein	1	66	–
Black tourmaline from biotite rock	1	26	–
Zone of finely-micaceous biotite	1	26	–
Phlogopite from the fringe of a beryl-bearing vein	10	30–600	60
Chloritic zone of the beryl-bearing plagioclase vein	1	9	–
Coarse-grained chlorite	1	13	–
Zone of fine-lamellar phlogopite	3	8–33	–
Biotite from chlorite-biotite schist	1	6	–
Tremolite from talc schist	1	1	–
Tremolite-talc schist	3	1–2	–
Talc-actinolite schist	3	1–3	–
Talc schist	3	0–1	1–0
Talc	3	3–50	–

2. A wide development of contamination phenomena, which include in the process of mineral formation a number of cations foreign to pegmatites (magnesium, titanium, chromium, etc.) that can compensate the replacement of silicon with beryllium in silicates.

Table 132 summarizes data on the distribution of disseminated beryllium in minerals and reaction rims of pegmatites and pneumatolites of the crossing line.[4]

Thus, the "crossing line" features are not the cause of beryllium concentration and formation of large accumulations of beryllium minerals formed at the same time (particularly micas) as an isomorphous impurity (Table 133).

It is evident that the relationship between beryllium dissemination and the reaction between mineral-forming emanations and solutions and the enclosing rocks have already been known for a long time to our geolo-

[4] Because very small beryl grains occurred in the described deposits, the material for analyses was sampled with utmost care, and its purity checked under a microscope.

gists, who would note that as the thickness of the reaction rims increased, the beryllium content of the vein body would be correspondingly reduced until beryl completely disappeared in those parts where the biotite reaction zone attained the greatest thickness.

The complex of beryllium minerals characteristic of "crossing-line" pegmatites and pneumatolites is most peculiar and is determined in the first place by the formation of beryllium-bearing vein bodies and their reaction rims. The main beryllium mineral of the veins proper and of the first reaction zone of the phlogopite-biotite composition, is beryl.

Study of beryl segregations in the quartz-plagioclase cores of vein suites, and of the interrelations between beryl on the one hand, plagioclase and quartz on the other, shows that beryl was formed later than plagioclase. Also the problem of the possible metasomatic origin of beryl as a result of replacement of plagioclase should be studied. Without attempting to reach

Table 133 Beryllium distribution in beryl-bearing vein bodies of "crossing-line" pegmatites

	% of the total beryllium content
For deposit as a whole	
Total quantity of Be	100
Quantity of Be combined in beryl	80
Quantity of Be combined with micas and other nonberyllium minerals	20
For mica veins	
Total quantity of Be	100
Quantity of Be combined in beryl	44
Quantity of Be combined with micas and other nonberyllium minerals	56
These include:	
Be combined in beryllium-margarite	42.5
Be combined in phlogopite	12.8

any final conclusion, let us note that the interrelationships between beryl and plagioclase in the quartz-plagioclase veins provide a sufficient foundation for discussing this problem. Beryl is always, apparently, earlier than quartz. Crushed beryl crystals cemented with quartz are common.

It already has been noted that, in the phlogopite-biotite rim of the veins, light-colored beryl passes into bright-green emerald whose color is due to an insignificant impurity of chromium captured during the alteration of the enclosing ultrabasic rocks. Here, the growth of beryl crystals apparently began during the early stage of formation of the reaction zone, as frequently the beryl and emerald crystals have cracks that are sealed with a finely micaceous mass in which beryl crystals are embedded. The long duration of crystal growth is borne out by the inclusion of biotite flakes in the outer zones of beryl and emerald crystals (the growth zones of beryl crystals containing biotite inclusions were noted to have the densest coloration).

Turning to the chemistry of formation of the phlogopite-biotite zone (energetic addition of alkalis and aluminum), we must note that the silicon/aluminum ratio established within the zone (3:1) corresponds to the ratio found in beryl that precisely determines the formation of this particular beryllium mineral.

The process was developed with much greater complexity during the formation of the chlorite and talc zones of the reaction complex; this process occurred with the addition of silicon and aluminum with their subsequent redistribution.

It is know that the chlorite zone (particularly those sections adjoining the phlogopite-biotite zone) is the enclosing complex for two other much less widespread beryllium minerals—phenacite (Be_2SiO_4) and chrysoberyl (Al_2BeO_4)—which commonly occur in close association.

It would seem that such an association of beryllium minerals, so different chemically, one of them containing silicon but no aluminum and the other containing aluminum but no silicon, is very rare. However, this is not so. Both minerals are typical products of the transformation by stages of the enclosing ultrabasic rocks under the action of acid emanations and solutions, the process called by the writer "desilication" (Fersman) or "neutralization" (Vlasov).

During the transformation of the enclosing rock, silicon, as the most mobile component of mineral-forming solutions, naturally migrates further than aluminum and much further than potassium, considerably dwarfing them in the composition of the advance portions of the metamorphosing emanations and solutions. This forms actinolite and talc in the enclosing serpentinites that contain no aluminum. In conditions of an acute deficiency of aluminum near the outer boundary of the mica zone, the beryllium silicate phenacite, crystallizes from the beryllium-containing siliceous solutions.

However, the subsequent development of the transformation of enclosing rocks substantially alters the composition of the later portions of the mineral-forming solutions in which the amount of silica noticeably decreases and the less mobile aluminum appears. This is the start of the formation of the chlorite reaction zone, which is associated with the addition of aluminum and with the subtraction of a part of the silica into the outer part of the reaction complex; this is a repeated and noticeable desilication of the rock to which silica had been added previously. As a result of this process, there forms an aluminum-enriched chlorite zone poor in SiO_2 (29 to 33 percent compared with 40 to 44 percent in serpentinite) and silica accumulates in the outermost zone, talc, of the reaction complex.

It is obvious that the beryllium minerals that have been formed change as the process of chloritization develops. When silicon is deficient and the role of aluminum has sharply increased, chrysoberyl is formed as crystals that, in many places, grow on or penetrate phenacite crystals.

It is known that the formation of the chlorite zone, and of phenacite and chrysoberyl in this zone, is mainly in veins where the desilication has been most intense and has resulted in the complete disappearance of the central oligoclase core, which is replaced in a number of places, as already mentioned, by lenticles and nodules of beryllium-margarite.[5] The origin of this interesting mineral is also related to the intensive desilication and to the subtraction of calcium, alkalis (including lithium), and beryllium in the enclosing rocks.

What are the causes of such a considerable mobility of beryllium in the formation of these deposits, a mobility that is absolutely uncharacteristic of normal beryl-bearing pegmatites? We can answer this question if we recall the tremendous role played in the formation of deposits of this type by fluorine and if we estimate the mobility and relative stability of fluorine compounds of beryllium.

Given a high concentration of fluorine, the transport of beryllium in emanations and solutions can take place, depending on the nature of the medium, either in the form of alkali fluoroberyllates or in the form of simple fluorides.

In conclusion, the late-hydrothermal dissolution of beryllium minerals, and the secondary beryllium transport and formation of secondary beryllium minerals in deposits of "crossing-line" pegmatites and pneumatolites, are in places noticeably developed, although they have been insufficiently studied. The most common process is the formation of bavenite after beryl, or unconnected with beryl. This process is analogous to that of normal pegmatites; it occurs in plagioclasites when calcium is present in late solutions. Other times the formation of bertrandite is observed.

The detailed study of the secondary transport and deposition of beryllium in "crossing-line" pegmatites and pneumatolites undoubtedly provides a great deal of new information for the understanding of the geochemistry of beryllium in the hydrothermal process and is likely to enrich science with the discovery of new beryllium minerals.

Beryllium in Alkalic Pegmatites

The geochemical history of beryllium in alkalic pegmatites so far has been studied little, but everything that has been said about the behavior of beryllium in the formation of alkalic rocks can be applied *a fortiori* to alkalic pegmatites. The increased concentrations of beryllium and a number

[5] Beryllium-margarite usually forms a thin fringe at the boundary between plagioclase and the phlogopite-biotite reaction zone, and is also disseminated as separate crystals in the phlogopite rock.

of high-valency cations (rare earths, titanium, etc.) in the agpaitic alkalic pegmatite process create favorable conditions for the isomorphous entry of beryllium into the structure of a number of silicate minerals in alkalic pegmatites. This is confirmed in the not very numerous, but already quite convincing, accounts that throw light on the distribution of beryllium in the minerals of alkalic pegmatites (Table 134). The higher beryllium concentration is characteristic only of minerals of the earlier paragenetic pegmatitic complexes, whereas the rock-forming minerals of the replacement stage usually do not contain any noticeable accumulation of beryllium. This can most probably be related to the substantial change in composition, in particular, of the alkalinity of solutions in the late stages of formation of alkalic pegmatites. It can be seen from the descriptions given above that the parageneses of the replacement stages of alkalic pegmatites are substantially more acid than the parageneses of primary-crystallization zones of these formations.

In particular, the relatively acid nature of replacement solutions that act in the final stage of formation of alkalic pegmatites is shown by the appearance of quartz, which is ubiquitous in the albitized zones of the most complex-zoned pegmatite bodies developed within the Khibiny and Lovozero alkalic masses.

The wide development of albitization that completes the alkalic pegmatitic process shows, within definite limits, an analogy between the replacement phenomena of alkalic and granitic pegmatites, particularly as this process determines in both kinds of pegmatites the highest beryllium concentrations.

The beryllium minerals in pegmatites of nepheline syenites and in granitic pegmatites are related to the final stages of pegmatite formation, because they are the characteristic late minerals of the sodium metasomatism stage of the complex-zoned pegmatites. From the geological aspect, the possibility of secondary concentration of beryllium in the metasomatism of early minerals of alkalic pegmatites, which contain an isomorphous admixture of beryllium (nepheline, etc.) is very interesting. At present, we lack sufficient data for drawing a final conclusion. However, the substantial lowering of beryllium content in the rock-forming minerals of the replacement complexes (compared with minerals of the zones of primary crystallization), and the appearance of beryllium minerals proper during the stage of replacement, provide a basis for assuming the secondary concentration of beryllium in late solutions. It is necessary to carry out special investigations in order to check this hypothesis.

The features of the alkalic process, expressed by the preponderence of $K_2O + Na_2O$ over Al_2O_3 and by the deficiency of SiO_2, determine the probability of beryllium transport in the pegmatitic process in the form of a beryllate complex, and the peculiar nature of the relatively rare beryllium minerals associated with alkalic pegmatites. By far the most

Table 134 Beryllium content in minerals of nepheline syenites

Minerals	Location	Limits of Be content in 10^{-4}%	Collection or source
	Minerals of primary crystallization zones		
Nepheline	Southern Norway	36–360	V.M. Goldschmidt and Peters, 1932
Nepheline	Khibiny rock mass	10–30	I.P. Tikhonenkov
Nepheline	Lovozero rock mass	10–30	M.V. Kuz'menko
Potassium feldspar	Southern Norway	3.6–36	V.M. Goldschmidt and Peters, 1932
Potassium feldspar	Khibiny	1–5	I.P. Tikhonenkov
Potassium feldspar	Lovozero	2	L.L. Shilin (1957)
Arfvedsonite	Khibiny	30	I.P. Tikhonenkov
Arfvedsonite	Southern Greenland	36	V.M. Goldschmidt and Peters, 1932
Aegirine	Southern Norway	360	V.M. Goldschmidt and Peters, 1932
Green aegirine	Khibiny	12–20	I.P. Tikhonenkov
Black aegirine, late after arfvedsonite	Khibiny	4–6	I.P. Tikhonenkov
Sodalite	Lovozero	50	L.L. Shilin (1957)
Lepidomelane	Lovozero	3–30	M.V. Kuz'menko
Lepidomelane	Southern Norway	3.6–36	V.M. Goldschmidt and Peters, 1932
Barkevikite	Southern Norway	36–360	V.M. Goldschmidt and Peters, 1932
Eudialyte	Lovozero	18	E.I. Semenov
Eudialyte	Khibiny	1–7	I.P. Tikhonenkov
Enigmatite	Khibiny	3	I.P. Tikhonenkov
	Minerals of replacement complexes		
	Main		
Albite	Lovozero	2–6	M.V. Kuz'menko
Natrolite	Lovozero	3–26	M.V. Kuz'menko
Hackmanite	Lovozero	6–13	M.V. Kuz'menko
Ussingite	Lovozero	5	L.S. Borodin
	Accessory		
Lepidolite	Lovozero	20–60	L.L. Shilin (1957)
Schizolite	Lovozero	3	I.P. Tikhonenkov
Steenstrupine	Lovozero	1080	M.V. Kuz'menko
Karnasurtite	Lovozero	1080	M.V. Kuz'menko
Erikite	Lovozero	1800	M.V. Kuz'menko
Thorite	Lovozero	>3600	E.I. Semenov
Catapleiite	Lovozero	540	E.I. Semenov
Zircon-halloysite	Lovozero	2520	E.I. Semenov
Hydrargillite	Lovozero	3–110	E.I. Semenov

common minerals are alkalic beryllium silicates; aluminosilicates are virtually absent among beryllium minerals in alkalic rocks.

Concluding the geochemistry of beryllium in the pegmatite process, we must stress again that the main factors determining beryllium migration and concentration in granitic and alkali pegmatites are the degree and form of albitization processes.

The sodic alkalic solutions containing such active mineralizing agents as F^{1-}, Cl^{1-}, and Co_3^{2-} have probably served as the most favorable medium in which the transport of beryllium in the form of complex beryllates can take place.

CHAPTER 10

Beryllium in the Hydrothermal-Pneumatolytic Process

The principle of the limited migration potential of beryllium and the association of its high concentrations exclusively with granitic pegmatites, proposed by V. M. Goldschmidt (1932) and supported by a number of investigators (Fersman, 1939, 1940; Rankama, Sahama, 1950) is not borne out by the evidence, and should be reviewed.

When beryllium-bearing intrusives are formed under physico-chemical conditions that eliminate the possibility of pegmatite formation and in the presence of extracting and mineralizing agents such as fluorine, beryllium with tungsten, tin, and molybdenum passes into the pneumatolytic phase and concentrates in the pneumatolytic products of the granitic magma and in hydrothermal veins. It should be noted also that the paragenesis and composition of beryllium minerals in hydrothermal-pneumatolytic deposits are usually determined by the nature of the enclosing rocks that have undergone pneumatolytic or hydrothermal processing (Table 135).

In most deposits, there is a clear relationship between beryllium and fluorine (close paragenesis of beryllium minerals with topaz and fluorite), which shows the important part played by fluorine in the subtraction of beryllium compounds from the magma.

From an analysis of the abundant descriptions of hydrothermal-pneumatolytic beryllium deposits, we may conclude that the addition and concentration of beryllium in the formation of these deposits are mostly related to the postmagmatic alteration of granites and enclosing rocks corresponding to the albitization and greisenization stages.

The phenomena of early albitization, exhibited in most beryllium-bearing granitic masses with varying intensities, is sometimes caused by the addition

Table 135 Paragenesis of beryllium minerals in hydrothermal-pneumatolytic deposits

Enclosing rocks	Characteristic beryllium minerals	Characteristic paragenesis
Granites and other acid and medium magmatic and metamorphic rocks	Beryl, bertrandite, euclase	Quartz, topaz, micas
Ultrabasic rocks	Beryl, phenacite, chrysoberyl	Ferro-magnesian micas, actinolite, chlorite, talc
Aluminous rocks	Beryl, chrysoberyl	Micas, topaz, more rarely fluorite
Carbonate rocks	Chrysoberyl, phenacite, helvite-danalite	Fluorite, micas

of sodium-containing emanations and solutions to the apical sections of dome-shaped protrusions of large intrusive bodies; at other times they are clearly autometasomatic. These phenomena, expressed in the partial albitization of granites and in the replacement of biotite with muscovite, are accompanied by the accumulation of beryllium as an isomorphous impurity in muscovite (Table 136).

The presence of beryllium-containing muscovite noticeably increases the mean beryllium content of such granites (Table 137). This feature sometimes enables one to determine the extent of beryllium participation in pneumatolytic processes and the possibility of formation (in connection with the given intrusive complex) of hydrothermal-pneumatolytic beryllium deposits.

When noticeable high beryllium concentrations are present in the early stages of the metasomatic alteration of granites, fine crystals of the beryllium mineral proper, beryl, are disseminated in the granites. Beryl is usually observed in granites whose mean beryllium content exceeds 20 to 30 $\times$ 10^{-4} percent (five times as much as the beryllium clarke for granites).

Early sodium metasomatism of the pneumatolytically altered granitic masses enriched in beryllium has in general a limited degree of development and is always accompanied by more intense processes of the acid stage of metasomatism (greisenization). The form of manifestation of postmagmatic processes of the analyzed stages within the intrusive mass is determined to a large extent by structural factors, in particular by the time of appearance and nature of fractures that can serve as paths of migration for the mineral-forming emanations and solutions.

When the appearance of fractures and the separation of postmagmatic solutions coincide in time, the fractures act as channels that remove the gaseous and liquid postmagmatic products, entirely controlling the development of high-temperature metasomatism. This results in the formation of typical greisen deposits in which concentrations of beryllium are clearly limited by the definite zones of greisen bodies related to fractures of various origin.

Table 136 Beryllium content of muscovite from muscovite granites and granite-porphyries

Muscovite sampling location	Be content in $10^{-4}\%$
From the poorly greisenized Sherlovaya Mountain granite-porphyry	45
From the Akcha-Tau granite	33–40
From the granite of the Voznesensk complex	20
From the granite of Kedrovsk deposit	22
From the granite of the Onon deposit	16

If contractional or other fractures in apical sections of the granitic mass occur later than the period of greatest separation of post-magmatic solutions, then autometasomatism, unrelated to any fracture system, is most widespread in such rock masses.

Unlike the greisen deposits proper, which are controlled by jointing, postmagmatic processes result in the formation of greisenized and albitized granitic masses characterized by disseminated rare-metal (including beryllium) mineralization.

As in some granitic masses of eastern Transbaikalia, beryllium is disseminated in the metasomatically altered granite, being captured as an isomorphous impurity in muscovite or (given a high beryllium concentration in solutions) forming small beryl crystals. Postmagmatic acid leaching (greisenization), most widely developed in the beryllium-bearing granites, succeeded the albitization, and took place mainly in the uppermost parts of granitic masses.

Although it is still too early to speak about regularities in the vertical zoning of greisenized beryl-bearing granitic masses, let us note that the individual examples studied indicate the following series of metasomatic changes of granites from the apical sections of the granite dome to its deep horizons: (1) quartz-muscovite greisen, (2) strongly greisenized muscovite granite, (3) weakly greisenized and partly albitized muscovite granite, (4) weakly albitized bimica granite, (5) normal bimica granite. In the analyzed rock masses, the highest concentration of beryllium occurs in two zones, that of the weakly greisenized and partly albitized granite, and the quartz-muscovite greisen of the near-contact zone. The intermediate zone of strongly greisenized granite appears to be impoverished in beryllium (Chapter 5). This may indicate that the secondary dissolution and redeposi-

Table 137 Beryllium content of some granitoid rocks to which the greisen and quartz veins are related

Nature of granites	Complex or deposit	Number of samples	Mean beryllium content in $10^{-4}\%$	Coefficient of concentration with respect to the clarke in granites ($5 \times 10^{-4}\%$)
Greisenized granite-porphyry	Sherlovaya Mountain	30	10	2.0
Muscovite	Talitsa	combined sample	25	4.1
Muscovite	Talitsa	combined sample	14	2.8
Muscovite	Akchatau	3	11	2.2
Muscovite	Kyzylta	5	10	2
Muscovite	Voznesensk	6	9	1.8
Bimica	Urda-Taptanai	6	7	1.4
Bimica	Kedrovsk deposit	2	13	2.6

tion of beryllium takes place when intensive greisenization is superposed on weakly greisenized and albitized granites characterized by an increased beryllium concentration related to the albitization stage. The secondary deposition of beryllium converted to solutions occurs apparently in the apical sections of the rock mass when the quartz-muscovite greisens form under the screen of the roof rocks.

Of the conditions that govern the possibility of migration or deposition of beryllium in postmagmatic processes, the acidity and alkalinity of the mineral-forming solutions are the main migration factor. This factor is most clearly shown in the formation of the greisen deposits of beryllium, related to the leaching along fractures.

Beryllium can be easily transported in acid and weakly alkaline solutions (Chapter 1), but its mobility rapidly decreases as the alkalinity of solutions increases. This is apparently the main reason for the separation of beryllium in the solid phase.

It can be seen from the facts given in Chapter 5 that there are two zones of beryllium concentration in greisen deposits. The first corresponds to the outer zone of greisen bodies and has a quartz-muscovite composition (zone of incomplete leaching). The concentration of beryllium occurs here under conditions of a sharp fall in acidity of the greisenizing solutions, within the leading metasomatic front as a result of saturation of replacement solutions with alkalis removed from the altered rocks.

The second zone is the zone of fracture filling in the central part of greisen bodies. The separation of beryllium in solid phase in the filled fractures occurs under conditions of a sudden change in the concentration of hydrogen ions in mineral-forming solutions. However, the increase in pH of solutions in fractures, which occurs in the final stage of greisen formation, is primarily the result of the removal of fluorine from solutions; as the temperature and acidity of the mineral-forming solutions decrease, fluorine becomes bound by aluminum in the composition of topaz in the inner quartz-topaz zones of greisen bodies (zone of incomplete leaching).

In fracture fillings of greisen bodies, beryllium separates out in solid phase as beryl, crystallizing in the central part of such formations as the end-product, after the main mass of fluorine-containing minerals has been precipitated from solutions.

The paragenetic features of various greisen zones indicate the possible change in composition of greisenizing solutions and also the change in the form of beryllium transport during the development of the greisenization.

In the main stage of greisen formation, characterized by mainly acid fluorine emanations and solutions, the most probable form of beryllium transport is beryllium fluoride, which is known to be a highly stable and readily migrating compound. The deposition of beryllium from solution may be effected either by increasing the concentration of alkalis (which would unavoidably result in the transition of beryllium into less stable complex compounds and, finally, in its precipitation) or by extracting fluorine from solutions in such sparingly soluble compounds as topaz or fluorite. The former case apparently occurs in solutions of the leading metasomatic front, while the latter takes place in solutions in the final stage of the greisenization. The paragenesis of minerals in the late formational stages of fracture filling, which follows the precipitation of fluorine-containing minerals, indicates that the solutions of the final stage were already mainly carbonate. This is shown in the crystallization of carbonates (siderite, calcite, rhodochrosite), the development of carbonate metasomatism (similar to sideritization of siderophyllite in the Shelovaya Mountain greisens), and the presence of inclusions of liquid carbonic acid in the late beryls in cavities.

The nature of beryl distribution in the vein bodies changes radically when passing from greisen formations to quartz veins with greisen rims. Unlike the substantially metasomatic greisen formations, where beryl is usually concentrated in the central part of the bodies occurring in the fractures, in the quartz (wolframite-quartz, molybdenite-quartz) veins with greisen rims, the beryl definitely tends to concentrate in the near-contact sections of vein bodies in the early stages of their formation. This tendency is greater where greisenization of the enclosing rocks is weaker.

In quartz veins with relatively thick greisen rims the beryl crystals are usually irregularly disseminated in the quartz, forming accumulations both at the contact with the greisenized rocks and in other parts of the vein. In quartz veins almost free of enclosing rims, accumulations of small beryl crystals form rather dense rims at the contact between the vein and the enclosing rock.

The features of beryl distribution in high-temperature quartz veins indicate the relation of its formation to the reaction between mineral-forming silicate solutions and the enclosing rocks—a reaction that causes alkalis and a certain quantity of aluminum to go into solution. When the hydrogen ion concentration decreases continuously, aluminum forms with beryllium a stable silicate of aluminum and beryllium—beryl. Beryllium has an active function in the metasomatic process that develops at the contact between the vein and the enclosing aluminosilicate rock. Beryl crystals that form in these sections replace the microcline of the granite, sometimes penetrating the altered granite to a depth of 2 to 3 cm from the contact. The usual paragenesis of beryl and fluorine-containing minerals characteristic of the high-temperature quartz-feldspar and quartz veins indicates that the transport of beryllium in the formation of these deposits has also occurred in the fluoride form.

As the concentration of alkalis extracted from the enclosing rocks increases in the solution, beryllium fluoride should be replaced by the less stable fluorberyllates. As the pH of the solution further increases, owing to the development of leaching around the veins, these fluoroberyllates decompose, resulting in the possible separation of beryllium in the solid phase. On the basis of paragenesis of the minerals and degree of development of circum-veinous leaching, we can see that the silicate solutions from which the high-temperature quartz veins were formed were considerably less acidic than the solutions of the early stages of the greisen process. The precipitation of beryllium under such conditions could have taken place in the initial stage of formation of quartz veins in their endocontact zone, which is a *sui generis* zone of exchange reaction with the enclosing rocks.

In the most general case studied, the agent that precipitates beryllium from the solutions being neutralized is aluminum, which enters the mineral formation process through leaching of rocks surrounding the veins.

A somewhat different picture is seen when postmagmatic greisening emanations and solutions are considerably enriched in iron, manganese, and a number of chalcophilic elements, in particular zinc. The greisens that form by interreaction between these solutions and enclosing granites are enriched in iron (hematitic greisens). The accumulations of hematite occur with quartz vein bodies containing fairly widespread sulfides.

The nature of the beryllium-bearing hydrothermal-pneumatolytic formations changes suddenly if formation takes place in a carbonate medium, as a result of interaction between the beryllium-containing emanations and solutions and various carbonate rocks. The paragenesis of these deposits, characterized by the activity of fluorine, points also to the essentially fluoridic nature of the beryllium-bearing emanations and solutions that have taken part in the formation of deposits. This is a direct analogy with the formation of greisen deposits that are the product of similar emanations and solutions in aluminosilicate rocks differing in composition. In these deposits, beryllium occurs together with the addition of lithium (formation of brittle lithium micas), tin, and at times tungsten; again there occurs the typical association of elements characteristic of the high-temperature postmagmatic stage of mineral formation related to the activity of essentially acid emanations and solutions enriched in fluorine.

It is natural that the beryllium minerals formed by reactions between fluoride solutions and limestones should differ considerably from minerals formed in the aluminosilicate medium. Ideally, the result of such an interaction caused by the increase of pH of the beryllium-containing solution, should be the formation of the simple beryllium oxide, bromellite. However, as a rule, the fluorine-containing emanations and solutions, which penetrate along fractures into limestones and from the peculiar high-temperature fluoritic deposits, contain a certain proportion of silicon that is highly mobile under these conditions. The presence of silicon determines the predominant role of such beryllium minerals as phenacite in deposits of this type. The nature of mineral formation becomes more complex when limestones contain some impurities that take part in the process of mineral formation and affect the nature of the crystallizing beryllium minerals. A particularly noticeable influence on the composition of beryllium minerals is exerted by epigenetic skarn-type formations, quartz, or other veins contained in limestones. In particular, as a result of fluoritization of scapolitic skarns disposed among limestones replaced with fluorite, chrysoberyl forms, whereas, according to I. N. Govorov, the superposition of fluoridic beryllium-containing solutions on quartz bodies transgressing limestones results in the formation of euclase.

From this point of view, the paragenesis of beryllium-bearing contact-metasomatic formations, formed by the superposition of fluorine-containing solutions of the acidic stage of metasomatism on limestone or ferruginous limestone reaction skarns, is very typical. The constancy of paragenesis and texture of the described formations from various parts of the world shows that these deposits were formed by closely similar mineral-forming solutions of the acidic stage of metasomatism, having a high concentration of fluorine and iron and a higher content of beryllium, tungsten, and some other elements.

We shall not dwell in detail on the general problems of the genesis of beryllium-bearing contact-metasomatic rocks, because this is outside the scope of the present work; but some fundamental characteristics of the process of their formation, which determines the behavior of beryllium, should be noted.

These characteristics include in particular the varying migration capability of silicon and aluminum in the postmagmatic solutions, which introduced contact metasomatism by separations of these rock-forming elements. The greater mobility of silicon (compared with aluminum) is the fundamental cause of both the enrichment in silicon of solutions of the leading metasomatic front impoverished in aluminum, and the relative enrichment in aluminum of the deepest front of metasomatism. The relatively low (compared with silicon) migration capability of aluminum determines the earlier precipitation of the basic mass of aluminum in solid phase; this naturally leads to the relatively enrichment in silicon of solutions of late metasomatic stages. The variation of the silicon/aluminum ratio in solutions, both in time and space, during the development of metasomatism affects the chemical composition of beryllium minerals forming in the various types of metsomatic rocks.

Thus, in various skarn zones of the same deposit, formed under conditions of quite different Si/Al ratios, chrysoberyl, which contained no silicon, and helvite (or phenacite), which contained no aluminum, formed. The formation of beryllium minerals of various composition may also take place within the same skarn zone as a result of superposition of late solutions enriched in silicic acid on the paragenesis of substantially aluminous minerals formed earlier. As a result of such a superposition, beryl or phenacite may crystallize in geode-like cavities or along fractures of skarns, which contain relatively early chrysoberyl. During the same stage bertrandite replaces chrysoberyl.

Interesting data were obtained in the determination of the Si/Al ratio in various types of Kazakhstan skarns, which contained various beryllium minerals. As one would expect, it was found that skarns containing chrysoberyl have a low atomic ratio $Si/Al < 1.1$ (from 0.3 to 1.1), whereas the helvite-containing skarns from the same deposits are substantially more acid and the atomic ratio Si/Al in them varies between 2 and 3.5. In beryllium-bearing skarns there is no relationship between the nature of the beryllium minerals and the alkali content of the rock. This additional proof bears out the decisive importance of the Si/Al ratio in mineral-forming solutions during the crystallization of beryllium minerals of any composition.

Another important factor on which the behavior of beryllium in the process of skarn formation depends is the absolute silicon concentration which, along with the Si/F ratio, determines the quantity of silicates present in the skarn. While capturing a large amount of beryllium as an isomorphous impurity (Table 138), the silicate minerals (particularly vesuvianite) hinder the formation of beryllium minerals proper. The predominance of silicates in skarns usually results in the dissemination of beryllium.

In particular, it was determined for the beryllium-bearing skarns from a number of Central-Asian deposits that, for the same mean beryllium content in the rock, the increase in vesuvianite content from 25 to 80 percent results in the corresponding decrease in that part of beryllium bound in beryllium

Table 138 Beryllium content of Vesuvianite specimens from various regions of the USSR

Deposit	Be content in 10^{-4}%
Lyupikko (SW Karelia)	650–1490
Khopunvaara (SW Karelia)	980–1610
Nadezhdo-Kommercheskoe deposit (Urals)	470–5400
Akhmatovskaya mine (Urals)	29
Chidan (Caucasus)	720
Karadzhal (central Kazakhstan)	
Fluorite-mica-magnetite skarns	360–3600
Fluorite-garnet-idocrase skarns	4–360
Akmaya (central Kazakhstan)	36–1100
Oigaing (Central Asia)	54–2520
Chettyndy (Central Asia)	29–5420
Tashty (Central Asia)	576
Bakaly-Sai (Central Asia)	432
Lyangar (Central Asia)	1080
Kara-Tyube (Central Asia)	72–360

minerals from 80 to 15 percent. Other examples are the skarn formations of the Iron Mountain deposit, New Mexico, U.S.A., in which the increase in the silicate content from 4.5 to 18.5 percent is accompanied by a decrease in helvite content from 11.2 to 0.7 percent (Table 114), while the predominant skarn silicate, vesuvianite, contains 1 percent beryllium oxide. Finally, the third and, apparently, main factor that determined the possibility of extraction and loss of beryllium from the magmatic source in the composition of post-magmatic emanations and solutions is the high concentration of fluorine in the magma and in its pneumatolytic and hydrothermal separations.

The high fluorine concentration in the mineral-forming solutions accompanied by a relatively low concentration of alkalis allows us to assume that, in the process under discussion, beryllium is transported both as beryllium fluoride and fluoberyllates. Again, the main factor that determines the lowering of the migration capability of beryllium and its precipitation in solid phase is the sudden rise in pH of the mineral-forming solution at the metasomatic front, as a result of fluorine being bound by calcium that comes from the replaced rocks rich in calcium. The rhythmic nature of variation in pH of the mineral-forming solution, characteristic of the process of diffusional metasomatism, is also, most probably, the main cause of the rhythmic precipitation of minerals and of the formation of the

Table 139 Limits of pH during the precipitation of iron and beryllium hydroxides from solutions of their fluoride compounds

Compound	pH limits on precipitation from solution
FeF_3	3.6 — 6.7
BeF_2	6.3 — 11.8
$(NH_4)_3FeF_6$	5.5 — 7.2
Na_2BeF_4	8.0 — 11.8

laminated structure of rocks. Indeed, the lamination of the beryllium-containing skarns is determined by the separation, in the process of formation of the metasomatic rock, of such elements as aluminum, silicon, and beryllium from iron. Taking into account that the separation of these elements into solid phases from the acid fluorine-containing solution is a function of the hydrogen ion concentration, we must stress that such a separation clearly corresponds to variations in pH at which the precipitation of aluminum and beryllium oxides takes place on the one hand, and that of iron oxides on the other.

Thus, A. V. Novoselova and Yu. T. Simanov (1955) determined experimentally the limits of pH for the precipitation of iron and beryllium hydroxides from solutions of their fluorides (Table 139); these limits confirm the regular nature of the separation of these elements in the process of the neutralization of fluoridic solutions containing iron and beryllium.

Thus, in the neutralization process of the leading front of the fluorine-containing solution reacting with rocks enriched in calcium, the first element to precipitate should be iron. At this neutralization stage beryllium remains in solution[1] and, diffusing further, separates in the solid phase, together with aluminum or silicon, immediately after iron, after the solution has reached the corresponding pH value. The new front of replacement solutions enriched in iron and beryllium diffuses after the leading front and reacts with the enclosing rock according to the same scheme. Successively deposited from the solutions are layers of iron oxides separating in the weakly acid medium, and layers of fluorite containing minerals of

[1] Excluding the insignificant part adsorbed by iron in the process of precipitation.

beryllium, aluminum, and silicon, which precipitate after the solutions have been completely neutralized.

In order to obtain a more complete geochemical picture of the role of beryllium in processes of skarn formation, the relationship between beryllium and iron in all contact-metasomatic deposits should be considered. Gathered data indicate that there is no direct relation between the formation of concentrations or iron and beryllium in contact metasomatism, and that their simultaneous accumulation in fluorite-magnetite ore is caused by fluorine-containing solutions that can transport, together with beryllium, considerable amounts of iron.

Study of the occurrence of beryllium in contact-metasomatic iron deposits of central Kazakhstan, Transbaikalia, etc., formed without a noticeable participation of fluorine, has shown that in these deposits beryllium does not betray any tendency towards concentration, and is usually present in proportions of ten-thousandths and thousandths of 1 percent. Analogous data were obtained by S. Landergren (1948) for the contact iron ores of Sweden, most of which contain not more than 10×10^{-4} percent Be.

Thus the accumulation of beryllium in contact-metasomatic formations, as in other high-temperature hydrothermal-pneumatolytic deposits, is determined wholly by the activity of postmagmatic fluorine-containing emanations and solutions of the acid stage of metasomatism.

Also, in this type of deposit, fluorine appears as the leading extracting and transporting agent for beryllium and takes an active part in the formation of its deposits.

In completing the analysis of the behavior of beryllium in the high-temperature stages of formation of postmagmatic deposits, we must emphasize the incompleteness of our knowledge in this field, which is due to the newness of the problem and the scarcity of available material. In particular, data that would indicate the behavior of beryllium in the stage of early sodium metasomatism is lacking, although the geochemical properties of beryllium suggest its active migration not only with mainly acid postmagmatic solutions of the acid metasomatic stage, but also with sodium-enriched solutions of the early sodic stage. Apparently, it is with this stage that the accumulation of beryllium is associated in some albitized and greisenized deposits characterized by a wide development of albitization. Indications of this stage are also possible beyond the granitic masses. From this aspect, the detailed study of albitized sections and zones in various (including carbonate) rocks near the beryllium-bearing intrusions is very interesting.

Very valuable data, both from the scientific and practical aspects, will undoubtedly be obtained from the detailed analysis of investigations into the distribution of beryllium in granitic masses in which its concentration is increased, and especially in the greisen rare-metal deposits.

Beryllium in Meso- and Epithermal Processes

The geochemical history of beryllium in meso- and epithermal processes has been little studied. Nonetheless, beryllium concentrations related to relatively low-temperature carbonate veins (Muso, Columbia; Bom Jesus dos Meiros, Brazil), the development of helvite mineralization in the late formation stages of some polymetallic deposits, and the presence of beryllium minerals (euclase, phenacite, milarite, and bavenite) in veins of the Alpine type all point to a wide range of beryllium migration in hydrothermal conditions.

The lack of knowledge of the paragenesis of beryllium minerals in most of these deposits prohibits an authoritative discussion of the geochemical features of the transport and deposition of beryllium in their formation. Characteristic of a number of deposits is the paragenesis of the beryllium- and fluorine-containing minerals (Muso–parisite; Bom Jesus dos Meiros–topaz; Cornwall–topaz, fluorite; Grandview–fluorite; Fremont–topaz), which indicates the function of the most common mobile association, beryllium-fluorine. Fluorine minerals do not occur in other deposits (Butte, etc.), and the question of the possible form of beryllium transfer remains open.

In veins that were formed in a high concentration of $(CO_3)^{2-}$, beryllium was probably transported in the form of carbonate. For the beryllium in other veins, a definite answer can apparently be reached only after a detailed study of the paragenesis of beryllium minerals in the given deposits.

Unlike the high-temperature hydrothermal-pneumatolytic deposits analyzed above, the leading factor that determines the formation of a particular beryllium mineral in the hydrothermal process is most probably the complex of sulfur and oxygen conditions (Betekhtin, 1949). High sulfur concentration in the mineral-forming solutions results in the formation of minerals of the helvite-danalite group. The most widespread mineral in sulfide deposits is the manganese end-member of the isomorphous series, helvite, because, under conditions of high concentration of the S^{2-} ion, iron and zinc, which have a greater affinity for sulfur, separate in the form of the corresponding sulfides. The formation of phenacite or bertrandite in sulfide deposits apparently occurs under conditions of a high oxygen potential in the latest stages of the hydrothermal process, when sulfur has either been bound in the solid phase in various sulfides or has been oxidized to the hexavalent state, forming the stable complex ion $(SO_4)^{2-}$.

It is significant that in all hydrothermal deposits containing phenacite, milarite, or bavenite, the leading role is played by oxygen compounds of heavy metals (magnetite, hematite—Fremont, France; Durango, Mexico) or carbonates and sulfates (Henneberg, Thuringia). The sulfides occurring in these deposits play a subordinate part.

The segregations of phenacite and bertrandite in sulfide formations correspond to the latest stages of their formation and are associated with fractures and streaks that transgress the sulfide ores. One sometimes notes the relation of these minerals to the late carbonate stage of mineral formation and the replacement by them of the earlier helvite.

Carbonic solutions in the range of low temperatures are apparently the most effective transporters of beryllium. This follows from all the available data analyzed in the descriptions and is also confirmed by the presence of beryllium in a number of carbonic mineral waters. In particular, in some carbonic mineral waters of eastern Transbaikalia, up to 6×10^{-5} g/liter of beryllium have been detected. Although the limited number of the samples analyzed prohibits final conclusions, it is interesting to note that the highest amounts of beryllium were discovered in sources situated within granitic masses containing beryllium concentrations. Be^{2+} was not detected in mineral waters situated in regions of development of granites with a normal or reduced beryllium clarke (e.g., Darasun).

The possibility of beryllium migration in low-temperature solutions most probably explains the presence of beryllium minerals in veins of Alpine type. However, the lack of information on these rare formation does not permit us to draw any concrete conclusions about the geochemical conditions of their formation.

CHAPTER 11

Beryllium in Hypergene Processes and Sedimentation

The features of beryllium migration in the hypergene zone have so far been studied little, and available references indicate only a very general picture of beryllium geochemistry in exogenous processes.

Most widely distributed beryllium minerals are highly stable against the agents of chemical weathering. In particular, this is true of beryl,[1] chrysoberyl, phenacite, euclase, and many other minerals, which account for over 90 percent of the beryllium that is concentrated in beryllium minerals. All of these minerals, during the weathering of their enclosing rocks, undergo mainly mechanical destruction and are disseminated by erosion with other detrital material. The low specific gravity of beryllium minerals hinders their accumulation in alluvial placer deposits. The strength and hardness of a number of beryllium minerals prevent their rapid abrasion; as a result, crystals of such minerals as euclase, phenacite,

[1] Indications, available in the literature, of cases of exogenous kaolinization of beryl are not well founded. In all deposits studied by the author the kaolinization of beryl is related to its alteration by late hydrothermal solutions. Yet deposits are known to occur where unaltered beryl crystals lie among completely kaolinized pegmatite (India, Brazil, etc.).

and chrysoberyl occur rarely in some eluvial-alluvial placers situated in the regions of the original deposits (Urals, India, Burma, Ceylon, Brazil). The most brittle of these minerals, beryl, which is usually in the form of almost unaltered crystals in the weathered crust and in the talus of beryl-containing pegmatites, occurs in alluvial placers, as a rule, in the form of detritus and small grains.

The minerals of the helvite-danalite group undergo much readier chemical alteration under conditions existing at the earth's surface. The cause of this instability is most probably the presence, in minerals of this group, of bivalent sulfur, which is unstably bound in their structure and is easily oxidized. The products of the hypergene alteration of minerals of the helvite-danalite group have not been studied. Judging from A. I. Ginzburg's observations in the danalite-containing pegmatite (eastern Trainsbaikalia), we assume that phenacite forms in individual cases by the supposedly hypergene alteration of danalite.[2] The alteration of danalite proceeds here apparently according to the scheme

$$Fe_4[BeSiO_4]_3S + H_2O + O_2 \rightarrow Be_2[SiO_4] + SiO_2 + FeO(OH)_nH_2O + Fe_2[SO_4]_3.$$

The extraction of beryllium by solutions containing $SO_4{}^{2-}$ is shown by the higher beryllium content in acid ground and mine waters in regions of contact-metasomatic and greisen deposits containing helvite or danalite.

Some alkalic beryllium silicates (leucophanite, epididymite, etc.), whose alteration under hypergene conditions results in the extraction of alkalis, have a relatively weak resistance to agents of chemical weathering. The products of such alteration are most probably the slightly studied secondary minerals of the bertrandite group (helbertrandite, beryllite), but their hypergene origin requires substantiating.

Summarizing available data of the nature and extent of the exogenous alteration of beryllium minerals, we should note that the amount of beryllium that is introduced into solutions of the hypergene zone and migrates with them is extremely insignificant. A much greater quantity of beryllium should pass into surface solutions by the destruction of silicates that compose acid rocks and that contain, as an isomorphous impurity, ten-thousandths and thousandths of 1 percent of beryllium.

When analyzing the features of beryllium migration in hypergene processes, K. Rankama and T. Sahama (1950) drew on the closeness of the ionic potentials of beryllium (5.86) and aluminum (5.26), concluding that their migration paths are similar at the surface of the earth's crust and agreeing in this respect with V. M. Goldschmidt. A. E. Fersman, in a number of his papers (1939, *et al.*), attached decisive significance to the

[2] The phenacite crystals were discovered by A. I. Ginzburg in the leached cavities of danalite, filled with brownish ochres of iron oxides; their hypergene origin requires confirmation.

Table 140 Occurrence of beryllium in water, brine, muds, and salt residues of salt lakes and seas

Analyzed material	Be content, in 10^{-4}%
Dry residues of seawater:	
Black Sea	<0.2
Kandalaksha Bay of the White Sea	<0.2
Deep-sea muds (Goldschmidt and Peters, 1932)	<1
Deep-sea red clay (Goldschmidt and Peters, 1932)	<1
Sediments of Tyrrhenian Sea (Landergren, 1948)	13
Muds of salt lakes in central Kazakhstan (6 lakes)	0.6
Muds of salt lakes of Turgai depression (5 lakes)	0.2
Muds of salt lakes of Caspian lowlands (5 lakes)	<0.2
Muds of salt lakes in the Crimea:	
Sakskoe, Sasyk-Sivash, Chokrakskoe, Aktashskoe, Otburgskoe, Donuzlav, Karleutskoe, Uzunlarskoe, Moinakskoe, western Sivash	0.6–0.8
Staroe, Krasnoe, eastern Sivash	<0.2
Epsomite (Caspian lowlands, Urals, central Kazakhstan, Crimea, etc.)	<0.2–1.5
Halite, thenardite, mirabilite, glauberite, gypsum (from various regions)	<0.2

active polarizing capability of beryllium and suggested the possibility of its being mainly adsorbed in the hypergene zone on clays and soils. Available data on the occurrence of beryllium in the hypergene zone wholly confirm Fersman's conclusions.

An investigation of the occurrence of beryllium in dry residues of fresh water from temporary and permanent rivers showed its virtual absence from the contained transported salts, although the beryllium content of the surrounding rocks exceeded, in individual places, the mean clarke by a factor of 1.5 to 2. Single samples of water from shallow rivers in regions of abundant beryl-bearing pegmatites also failed to disclose the presence of beryllium in the dry residue. Also, beryllium has not been detected in water samples from the Black Sea and from the Kandalaksha Bay of the White Sea, and in brines, mud, and salt residues of salt lakes (Table 140) it is present only in negligible quantities if not completely absent; thus it is obvious that the mobility of beryllium at the surface of the earth's crust is very poor.

Analytical data relating to the occurrence of beryllium in sedimentary rocks do not bear out its preferential relation to aluminum. When the concentration of aluminum in bauxites exceeds the mean clarke of the earth's crust by a factor of 3 to 5, the relative concentration of beryllium in these rocks in relation to its mean clarke varies within the limits 0.3 to 4, exceeding this only in a few places (Table 141).

The absence of a distinct relationship between aluminum and beryllium

Table 141 Occurrence of beryllium in bauxites and sedimentary iron ores

Analyzed material	Be content, in 10^{-4}%
Bauxites of Tikhvin deposit (combined sample)	12
Bauxites of the Krasnaya Shapochka deposit (Urals) (combined sample)	9
Bauxites of Amangel'din deposit (Kazakhstan) (combined sample)	6
Bauxites (T. Szelenyi, 1937)	1.8–36
Bauxites of Arkansas deposits, United States (M. Gordon, K. Murata, 1952)	0–20 mean 5
Bauxites (K.B. Krauskopf, 1956)	mean 2, maximum 60
Sedimentary (lake) iron ores (Karelia)	5
Bog iron ores (S. Landergren, 1948)	7
Marine iron ores (S. Landergren, 1948)	10
Sedimentary iron ores (V.M. Goldschmidt and Peters, 1932)	<3.6
Sedimentary manganese ores (V.M. Goldschmidt and Peters, 1932)	<3.6
Lateritic and bauxitic iron ores (S. Landergren, 1948)	5

concentration in the formation of residual bauxite deposits is borne out in particular by the bauxite deposits of Arkansas, U.S.A., studied in detail by M. Gordon and K. Murata (1952). These formed as a result of the hypergene alteration of nepheline syenites. When the aluminum concentration of bauxites exceeds that of nepheline syenites by the factor of 2.7, beryllium is concentrated only by a factor of 1.3. Again, in most bauxite specimens studied, beryllium is either absent or present in a smaller quantity than in nepheline syenites.[3] Thus, bauxites, which carry the highest aluminum concentrations in the hypergene zone, apparently do not have a large accumulation of beryllium. Further, in clays and particularly kaolinites, which have only a relatively low aluminum concentration (< 2) the coefficient of enrichment in beryllium, compared with its mean clarke, attains 100, the highest beryllium content (up to hundredths and even tenths of 1 percent) has been detected in clays that occur near deposits somewhat enriched in beryllium (particularly in those containing helvite or danalite). Away from the beryllium source the beryllium content of the clays drops relatively sharply to the normal clarke level. The sands, sandstones, and other clastic rocks, even in regions of beryllium deposits, do not as a rule have an increased beryllium content (Table 142).

Thus, the adsorption of beryllium in clays is undoubtedly one of the main causes that determine the rapid precipitation of beryllium from hypergene solutions and its very limited mobility in surface channels.

[3] Beryllium was discovered only in 4 (out of 14) specimens and its mean content (Table 141) is wholly determined by a relatively high concentration (20×10^{-4} percent) in one of the specimens.

The main factor that determines the characteristic migration properties of beryllium in the hypergene zone is its high ionic potential (5.88), which is expressed in the considerable energy of the field of force of the Be^{2+} ion and its great ability to combine with finely dispersed particles.

The adsorption role of colloidal and finely dispersed systems in the process

Table 142 Occurrence of beryllium in some sedimentary and metamorphosed rocks

Rock and location	Number of samples	Be content in 10^{-4}%
Clays (redeposited) from various regions of the Russian platform	26	<0.2–5 mean 2
Clays from various regions of Central Asia	6	< 2–6 mean 3
Clays (redeposited) from eastern Siberia (Yenisei range)	14	< 2–3 mean 1.5
Clays from various regions of Transbaikalia	14	<0.2–10 mean 3
Eluvial and redeposited clays near beryllium deposits	8	3–300
Kaolins from Hungary and Yugoslavia (T. Szelenyi, 1937)	–	1–180
Clays (T. Szelenyi, 1937)	–	1–36
Sands from various regions of the Russian platform and eastern Siberia	–	<0.2–2 mean <0.5
Clay shales – mixture (V. Goldschmidt et al., 1932)	–	6
Metamorphosed shales from regions of beryl-bearing pegmatites in the United States (W. Stoll, 1945)	40	5
Black shales (K.B. Krauskopf, 1956)		maximum 4 (?) mean 1 (?)
Schists from various regions of eastern Transbaikalia	10	1–5 mean 3.5
Schists from various geosynclinal regions of the USSR	22	1–8 mean 3.8
Clays from various areas of the USSR	50 (mixture)	7
Clays from various areas of the USSR, excluding four samples taken in areas of beryllium deposits	46 (mixture)	3
Limestones from various areas of the USSR	14	<0.2–2 mean <0.2
Marbles from eastern Transbaikalia	2	0.5
Silicified limestones from the Caucasus	4	0.9–0.5
Dolomites from the Moscow region	4	<0.2–4
Carbonate rocks of southern Lappland (T. Sahama, 1945)	–	0
Insoluble residue of limestones in Apennines (Pierruccini, 1943)	–	0.9–2.5
Shells of fossil molluscs from Myachkovo (Moscow region)	14	<3–3
Phosphorites (K.B. Krauskopf, 1956)	4	maximum 100 (?) mean 5

of beryllium precipitation from aqueous solutions can be illustrated by the following example. In a mine-water sample from a pegmatitic beryllium deposit, 1×10^{-5} g/liter Be was found. After some time a colloidal precipitate formed that consisted mainly of iron, manganese, and silicon hydroxides. When the precipitate was filtered off and analyzed, the beryllium content was found to be 0.03 percent. Beryllium was not found in the dry residue of the filtrate after evaporation.

The investigation of V. P. Petrov and N. V. Lizunov (1946), carried out on the eluvial and redeposited clays of the Urals, showed a wide occurrence of beryllium in redeposited clays and in eluvial clays formed from granites and related veins. Of interest is their conclusion on the more frequent presence of beryllium in redeposited clays compared with eluvial clays (kaolins), caused by the dissemination of beryllium during the redeposition of the clays. Available analytical data indicate that eluvial clays have a higher beryllium content than redeposited clays. It should be noted here that the beryllium content of any clays, particularly eluvial types, is determined by the distribution and content of the element in the original endogenous rocks. The ability of beryllium to precipitate rapidly from hypergene solutions as a result of its capture in colloidal and finely dispersed systems results in a generally nonuniform distribution in sedimentary rocks of the hypergene zone. In particular, there is a noticeable enrichment of beryllium in clayey sediments in regions of alkalic rocks with increased beryllium content (Table 143), and also in some clays occurring near greisen or skarn deposits containing helvite or danalite. Redeposited clays formed from various rock types (acid, medium, or alkalic) contain, as a rule, insignificant proportions of beryllium, usually not exceeding, and commonly less than, the beryllium clarke of the earth's crust.

The mean beryllium content of a mixture of 50 redeposited clays from various parts of the USSR was found to be 7×10^{-4} percent, which is close to the results obtained by V. M. Goldschmidt for a mixture of clay shales (6×10^{-4} percent) and is almost twice the beryllium clarke of the

Table 143 Occurrence of beryllium in recent sediments, soils, and plants of the Khibiny rock mass

Sample characteristic	Be content, in 10^{-4}%
Soil from Mt. Kuivchorr	440
Soil from Mt. Yukspor	360
Ash of Vaccinium myrtillus, Mt. Kuivchorr	250
Ash of meadow grass (Poa), Mt. Yukspor	3.6
Ash of birch branches	14
Ash of spruce, detrital deposits of river Kuniok	not detected
Mud of lake Il'ma (Lovozero rock mass)	36

lithosphere. However, after four samples from regions of beryllium deposits, with an abnormally high beryllium content, had been eliminated, the mean beryllium content of the mixture was found to be 3×10^{-4} percent. This figure probably corresponds more realistically to the mean beryllium content of redeposited clays, but it should be determined with greater accuracy. Our figures of the beryllium content of various shales were also found to be much lower than those of V. M. Goldschmidt. It is interesting to note that the mean beryllium value, calculated for shales (3.8×10^{-4} percent), was found to be close to the beryllium clarke derived for biotite granites. A somewhat higher mean beryllium value for metamorphosed shales can be obtained from the data of W. Stoll (1945) for shales developed in regions of a wide occurrence of beryl-bearing pegmatites.

Increased amounts of beryllium in quaternary sediments near beryllium deposits, caused by its weak ability to migrate in the hypergene zone, can be successfully utilized for prospecting for beryllium deposits. The first field investigations of this type conducted by the author, have entirely borne out the possibility of utilizing the metallometric prospecting method not only in skarn and greisen deposits, but also in pegmatitic beryllium deposits, even when the overburden is 2 m thick.

The beryllium content of limestones usually does not attain the sensitivity threshold of available analytical methods and depends closely on the clayey material present. This was convincingly demonstrated by R. Pierruccini (1943) for some limestones of the Appennines (Table 145), in which all of the beryllium present was combined with the insoluble clay fraction of the limestone. Somewhat higher beryllium concentrations were found in individual samples of dolomites of the Moscow area, and in the silicified limestones of a number of Caucasian regions (Table 146); however, in general, the carbonate rocks of the USSR have a much lower beryllium content than the clarke in the lithosphere.

The regularities of beryllium occurrence in soils are noteworthy. Work done by A. P. Vinogradov (1950) on the geochemistry of the soil mantle indicates the preferential relation between beryllium and clayey soils, although there are indications that chalky soil may contain up to 7×10^{-4} percent Be. In regions of beryllium minerals and rocks with a higher beryllium content, there are soils with a relatively high concentration of this element. Thus, for example, A. S. Dudykina and E. I. Semenov (1957) note that in soils covering the Khibiny and Lovozero nepheline syenites there are, along with other rare elements, considerable beryllium concentrations, attaining 440×10^{-4} percent (Table 143).

Beryllium concentrations varying between 7 to 15×10^{-4} percent were also found in soils in a number of areas with beryllium-bearing pegmatites (eastern Transbaikalia, Mongolian Altai).

In this connection, results point to a higher beryllium content in the ash of plants that grow on soils enriched with beryllium. A. S. Dudykina and E. I. Semenov found 250×10^{-4} percent Be in the ash of *Vaccinium myrtillus* from Mt. Kuivchorr (Khibiny rock mass), which grew on a soil containing 440×10^{-4} percent Be, and 3.6×10^{-4} percent Be in meadow grass (Poa) from Mt. Yukspor (beryllium content of soil 360×10^{-4} percent.) W. Stoll (1945) notes also the usual increase of beryllium content in

Table 144 Relative occurrence of beryllium in fossil coal in various areas of the USSR

Range of Be content, in percent	Relative occurrence in relation to the total number of samples, in percent		
	USSR in Europe	Caucasus	Other areas
0.1 — 1	—	—	—
0.01 — 0.1	0.3	—	0.8
0.001 — 0.01	6	12.3	4.5
0.001	43.4	75.4	33.3
<0.001	50	12.3	61.4

the ash of plants that grow in the neighborhood of beryl-bearing pegmatites. The investigation of grasses within one of the beryl-bearing pegmatite fields in the Altai showed a content of 5 to 8×10^{-4} percent Be in the ash of grasses growing on gabbro.

Away from the beryllium source, the beryllium content of the plant ash sharply decreases. Thus, for example, beryllium was not detected in the ash of spruce growing on thick detritus in the valley of the river Kunnok within the Khibiny rock mass. The soils and plants situated directly on the nepheline syenites contain, as already indicated, a noticeable beryllium concentration. Similarly, beryllium was not detected in the ashes of trees and grasses growing on sedimentary rocks impoverished in beryllium (a series of regions in eastern Transbaikalia, Altai, and in the provinces of Moscow and Leningrad).

When describing the function of beryllium in the biogeochemical process, V. M. Goldschmidt and C. Peters (1932) pointed to considerable beryllium concentrations, attaining 0.01 percent, in the ashes of coals from various areas.

When studying the occurrence of beryllium in the ash of coal mined in some coalfields of the USSR, V. A. Zil'bermints and A. K. Rusanov (1936) failed to establish in them a wide incidence of high beryllium concentrations (Table 144).

For the Donets coal field, the highest mean beryllium concentration was found in the marginal parts of the coal field (Table 145), the content decreasing gradually towards the central area.

The highest beryllium contents are associated with coal varieties with the lowest ash content (mean ash content < 3.5 percent). The mean ash content of coals, in which less than 10×10^{-4} percent Be was found, exceeded 6.7 percent. These results show there is no relationship between beryllium concentration in coals and the clastic constituents.

High beryllium concentrations were not detected in the ash of low-grade coal from Texas, Colorado, North and South Dakota, U.S.A., investigated by M. Deul and C. Annell (1956). Beryllium content of coal ash from these

Table 145 Mean beryllium content of coals from various districts of the Donets coalfields

Location	Number of determinations	Mean Be content in 10^{-4}%
Lisichanskii	19	15
Almazno-Mar'evskii	118	11
Tsentral'nyi	94	4
Stalinsko-Makeevskii	54	9

areas varied between 1 and 10×10^{-4} percent. Thousandths and ten-thousandths of 1 percent of beryllium were also noted in the oil ash from various areas of the United States. (R. Erickson *et al.*, 1954).

We do not yet have sufficient evidence for deciding whether beryllium bound in coal is of syngenetic or epigenetic origin. However, considerable variations of beryllium content in coals from various coalfields undoubtedly reflect the geochemical peculiarities of each specific province and of the epoch of coal accumulation. Further investigations will explain these irregularities.

Concluding the brief description of the relation between beryllium and fossil organic residues, we should note that there is a fairly wide occurrence of insignificant amounts of beryllium ($n \times 10^{-4}$ percent) in the bones of fossil animals (V. V. Lavrov, 1956). Phosphorus appears to be the precipitating agent of beryllium in animal organic remnants. In this connection, K. B. Krauskopf (1956) suggests that phosphorites contain up to 0.01 percent of beryllium. One should keep this suggestion in mind when investigating precipitates rich in phosphorus, although such high beryllium content in phosphorites is apparently exceptional.

Thus, in summarizing the available data on the occurrence of beryllium in rocks of the hypergene zone, let us stress again its weak ability to migrate and its clearly manifested property of being captured in dispersed and colloidal systems near the original source. Further migration of beryllium thus precipitated is probably effected in the erosion by water and redeposition of clays, along with the primary clayey material that has adsorbed the beryllium.

CHAPTER 12

Beryllium Clarke in the Earth's Crust

In order to calculate the mean beryllium content of the rocks of the USSR, a large number of mean composite samples, collected systematically in various intrusive masses, were used. On the basis of the results obtained—with consideration of the incidence of various rocks within the USSR (Solov'ev, 1952)—the beryllium clarke for the USSR was calculated (Table 146).

Table 146 Calculation of the beryllium clarke for the USSR

Rocks	Occurrence in the USSR, according to S.P. Solov'ev (1952)	Mean beryllium content, in 10^{-4}%	Area multiplied by content $\times 10^{-4}$
Acid intrusive granites	48.7	5	243.5
Acid effusive rocks	13.5	6	81.0
Basic and ultrabasic (intrusive and effusive)	37.4	0.5	18.7
Alkalic rocks	0.4	7	2.8
Total	100		346.0
Mean Be content	$\frac{346 \times 10^{-4}}{100} = 3.46 \times 10^{-4} \approx 3.5 \times 10^{-4}$		

Table 147 Mean beryllium content of various magmatic rocks (in 10^{-4} percent)

Rock types	V. M. Goldschmidt (1932)	Sandell (1952)	A. A. Beus (1955)
Ultrabasic	0	<0.2	<0.2
Basic	<3.6	1 and less	0.4
Intermediate (diorites)	—	1.6	1.8
Acidic	3.6	3	5
Alkalic	36	—	7

Table 148 Beryllium clarke for the upper part of the lithosphere (in 10^{-4} percent)

Clarke and Washington (1921)[a]	V. I. Goldschmidt (1932)	A. E. Fersman (1933-1939)[a]	A. P. Vinogradov (1949)	Sandell (1952)	A. A. Beus (1955)
10	1.8	4	6	2	3.5

[a] Allowing for hydrosphere

The beryllium clarke determined for so considerable a part of the world can probably be accepted as the real mean value for the upper, sialic part of the lithosphere (Table 147 and 148).

Literature

Alimarin, I. P. (1932), Occurrence of beryllium in minerals and rocks of the USSR (K voprosu o rasprostranenii berilliya v mineralakh i porodakh SSSR) *Min, Syr'e,* No. 9.

Aminoff, G. (1923), Omen association med barylit och hedifan vid Langban, *Géol., För. Förh.*, Stockholm, vol. 45.

——— (1924), Über ein neues Mineral von Langban, *Zs. f. Kristallogr,* vol. 60.

——— (1925), Über Beryllumoxyd als Mineral und dessen Kristallstructur, *Zs. f. Kristallogr,* vol. 62.

——— (1926), Zur Kristallographie des Trimerites, *Geol. För. Förh.*, Stockholm, vol. 46, H. 1.

——— (1933), On the structural and chemical composition of Swedenborgite, *Ihungl. Svenska Vetenskaps.* Handl., Upsala, ser. 3, vol. 11.

Anderson, B. W. (1952a), More notes on the new gemstone taaffeite, *Gemmologist,* vol. 21, No. 247.

——— (1952b), Two new gemstones, taaffeite and sinhalite, *Gems a. Gemol.*, vol. 7, No. 6.

——— and G. F. Claringbull (1951), Taaffeite a new beryllium mineral, found as a cut gemstone, *Min. Mag.*, vol. 29, No. 25.

Arnold, J. R. and H. Al-Salih, (1955) Beryllium[7] produced by cosmic rays, *Science,* vol. 121.

Atkinson, R. (1931), Atomic synthesis and stellar energy, *Astrophys. Journ.*

Avdeev, I. V. (1842), Glucinium (beryllium) and its compounds (O Glitsinie (berillie) i ego soedineniyakh), *Gor. Zhurn.*, pt. 3, book 9.

Badalov, S. T. (1955), Genesis of calamine (O genzise kalamina), *Zap, uzb. Otd. vses. min. Obshch,* issue 8.

——— (1956), Some results of the investigation of hydrothermal helvite (Nekotorye rezul'taty izucheniya gidrotermal'nogo gel'vina), *Zap. uzb. Otd. vses. min. Obshch,* issue 10.

Belov, N. V. (1942), New silicate structures, (Novye silikatnye struktury), *Dokl. Akad. Nauk SSSR,* Nos. 4 and 37.

——— (1947), Structure of ionic crystals and metallic phases (Struktura ionnykh kristallov i metallicheskikh faz), *Akad, Nauk SSSR,* Moscow.

——— (1950), Essays on structural mineralogy, (Ocherki po strukturnoi mineralogii), *Min. Sb. l'vovsk. geol. Obshch,* No. 4.

——— (1954a), Essays on structural mineralogy. Some features of the geochemistry of boron in the light of its crystallization (Ocherki po strukturnoi mineralogii. Nekotorye osobenosti geokhimii bora v svete ego kristallizatsii), *Min. Sb. l'vovsk. min. Obshch.,* No. 8.

——— (1954b), Nepheline structure (Struktura nefelina), *Tr. Inst. Kristallogr. Akad. Nauk SSSR,* issue 10.

——— and T. N. Tarkhova (1949), Crystalline structure of milarite (Kristallicheskaya struktura milarita), *Dokl. Akad. Nauk SSSR,* vol. 69, No. 3.

——— ——— (1951), Crystalline structure of milarite (Kristallicheskaya struktura milarita), *Tr. Inst. Kristallogr. Akad. Neuk SSSR,* issue 6.

Bel'kov, I. V. (1958), Yttrium mineralization of amazonitic pegmatites in alkalic granites of the Kola Peninsula (Ittrievaya mineralizatsiya amazonitovykh pegmatitov v shchelochnykh granitakh Kol'skogo poluostrova), *Sb. Voprosy Mineralogii i Geologii Kol'skogo Poluostrova, Akad. Nauk SSSR,* issue 1.

Betekhtin, A. G. (1949), Effect of the sulfur and oxygen cycle on the paragenetic relations of minerals in ores (O vliyanii rezhima sery i kisloroda na parageneticheskie sootnosheniya mineralov v rudakh), *Izv. Akad, Nauk SSSR,* ser. geol., No. 3.

——— (1950), Mineralogiya (Mineralogy), *Gosgeolizdat,* Moscow.

Beus, A. A. (1948), Vertical zoning of granitic pegmatites in the pegmatite field of Aksu-Pushtiru, Turkestan ridge (Vertikal'naya zonal'nost' granitnykh pegmatitov na primere pegmatitivogo polya Aksu-Pushtiru Turkestanskii khrebet), *Dokl, Akad. Nauk SSSR,* vol. 60, No. 7.

——— (1950), The nature of the aplite-like zone of granitic pegmatites (O prirode aplitovidnoi zony granitnykh pegmatitov), *Tr. min. Muzeya Akad. SSSR,* issue 2.

——— (1951), Zonation of granitic pegmatites (O zonal'nosti granitnykh pegmatitov), *Izv. Akad. Nauk SSSR,* ser. geol., No. 6.

——— (1953a), Zoning of granitic pegmatites (O zonal' nosti granitnykh pegmatitov), *Akad. Nauk SSSR,* Moscow.

——— (1953b), Isomorphism of beryllium in connection with the phenomena of its concentration and dissemination (Ob izomorfizme berilliya v svyazi s yaleniyami ego kontsentratsii i rasseyaniya), *Dokl. Akad. Nauk SSSR,* vol. 90, No. 3.

——— (1954), Problem of the origin of zonation of granitic pegmatites (K voprosu o proiskhozdenii zonal'nosti granitnykh pegmatotiv), *Dokl, Akad. Nauk SSSR,* vol. 97, No. 1.

——— (1955), Estimation of pegmatitic beryllium deposits (K voprosu ob otsenke pegmatitovykh mestorozhdenii berylliya), (in Chinese), translated by Van Yao-tszen, Peking.

——— (1956a), Beryllium. Evaluation of deposits during prospecting and exploratory work (Berillii. Otsenka mestoroshdenii pri poiskakh i razvedkakh, Moscow, *Gosgeolizdat.*) English translation, W. H. Freeman and Company, San Francisco and London, 1962.

——— (1956b), Geochemistry of beryllium (Geokhimiya berilliya), Report read at the 20th session of the Intern. Geol. Congress in Mexico, *Geokhimiya,* No. 5.

——— (1956c), Characteristics of diadochic entry of beryllium into crystal structures of minerals (Osobennosti izomorfnogo vkhozhdeniya berilliya v kristallicheskie struktury mineralov), *Geokhimiya,* No. 1.

——— (1957), Beryllium vesuvianite (O berillievom vezuviane), *Tr. min. Muzeya Akad. Nauk SSSR,* issue 8.

——— and S. N. Fedorchuk (1955), Beryllium clarke of granitic pegmatites (O klarke berilliya v granitnykh pegmatitakh), *Dokl. Akad. Nauk SSSR,* vol. 104, No. 1.

——— and L. I. Sazhina (1956), Beryllium clarke of acid magmatic rocks of the USSR (O klarke berilliya v kislykh magmaticheskikh porodakh SSSR), *Dolk. Akad. Nauk SSSR,* vol. 104, No. 1.

——— and N. E. Zalashkzova (1956), Genesis of the sodium variety of beryl in granitic pegmatites (O genzise natrievoi modifikatsii berilla v granitnkh pegmatitakh), *Min. Sb. l'vovsk. geol. Obshch,* No. 10.

Biscoe, J. and B. E. Warren (1933), The structure of euclase $HBeAlSiO_5$, Zs. f. *Kristollogr,* Abt. A, vol. 86, Nos. 3 and 4.

Bleshinskii, S. V. and V. F. Abramova (1955), Chemistry of beryllium (Khimiya berilliya), Frunze, *Akad. Nauk Kirgiz SSSR.*

Boldyrev, A. K. (1932), Tigerek beryl deposit in the Altai. In book: Papers of the "4th All-Union Geological Conference on Nonferrous Metals," issue 5. Minor and rare metals (Tigerekskoe mestorozhdenie berilla na Altae. V kn: "Trudy IV Vsesoyuznoi geologicheskoi konferentsii po tsvetnym metallam," vyp. 5. Malye i redkie metally), *Tsvetmetizdat,* Moscow, Leningrad.

——— and Ya. A. Lui (1929), Exploration of primary deposits of tungsten, tin, bismuth, and beryllium ores in Sherlovaya Mountain (Razvedka korennykh mestorozhdenii rud vol'frama, olova, vismuta i berilliya na Sherlovoi gore), Gorn. Zhurn., Nos. 8 and 9.

Borneman-Starynkevich, I. D. and V. S. Myasnikov (1950), Isomorphous replacements in clinohumite (Ob izomorfnykh zameshcheniyakh v klinogumite), *Dokl. Akad. Nauk SSSR,* vol. 71, No. 2.

Borodin, L. S. (1954), Belovite—a new mineral from alkalic pegmatites (Belovit—novyi mineral iz shchelochnykh pegmatitov), *Dokl. Akad. Nauk SSSR,* vol. 96, No. 3.

——— (1956), Occurrence of beryllium in the Khibiny alkalic rock mass and the beryllium clarke in nepheline syenites (O rasprostranenii berilliya v Khibinskom shchelochnom massive i o klarke berilliya v nefelinovykh sienitakh), *Dokl. Akad. Nauk SSSR,* vol. 109, No. 4.

Borovik, S. A. and A. F. Sosedko (1937), Occurrence of gallium in specimens of the expedition of the Lomonosov Institute of the Academy of Sciences of the USSR (Nakhozhdenie galliya v obraztsakh ékspeditsii Lomonsovkogo instituta Akademii Nauk SSSR), *Dokl. Akad. Nauk SSSR,* vol. 14, No. 1.

Böse, R. (1936), Optishe und spektrographische Untersuchungren an Beryllen, insebesondere bei höheren Temperaturen, *N. J. F. Min. Geol. u. Paleont,* vol. 70

Bragg, W. L. (1930), Structure of Silicates, *Akademische Verlagsgesellschaft* m. b H., Leipzig, vol. 69.

——— (1931), Atomic Structure of Minerals, Cornell University Press, Ithaca.

Brandenberger, E. (1932), Die Kristallstruktur non Beryllium fluorid, *Schweiz. min. u. petrog. Mitt.*, vol. 12.

Brezer, V. M. (1937), Some data of the geochemistry of reactional fringes of emerald mines (Nekotorye dannye o geokhimii reaktsionnykh kaim Isumrudnykh kopei), *Uch. Zap. sverdlovsk. gos. Universiteta*, No. 1.

Brögger, W. G. (1890), Die Mineralien der Syentpegmatitgänge der Südnorwegischen Augitund Nephelinsyenite, *Zs. f. Kristollogr. u. Min.*, vol. 16.

——— (1906), Die Mineralien der Südnowegischen Granitpegmatitgänge, *Vidensk. skrift., Math. Natur. Kl.*, Kristiania, vol. 6.

———, T. J. Vogt, and J. Schetelig (1922), Die Mineralien der Südnorwegischen Granite-Pegmatitgänge. 2. Silikate der seltenen Erden, *Vidensk. skrift., Math. Natur. Kl.*, Kristiania, vol. 6.

Budnikov, P. P. and A. M. Cherepanov (1950), Synthesis of phenacite (K sintezu fenakita), *Dokl. Akad. Nauk SSSR*, vol. 74, No. 5.

Burkser, E. S., N. P. Kapustin, and V V. Kondoguri (1937), Helium, radium, and thorium in beryllium minerals of the USSR (Gelii, radii i torii v berillievykh mineralakh SSSR), *Dokl. Akad. Nauk SSSR*, vol. 15, No. 4.

Cameron, E. N., R. B. Rowe, and P. L. Weis (1953), Fluid inclusions in beryl and quartz from pegmatites of the Middletown District, Conn., *Amer. Min.*, vol. 38, Nos. 3 and 4.

Cherdyntsev, V. V. and L. V. Kozak (1949), Origin of excess helium in some minerals (O proiskhozhdenii izbytochnogo geliya v nekotorykh mineralakh), *Dokl. Akad. Nauk SSSR*, vol. 69, No. 6.

Chernik, G. P. (1900), On the composition of gadolinite from the Batum province (Neskol'ko slov po povodu sostava odnogo vida gadolinita iz Batumskoi oblasti), *Zhurn. fiz. khim. Obshch.*, vol. 32.

——— (1950a), Result of the analysis of two gadolinite varieties and their inclusions (Rezul'tat analiza dvukh raznovidnostei gadolinita i naidennye v nem vklyucheniya), *Zap. sib. min. Obshch.*, vol. 43.

——— (1905b), Results of the investigation of chemical composition of some specimens of Scandinavian gadolinites (Rezul'taty issledovanii khimicheskogo sostava neskol'kikh obraztsov skandinavskikh gadolinitov), *Zap. SPb. min. Obshch.*, pt. 43.

——— (1907), Results of the investigation of chemical composition of two allanite varieties (Rezul'taty issledovaniya khimicheskogo sostava dvukh raznovidnostei ortita), *Zap. SPb. min. Obshch.*, pt. 45.

Chernyshkova, L. P. (1957), Geological features of Volhynian pegmatites; their morphology and internal structure. In the book: *Trudy VNIIP* (Geologicheskie osobennosti pegmatitov Volyni; ikh morfologiya i vnutrennee stroenie. V kn: Trudy VNIIP), vol. 1, issue 1.

Claringbull, G. F. (1940), Occurrence of bavenite in Switzerland, *Min. Mag.*, vol. 25, No. 168.

Crane, H. R. and C. C. Lauritsen (1935), Masses of Be^8, Be^9, and Be^{11}, *Phys. Rev.*, vol. 47.

Crookshank, H. (1948), Minerals of the Rajputana pegmatites, *Min. Geol. and Met. Inst. India, Trans.*, vol. 42, No. 2.

Daiton, A. D., P. H. Fowler, and D. W. Kent (1954), Abundance of lithium, beryllium, and boron in primary cosmic radiation, *Phil. Mag.*, vol. 43.

Dana, J. D., and E. S. Dana (1944, 1951), The System of Mineralogy, 7th edition revised by C. Palache, H. Berman, and C. Frondel, New York, John Wiley and Sons. vol. 1, 1944, vol. 2, 1951.

Deul, M. and C. S. Annell (1956), The occurrence of minor elements in ash of low-rank coal from Texas, Colorado, North Dakota, and South Dakota, *U.S. Geol. Surv. Bull.*, 1956, Bull. 1036.

Dilaktorskii, N. L. (1931), Alteration of beryls at high temperatures (Ob izmenenii berillov pri vysokikh temperaturakh), *Izv. vses. geol.-razv. Ob'ed,* vol. 50, issue 85.

Doelter, C. (1914–1925) Handbuch der Mineralchemie, Dresden, Leipzig, Bd. 1–4.

Dorfman, M. D. (1952), Determination of the genesis of beryl (K vopruso ob opredelenii genezisa berilla), *Dokl. Akad. Nauk SSSR,* vol. 82, No. 4.

Dovgal', N. D. (1934), The Tigerek beryl deposit on the basis of research conducted in 1933 (Tigeretskoe mestorozhdenie berilla po rabotam 1933 g.), *Vestn. zap.-sibir. geol. Tresta,* No. 4.

Dudykina, A. F. and E. I. Semenov (1957), The Lovozero and Khibiny rock masses—a rare-metal biogeochemical province (Lovozerskii i Khibinskii massivy—redkometal'naya biogeokhimicheskaya provintsiya), *Tr. Inst. Min. i. Geokim. redk. Elem. Akad. Nauk SSSR,* issue 1.

DuToit, L. G. (1919), Plumasite (corundum aplite) and titaniferous magnetite rocks, Natal, *Trans. Geol. Soc. S. Africa.*

——— (1928), The origin of corundum aplite, *Econ. Geol.* vol. 33, No. 7.

Eremeev, P. V. (1893), Inner structure of aquamarine from the snow-covered flattened Tigerek mountain summits in the Altai (O vnutrennen stroenii akvamarina iz Tigerekskikh belkov na Altae), *Zap. SPb. min. Obshch,* vol. 35.

——— (1895), Beryl crystals from the Ilmen hills, Murzinki village, and from the Kukeserken ridge in Nerchinsk district (Kristally berylla iz Il'menskikh gor, derevni Murzinki i iz Kukheserkenskogo kryazha v Nerchinskom okruge), *Zap. SPb. min. Obshch,* pt. 33, issue 1, proceedings of meetings.

Ermakov, N. P. (1950), Investigations of mineral-forming solutions (Issledovaniya mineraloobrazuyuschikh rastvorov), *L'vov, University Press.*

——— (1955), Origin of chambered type pegmatites (Prpiskhozhdenie pegmatitov kamernogo tipa), Summaries of reports read at the Jubilee Session of Moscow University, Geological Faculty, Moscow.

Erickson, R. L., A. T. Meyers, and C. A. Horr (1954), Association of uranium and other metals with crude oil, asphalt, and petroliferous rock, *Bull. Amer. Assoc. Petrol. Geol.,* vol. 38, No. 10.

Es'kova, E. M. (1957), Genthelvite from alkalic pegmatites, (Gentgel'vin iz shchelochnykh pegmatitov), *Dokl. Akad. Nauk SSSR,* vol. 116, No. 3.

Fersman, A. E. (1922), Precious and colored gemstones of Russia (Dragotsennye i tsevtnye kamni Rossii), *Petrograd,* vol. 1.

——— (1925a), Precious and colored gemstones of the USSR (Dragotsennye i tsbetnye kamni SSSR), Leningrad, vol. 2.

——— (1925b), Emerald mines and their origin (Izumrudnye kopi i ikh proiskhozhdenie), *Ural'skii tekhnik*, No. 5.
——— (1925c), Origin of emerald mines in the Urals (Proiskhozhdenie izumrudnykh kopei na Urale), *Dokl. Akad. Nauk SSSR*, ser. A., April–June.
——— (1933–1939), Geochemistry (Geokhimiya), *Goskhimtekhizdat*, 2nd ed., vols. 1–4.
——— (1939), Geochemical and mineralogical methods of prospecting for commercial minerals (Geokhimicheskie i mineralogicheskie metody poiskov poleznykh iskopaemykh), *Akad. Nauk SSSR*, Moscow, Leningrad.
——— (1940), Pegmatites (Pegmatity), *Akad. Nauk SSSR*, Moscow, Leningrad, 3rd ed., vol. 1.
——— (1946), History of culture of gemstones in Russia (Iz istorii kul'tury kamnya v Rossii), *Akad. Nauk SSSR*, Moscow, Leningrad.
Fleischer, M. (1950), New mineral named bowleyite, *Amer. Min.*, vol. 35, Nos. 11 and 12.
——— and G. Switzer (1953), The bavenite problem, *Amer. Min.*, vol. 38, Nos. 11 and 12.
Flink G. (1900), On minerals from Narsaruk on the Firth of Tunugdliarfik in Southern Greenland, *Meddl. om. Grønl.*, vol. 24.
Frondel, C. (1955), The heat treatment of beryl, *Mineralogist*, vol. 22, No. 1.
Gavrusevich, B. A. (1932), Data on the mineralogy of granitic pegmatites in the upper parts of river Lyailyak (Materialy k mineralogii granitnykh pegmatitov verkhov'ev r. Lyailyak), *Tr. pamir. Eksp. Akad. Nauk SSSR*, issue 4.
——— (1946), Causes of beryl coloration in emerald mines in the Urals (Pro prychyny zabarvlennya beryli v Izumrudnykh kopalen' na Urali), *Naukov. Zap. kyyiv. Univ.*, issues 1 and 5.
——— and F. Ya. Sarapulov (1941), Change of color and optical properties of beryllium on heating (K voprosu ob izmenenii okraski i opticheskikh svoistv berillov pri nagravenii), *Dokl. Akad. Nauk SSSR*, vol. 31, No. 8.
Georgievskaya, O. G. (1955), Genesis of the rhythmic-folded laminated texture of ore bodies of some contact-metasomatic deposits (K vopruso o genezise ritmichno-vitievato-poloschatoi tekstury rudnykh tel nekotorykh kontaktovo-metasomatischeskikh mestorozhdeneii), *Dokl. Akad. Nauk SSSR*, vol. 101, No. 5.
Gerasimovskii, V. I. (1939a), Pegmatites of the Lovozero alkalic rock mass (Pegmatity Lovozerskogo shchelochnogo massiva), *Tr. Inst. geol. Nauk Akad. SSSR*, ser. min.-geokhim, issue 18, No. 5.
——— (1939b), Chkalovite (Chkalovit), *Dokl. Akad. Nauk SSSR*, vol. 22, No. 5.
Gerling, E. K. and A. A. Polkanov (1958), Problem of the absolute age of the preCambrian of the Baltic shield (Problema absolyutmogo vozrasta dokembriya baltiiskogo shchita), *Geokhimiya*, No. 8.
Ginzburg, A. I. (1948), Prospecting features of rare-metal pegmatites (Poiskovye redkometal'nykh pegmatitov), *Razvedka Nedr*, No. 3.
——— (1952a), Mineral-geochemical indicators and their importance in prospecting for rare-metal ores in pegmatites (O mineralakh-geokhimicheskikh indikatorakh i ikh znachemii pri poiskakh rud redkikh metallov v pegmatitakh), *Tr. min. Muzeya Akad. Nauk SSSR*, Issue 3.
——— (1952b), Some groups of rare-metal pegmatites, formed in various

geological conditions, and their evaluation (O nekotorykh gruppakh redkometal'nykh pegmatitov, obrazovavshikhsya v razlichnykh geologicheskikh usoloviyakh i ikh otsenka), *Razvedka Nedr,* No. 2.

——— (1955a), Chemical composition of beryl (K vopruso khimicheskom sostave berilla), *Tr. min. Muzeya Akad. Nauk SSSR,* issue 7.

——— (1955b), Mineralogical-geochemical characteristics of lithium pegmatites (Mineralogo-geokhimicheskaya kharakteristika litievykh pegmatitov), *Tr. min. Muzeya Akad. Nauk SSSR,* issue 7.

——— (1957), Bityite—lithium-beryllium-margarite (Bitiit—litievo-berillievyi margarit), *Tr. min. Muzeya Akad. Nauk SSSR,* issue 8.

——— and D. I. Gorzhevskii (1957), Interrelationships between rare-metal pegmatites and some types of ore veins (K vopruso o vzaimnootnoshenii rekometal'nykh pegmatitov i nekotorykh tipov rudnykh zhil), *Izv. Akad. Nauk SSSR,* ser. geol., No. 6.

Glass, J. J. and J. W. Adams (1953), Genthelvite crystal from El Paso County, Colorado, *Am. Min.,* vol. 38, Nos. 9 and 10.

———, R. H. Jahns, and R. E. Stevens (1944), Helvite and danalite from New Mexico and helvite group, *Am. Min.,* vol. 29, Nos. 5 and 6.

Goldschmidt, V. M. (1945), The geochemical background of minor element distribution, *Soil Sci.,* vol. 60, No. 1.

———, H. Hauptmann, and C. Peters (1933), Über die Berücksichtigung seltener Elemente bei Gesteinsanalysen, *Naturwiss,* vol. 21.

——— and C. Peters (1932), Zur Geochemie des Berylliums, *Nachr. Ges. Wiss. Gottingen. Math.-Phys.,* Kl.

Gordon, M. and K. J. Murata (1952), Minor elements in Arkansas bauxite, *Econ. Geol.,* vol. 47, No. 2.

Goria, C. (1953–1954), Structura della berillio-akermanite, *Attl. Accad. Sci. Torino. Cl. sci. fis. mat. a natur.,* vol. 88, No. 1.

Gossner, B. and J. Besslein (1934), Über kristallographische Beziechungen Zwischen Silikaten und Phosphaten. Ein Beitrag zur Kenntnis Beryllonites, *Cbl. f. Min. Geol. u. Paleontol.,* Abt. A.

Greenstein, J. L. and E. Tandberg-Hanssen (1954), The abundance of beryllium in the sun, *Astroph. Jour.,* vol. 119.

Grigor'ev, I. F. (1944), Danalite in the pegmatites of Imalkin deposit of eastern Transbaikalia (Danalit v pegmatitakh Imalkinskogo mestorozhdeniya vostochnogo Zabaikaliya), *Dokl. Akad. Nauk SSSR,* vol. 44, No. 3.

Grum-Grzhimailo, S. V. (1940), Coloration of minerals, due to chromium (Ob okraske mineralov, vyzyvaemoi khromom), *Tr. Kristallogr. Labor. Akad. Nauk SSSR,* issue 2.

Hahn, T. (1953), Modellbeziehungen zwischen Silikaten und Fluoberyllaten, *N. J. Min. Abhandl,* vol. 86, No. 1.

Heide, F. (1955), Beryllium minerals from Henneberg near Wurzbach in Thuringia (Berylliummineralien vom Henneberg bei Würzbach in Thür), *Chemie der Erde,* vol. 16.

Heinrich, E. W. (1953), Zoning in pegmatite districts, *Amer. Min.,* vol. 38, Nos. 1 and 2.

Hewett, D. F. (1937), Helvite from the Butte district, Montana, *Amer. Min.,* No. 6.

Hidden, W. E. (1905), Results of late mineral research in Llano County, Texas,

Amer. Jour. Sci., ser. 4, vol. 19.

——— and J. B. Mackintosh (1844), On herderite from Oxford County, Maine, *Amer. Jour. Sci.*, vol. 27, Nos. 157–162.

Hintze, C. (1897), Hanbuch der Mineralogie, Bd. 20, Leipzig.

Hurlbut, C. S. (1937), Aminovit, a new mineral from Langban, *Geol. För. Förh.*, Stockholm, vol. 59.

——— (1955), Beryllian idocrase from Franklin, New Jersey, *Amer. Min.*, vol. 40, Nos. 1 and 2.

Iimori, T. (1938), Tengerite found in Iisaka and its chemical composition, *Sci. Papers, Inst. Phys. a. Chem. Res.*, Tokyo, vol. 34.

——— (1939), Be-bearing variety of allanite, *Sci. Papers. Inst. Phys. a. Chem. Res.*, Tokyo, vol. 36.

Ikornikova, N. Yu (1939), Crystallographic investigation of beryl crystals from Sherlovaya (Kristallograficheskoe issledovanie kristallov berilla Sherlovoi gory), *Zap. vseross. min. Obshch.*, pt. 68, issue 4.

Ito, T. (1947), the Structure of eudidimite, *Amer. Min.*, vol. 32, Nos. 7 and 8.

———, N. Morimoto and R. Sadanga (1952), The crystal structure of milarite, *Acta Crystallogr.*, vol. 5, pt. 2.

———, and J. West (1932), The structure of bertrandite $H_2Be_4Si_2O_9$, *Zs. f. Kristallogr*, A, vol. 83, Nos. 5 and 6.

Jahns, R. H. (1944), "Ribbon Rock," an unusual beryllium-bearing tactite, *Econ. Geol.*, vol. 39.

Jakob, J. (1938), Drei Analysen von Beryl, *Schweiz Min. Petrogr. Mitt.*, vol. 18, No. 2.

Kalugin, P. (1880), The Murzin and Alabashin mines of colored gemstones (Murzinskie i Alabashinskie kopi tsvetnykh kamnei), *Zap. SPb. min. Obshch.*, vol. 24.

Kerr, P. F. (1946), Kaolinite after beryl from Alto do Giz, Brazil, *Amer. Min.*, vol. 31, Nos. 9 and 10.

Khlopin, V. G. (1949), Determination of the absolute geological age by the helium method in nonradioactive minerals with dense crystal packing (K vopruso ob opredelenii absolyutnogo geologicheskogo vozrasta po gelievomu metodu v neradioktivnykh mineralakh s plotnoi kristallocheskoi upalovkoi), *Dokl. Akad. Nauk SSSR*, vol. 69, No. 6.

——— and Sh. A. Abishev (1941), Radioactivity and helium content of beryllium, boron, and lithium minerals of the USSR (Radioakticnost' i soderzhanie geliya v berillievykh, boronykh i litievykh mineralakh SSSR), *Dokl. Akad. Nauk SSSR*, vol. 32, No. 9.

Kholmov, G. V. (1929), Results of the mineralogical-petrographical evaluation of the Sherlovaya Mountains, tungsten deposit, Transbaikalia, in the summer of 1928 (Rezul'taty mineralogo-petrografischeskoi otsenki Sherlovogorskogo vol'framovogo mestrozhdeniya, Zabaikalie, letom 1928 g.), *Izv. geol. Kom.*, vol. 48, No. 10.

Kitaev, A. G. (1928), Deposit of corundum, helvite, and rare-earth minerals in Southern Urals (Mestotozhdenie korunda, gel'vina i redkozemel'nogo mineral-ala na Yuzhnom Urals), *Min. Syr'e*, No. 1.

Koksharov, N. A. (1852–1862), Materials for the mineralogy of Russia (Materialy dlya mineralogii Rossii), vol. 1–4, St. Petersburg.

Kopaleishvili, T. I. (1956), Nuclear reaction $Be^9(p,d)Be8$ (O yadernoi reaktsii $Be^9(p,d)Be^8$), *Zh. ėksper. teor. Fiz.*, vol. 30, issue 6.

Korzhinskii, D. S. (1953), Outline of metasomatic processes. In the book: Basic problems in the theory of magmatic ore deposits (Ocherk mestasomaticheskikh protsessov, V kn. niyakh), *Akad. Nauk SSSR,* Moscow.

Kostylova, E. E. (1937), Mineralogical outline of the Khibiny and Lovozero tundras. In the book: Minerals of the Khibiny and Lovozero tundras (Mineralogicheskii ocherk Khibinskikh i Lovozerskikh tundr. V kn. Mineraly Khibinskikh i Lovozerskikh tundr), *Akad. Nauk SSSR,* Moscow, Leningrad.

Krauskopf, K. B. (1956), Sedimentary deposits of rare metals, *Econ. Geol.*, 50th Anniv. vol.

Ksanda, C. J. and N. E. Merwin (1938), Bavenite: symmetry, unit cell, *Amer. Min.*, vol. 18, No. 8.

Kulibin, S. N. (1829), Description of the Adun-Chilon ridge (Opisanie kryazha Adun-Chilon), *Gorn. Zhurn*, book 10, pt. 4.

Kurbatov, I. D. and V. A. Kargin (1927), Change of the green color of beryl into blue (Ob izmenenii zelenoi okraski berilla v goldbuyu), *Priroda,* vol. 16, Nos. 7 and 9.

Kutukova, E. I. (1946), The bavenite of the emerald mines (Bavenit izumrudnykh kopei), *Dokl. Akad. Nauk SSSR,* vol. 54. No. 8.

Kuz'menko, M. V. (1954), Beryllite—a new mineral (Berillit—novyi mineral), *Dokl. Akad. SSSR,* vol. 99. No. 3.

——— (1957), Classification and genesis of alkalic pegmatites (K vorpsuo o klassifikatsii i genezise shchelochnykh pegmatitov), *Tr. Inst. Min. i Geokhim. redk. Elem. Akad. Nauk SSSR,* issue 1.

Kuznetsova, E. V. (1931), Data on pegmatite veins of the Dzirul rock mass in Transcaucasia (Materialy po pegmatitovym zhilam Dzirul (skogo massiva v Zakavkaz'e), *Izv. vses. geol.-razv. Ob'edin,* vol. 50, issue 98.

——— (1936), Classification scheme of preCambrian granitic pegmatites of Upper Balkariya (Skhema klassifikatsii dokembriiskikh graninykh pegmatitov Gornoi Balkarii), *Zap. ross. min. Obshch.,* pt. 65, issue 2.

——— (1946), Pegmatitic fields of Upper Karbarda, In the book: Natural resources of the Karbardian ASSR (Pegmatitovye poly Gornoi Karbardy, V kn: Prirodnye resursy Karbardinskoi ASSR), *Akad. Nauk SSSR,* Moscow, Leningrad.

Lacroix, A. (1908), Les mineraux des filons de pegmatite a tourmaline licique de Madagascar, *Bull. Soc. Franc. Min.,* vol. 31.

——— (1909), Sur l'existence de la rhodizite dans les pegmatites de Madagascar, *C. R. Acad. Sci.,* Paris, vol. 149.

——— (1910), Nouvelles observations sur les mineraux des pegmatites de Madagascar, *Bull. Soc. Franc. Min.,* vol. 33.

Landergren, S. (1948), On the geochemistry of Swedish iron ores and associated rocks, *Sverig. geol. undersokn.,* ser. C., Arsbok 42, No. 496.

Landes, K. K. (1932), The Baringer Hill, Texas pegmatite, *Amer. Min.,* vol. 17, No. 8.

Largest beryl crystal (1953), *Mineralogist,* vol. 21, No. 496.

Larsen, E. S. (1928), Hydrothermal origin of corundum and albite bodies, *Econ. Geol.,* vol. 33.

Lavrov, V. V. (1956), Geochemistry of the fossil bones of animals (Geokhima iskopaemykh kostei zhivotnykh), *Izv. Akad. Nauk Kaz. SSR,* ser. geol., issue 23.

Levitskii, O. D. (1933), Geological-petrographical outline of Sherlovaya Mountain, In book: On the geologic front of eastern Siberia (Geologo-petrograficheskii ocherk Sherlovoi gory, V kn: Na geologicheskom fronte Vostochnoi Sibiri), *OShZ,* Moscow, Irkutsk.

——— (1939), Tungsten deposits of eastern Transbaikalia. In the book: Deposits of rare and minor metals in the USSR (Vol'framovye mestorozhdeniya Vostochnogo Zabaikaliya, V kn: Mestorozhdeniya redkikh i Malykh metallov v SSSR), *Akad. Nauk SSSR,* Moscow, Leningrad, pt. 2.

Lindberg, M. L. and K. J. Murata (1953), Faheyite, a new phosphate mineral from Sapucaia pegmatite mine, Minas Gerais, Brazil, *Amer. Min.*, vol. 38, Nos. 3 and 4.

Lindberg, M. L., W. T. Pecora, and A. L. de M. Barbosa (1953), Moraesite, a new hydrous beryllium phosphate from Minas Gerais, Brazil, Amer. Min., vol. 38, Nos. 11 and 12.

Lindström, G. (1888–1889), Analise des Hyalotekit non Langban, *Zs. f. Kristallogr.,* vol. 15, H. 1.

Lodochnikov, V. N. (1935), The so-called desilication hypothesis (O tak nazyvaemoi desilikatsionnoi gipoteze), *Problemy sov. Geol.*, vol. 5, No. 1.

MacAlister, J. F. (1900), The emerald mines of N. Etbai, *Geogr. Jour.*, vol. 16.

Machatschki, F. (1928), Untersuchungen über das Sistem $BeO\text{-}SiO_2$, *Sonderdruck aus Zs. f. phys. Chem.*, vol. 133, Nos. 3 and 4.

——— (1932), Zur formel des vesuvuan, *Zs. f. Kristallogr,* vol. 81, Nos. 1 and 2.

——— (1938), Welche Schlusse sind aus der Existenz von Berylliumorthiten auf die Struktur der Epidote zu ziehen, *Tschermaks min. u. petrogr. Mitt.,* 3 Folge, vol. 1, No. 1.

——— (1948), Kristallochemische Probleme 1: Epidot, *Tschermaks min. u. petrog. Mitt.* 3 Folge, vol. 1, No. 1.

——— (1953), Spezielle Mineralogie auf geochemischer Grundlage, Wien.

——— and E. Stradner (1953), Ein weiterer Fall der Baugleicheit eines Berillium phosphaten mit einem Borosilikat: $CaBe_2Si_2O_8$. *Anz. Osterr. Akad. Wiss. Math. Natur. Kl.,* vol. 90, Nos. 1–15.

Mamasakhlisov, V. I. (1947), Fission of beryllium in nuclei with γ-rays (Rasshcheplenie yadra berilliya γ-luchami), *Tr. Inst. Fiz. i Geofiz. Akad Nauk Gruz. SSR.*, vol. 10.

Mendeleev, D. I. (1898), Periodic regularity of chemical elements (Periodicheskaya zakonnost' khimicheskikh elementov), *Entsiklopedicheskii Slovar'*, St. Petersburg, vol. 23.

Menge, I. N. (1826), Geonostic observations in the Urals and the Ilmen Mountains (Geonosticheskie nablyudeniya nas Uralom i preimushchestvenno nad Il'menskimi gorami), *Gorn. Zhurn.*, book 2, pt. 4.

Miklashevskii, P. I. (1862), Description of the Uralian emerald mines and their surroundings (Opisanie Ural'skikh izumrudnykh kopei i ikh okrestnostei), *Gorn. Zhurn,* book 7, pt. 3.

Momdzhi, G. S. (1955), Excitation potentials (O potentsialakh vozbuzdeniya), *Dokl. Akad. Nauk SSSR,* 1955, vol. 101, No. 4.

Mrose, M. E. (1952), Hurlbutite, $CaBe_2(PO_4)_2$, a new mineral, *Amer. Min.*, vol. 37, Nos. 11 and 12.

Nakai, T. (1938), On calcio-gadolinite, a new variety of gadolinite found in Tadati village, Nagano prefecture, *Bull. Chem. Soc. Japan.*, vol. 13.

Naprasnikov, D. I. (1933), The mineral beryl in pegmatite veins of Northern Caucasus (Mineral berill v pegmatitovykh zhilakh Severnogo Kavkaza), *Geol. na Fronte Industr.*, No. 3.

Nekrasov, B. V. (1946), Electroaffinity of chemical elements (Elektrosrodstvo khimicheskikh elementov), *Zhurn. obshch. Khim.*, vol. 16, issue 11.

——— (1954), Course of general chemistry (Kurs obshchei khimii), *Goskhimizdat*, Moscow.

Nenadkevich, K. A. (1911), Contributions to the knowledge of the chemical composition of minerals in Russia. 6. Cesium beryl. Vorobyenite (Materialy k poznaniyu khimicheskogo sostava mineralov Rossii. 6. Tsezievyi berill. Vorob'evit), *Tr. Geol. Muzeya Akad. Nauk SSSR*, vol. 5.

Nikolaev, V. A. (1953), Genesis of hydrothermal solutions. In the book: Basic problems in the theory of magmatic ore deposits (K vopruso o genezise gidrotermal'nykh rastvorov. V kn: Osnovnye problemy v uchenii of magmatogennykh rudnykh mestoroshdeniyakh), *Akad. Nauk SSSR*, Moscow.

Novoselova, A. V. and Yu. T. Simanov (1955), Structure and transformations of fluoridic beryllium compounds (Stroenie i prevrashcheniya ftoristykh soedinenii berilliya), *Uch. Zap. mosk. Univ.*, issue 174.

Oftedal, I. (1939), Beryllium in radioactive minerals, *Norsk. Tidsskr,* vol. 19, No. 4.

Oppenheim, V. (1948). The Muzo emerald zone, Colombia, South America, *Econ. Geol,* vol. 43.

Ormont, B. F. (1950), Structures of inorganic substances (Struktury neofganicheskikh veshchestv), *Gostekhteoretizdat,* Moscow.

Palache, C. (1931), On the presence of milarite, *Amer. Min.*, vol. 16.

——— and E. V. Shannon (1928), Beryllonite and other phosphates from Newry, Maine, *Amer. Min.*, vol. 13, No. 7.

——— and L. Bauer (1930), On the occurrence of beryllium in the zinc deposit of Franklin, New Jersey, *Amer. Min.*, vol. 15, No. 1.

Parker, R. L. and F. Quervain (1940), De Gadalonite aus den Schweizeralpen, *Scweiz. min. u. petrog. Mitt.*, vol. 20, No. 1.

Pasheva, Z. P. and T. N. Tarkhova (1953), Crystalline structure of milarite (O kristallicheskoi strukture milarita), *Dokl. Akad. Nauk SSSR,* vol. 88, No. 5.

Pauling, L. (1930), The structure of sodalite and helvite, *Zs. f. Kristallogr.*, vol. 74, No. 2.

——— (1940), The nature of the chemical bond, Cornell University Press, Ithaca.

———, H. Klug, and A. N. Winchell (1935), The crystal structure of swedenborgite $NaBe_4SbO_7$, *Amer. Min.*, vol. 20, No. 7.

Peters, B. (1955), Radioactive beryllium in the atmosphere and on the earth, *Prod. Indian Acad. Sci. Sect. A.*, vol. 41, No. 3.

Petrov, V. P. and N. V. Lizunov (1946), Content of trace elements in Urals refractory clays and kaolins, In the book: Problems of mineralogy, geochemistry, and petrography (Sodershanie mikroelementov v ural'skikh ogneupornykh glinakh i kaolinakh, V kn: Voprosy mineralogii, geokhimii i petrografii), *Akad. Nauk SSSR*, Moscow, Leningrad.

Pierruccini, R. (1943), Determinazione spekttrografica del berillo in alcune rocce sedimentarie dell'apennini tosco-emiliano, *Spectrochim.* Acta. Berlin, vol. 2.

Pilipenko, P. P. (1909), Bertrandite in the Altai, (O bertrandite na Altae), *Izv. Akad. Nauk*, 6 ser., No. 16.

Porvatov, B. M. and M. A. Karasik (1925), Principles of investigation of reliability of emerald mines in the Monetnaya section (Printsipy izucheniya blagonadezhnosti izumrudnykh kopei v Monetnoi dache), *Ural'sk. Tekhnik*, No. 4.

Pough, F. H. (1936), Phenakit, seine Morphologie und Paragenesis, *N. J. Min. Geol. u. Paleont.*, Abt. A, vol. 71.

Povarennykh, A. S. (1955a), Crystal-chemical classification of borates (O kristallokhimicheskoi klassifikatsii boratov), *Tr. min. Muzeya Akad. Nauk SSSR*, issue 7.

________ (1955b), Some basic problems of crystal chemistry and their significance in mineralogy (O nekotorykh osnovnykh voprosakh kristallokhi mii ikh ponimanii v mineralogii), *Zap. vses. min. Obshch*, pt. 84, issue 4.

Preiss, E. and S. Glizezynski (1950), Über den Berilliumgehalt einiger wavellite., *Geochim. Cosm. Acta.*, vol. 1, No. 2.

Pyatenko, Yu. A., G. B. Bokii, and N. V. Belov (1956), X-ray investigation of the crystal structure of chkalovite (Rentgenometricheskoe issledovanie kristallicheskoi struktury chkalovita), *Dokl. Akad. Nauk SSSR*, vol. 108, No. 6.

Pyatnitskii, P. P. (1929), Geological investigations in the emerald area of the Urals. 1. Genetic relationships of rocks in the suite of emerald schists (Geologicheskie issledovaniya v izumrudnom raione na Urale. 1. Geneticheskie sootnosheniya gornykh porod svity izumrudnykh slantsev), *Izv. geol. Kom.*, vol. 48, No. 3.

________ (1932a), Geological investigations in the emerald area of the Urals. Problem of formation of emeralds (Geologicheskie issledovaniya v izumrudnom raione na Urale. K. vopruso ob obrazovanii izumrudov), *Tr. gl. geol. razv. Upr.*, issue 75.

________ (1932b), Geological investigations in the emerald area of the Urals. 3. Geological conditions of the occurrence of emeralds outside the USSR (Geologicheskie issledovaniya v izumrudnom raione na Urale. 3. Geologicheskie usloviya hakhozhdeniya izumrudov vne SSSR), *Tr. vese. geol.-razv. Ob'edin*, issue 189.

________ (1934), Emeralds. Their location and origin (Izumrudy. Ikh mestonakhozhdenie i proiskhozhdenie), *Gos. nauchn. gorno-geol. neft. Izdat.*, Moscow, Leningrad, Novosibirsk.

Quensel, P. (1944), Berylliumorthit (murmontit) frän Skuleboda fältspatbrott, *Arkiv for Kemi, Min. o. Geol.*, vol. 18 A, No. 22.

Rankama, K. and T. Sahama (1950), Geochemistry, University of Chicago Press, Chicago.

Rayleich, L. (1933), Beryllium and helium. *Nature*, London, vol. 131.

Rezek, A. and K. Tomic (1942), Beryllium in Sediment des Mineralwassers, der Tempel-Quelle in Rohitsch-Sauerbrunn, *Der Balneologe*, vol. 9.

Ringwood, A. E. (1955a), The principles governing trace element behavior during magmatic crystallization. pt. 1. The influence of electronegativity, *Geochim. et Cosmochim. Acta.*, vol. 7, Nos. 3 and 4.

——— (1955b), The principles governing trace element behaviour during magmatic crystalization. pt. 2. The role of complex formation, *Geochim. et Cosmochim Acta.*, vol. 7, Nos. 5 and 6.

Rodolico, F. and R. Pierruccini (1942), Il berillio nella differenziazione del magma selagitico, *Rend. Soc. Min. Italiana*, No. 1.

Rose, G. (1846), On the phenacite of Ilmen Mountains, a new locality for this mineral (Über den Phenakit vom Ilmengebirge, einem neuen Fundorte desselben), *Poggend. Ann.*, vol. 69; *Bericht*, Berlin.

Rowledge, H. P. and J. D. Hayton (1948), Two new beryllium minerals from Londonderry, *Journ. Roy. Soc. West Australia*, vol. 33.

Ryss, I. G. (1956), Chemistry of fluorine and of its inorganic compounds (Khimiya ftora i ego neorganicheskikh soedinenii), *Goskhomizdat*, Moscow.

Sahama, T. G. (1945), Spurenelemente der Gesteine im südlichen finnisch. Lapland, *Bull. Commiss. geol. de Finland*, No. 135.

Sandell, E. B. (1940), Morin reaction for beryllium, *Ind. Eng. Chem. Analyt.*, vol. 12, No. 12.

——— (1949), Determination of beryllium in silicate rocks, *Anal. Chem. Acta.*, vol. 3, No. 1.

——— (1952), Beryllium content of igneous rocks, *Geochem et Cosmochem.* Acta., vol. 2.

——— and S. S. Goldich (1943), The rarer metallic constituents of some American igneous rocks, *Jour. Geol.*, vol. 51, Nos. 2 and 3.

Sazhina, L. I. and A. A. Sitnin (1954), Occurrence of rubidium in beryls (O rasprostranenii rubidiya v berillakh), *Tr. Inst. Min. Geokhim. i. Kristallokhim.*, issue 2.

Schaller, W. T. and J. G. Fairchild (1932), Bavenite, a beryllium mineral pseudomorphous after beryl, from California, *Amer. Min.*, vol. 17, No. 9.

Semenov, E. I. (1957a), Helbertrandite and spherobertrandite—new beryllium minerals of alkalic pegmatites (Gel'bertradit i sferobertrandit—novye berillievye mineraly shchelochnykh pegmatitov), *Tr. Inst. Min. i. Geokhim. redk. Elem. Akad. Nauk SSSR*, issue 1.

——— (1957b), Leucophane in alkalic pegmatites of the Kola Peninsula (Leikofan v shchelochnykh pegmatitakh Kol'skogo poluostrova), *Tr. Inst. Min. i. Geokhim. redk. Elem. Akad. Nauk SSSR*, issue 1.

Severgin, V. M. (1795), Siberian beryl or aquamarine (O sibirskom berille ili akvamarine), *Nov. ezhemesyachn, Soch.*, pt. 106, April.

Shaub, B. M. (1937), Contemporaneous crystallization of beryl and albite vs. replacement, *Amer. Min.*, vol. 22, No. 10.

Shcherbakov, D. I. (1936), Genetic types of beryllium deposits in the USSR (Geneticheskie tipy berillievykh mestorozhdenii SSSR), *Redkie Metally*, No. 1.

Shilin, L. L. (1956), Karpinskyite—a new mineral (Karpenskit—novyi mineral), *Dokl. Akad. Nauk SSSR*, vol. 107, No. 5.

——— and E. I. Semenov (1957), The beryllium minerals epididymite and eudidymite in alkalic pegmatites of the Kola Peninsula (Berillievye mineraly épidimit i évdidmit v shchelochnykh pegmatitakh Kol'skogo poluostrova), *Dokl. Akad. Nauk SSSR*, vol. 112, No. 2.

Shilin, L. L. and L. P. Tsareva (1957), Occurrence of beryllium in rocks and minerals of the pegmatitic veins of the Lovozero and Khibiny rock tundra (O rasprostranenii berilliya v porodakh i mineralakh pegmatitivykh zhil Lovoserskikh i Khibinskikh tundr), *Geokhimiya,* No. 4.

Simpson, E. (1914), The rare minerals and their distribution in Western Australia, *Geol Surv. W. Australia Bull,* No. 59.

——— (1948), Minerals of Western Australia, Perth, W. Australia, vol. 1.

Skal'kovskii, K. A. (1868), Discovery of helvite in Russia (Ob otkrytii russkogo gel'vina), *Gorn. Zhurn.*, pt. 4, book 10.

Smith, J. C. (1956), Unit cell and space group of barylite, *Amer. Min.*, vol. 41, Nos. 5 and 6.

Smol'yaninov, N. A. (1940), Mineralogical features of the Dzhidin deposits in the Buryat-Mongolian ASSR (Osobennosti mineralogii Dzhindinskogo mestorozhdeniya v Buryat-Mongol'skoi ASSR), *Tr. Inst. geol. Nauk Akad Nauk SSSR,* issue 39, Min. geol. ser., No. 8.

Sobolev, V. S. (1944), Crystal chemistry of double salts and their role in petrology and mineralogy (Kristallokhimiya dvoinykh solei i ikh rol' v petrologii i mineralogii), *Izv. Akad. Nauk SSSR,* ser. geol., No. 5.

——— (1949), Introduction to the mineralogy of silicates (Vvdenie v mineralogiyu silikatov), University of L'vov Press.

——— (1956), Dependence of the properties of silicates on their structure (Zavisimost' svoistv silikatov ot ikh struktury), *Geokhimiya,* No. 6.

Sobolev, B. P. and A. V. Novoselova (1959), Role of fluorine compounds in the transport of beryllium and in the formation of phenacite (O roli ftoristykh soedinenii v perenose berilliya i obrazovanii fenakita), *Geokhimiya,* No. 1.

Solov'ev, S. P. (1952), Distribution of igneous rocks in the USSR (Raspredelenie magmaticheskikh gornykh porod v SSSR), *Gosgeolizdat,* Moscow.

Sosedko, A. F. (1934), Commercial minerals of the Turkestan ridge. In the book: Tadkhik-Pamir expedition of 1933 (Poleznye iskopaemye Turkestanskogo khrebta. V kn: Tadzhiko-Pamirskaya ékspeditsiya 1933 g.), *Akad. Nauk SSSR,* Moscow, Leningrad.

——— (1935), Contributions to the mineralogy and geochemistry of the Altyn-Tau pegmatites (Materialy po mineralogii i geokhimii pegmatitov Altyn-Tau), *Tr. Sov. po. Izuch. proizvod. Sil. SSSR,* issue 5, (ser Karakalpakskaya).

——— (1937), Pegmatites of the southern slopes of the Turkestan ridge (Pegmatity yuzhnykh sklonov Turkestanskogo khrebta), *Mat. Tadzh.-Pamir. eksp. Akad. Nauk SSSR,* issue 68.

Sosedko, T. A. (1957), Change of structure and properties in beryls with an increased alkali content (Izmeneie struktury i svoistv v berillakh s povyshennym soderzhaniem shchlochei), *Zap. vses. min. Obshch.*, pt. 86, issue 4.

Stoll, W. C. (1945), The presence of beryllium and associated elements in the wallrocks of some New England pegmatites, *Econ. Geol.*, vol. 40, No. 2.

Strand, T. (1953), Euclase from Iveland, occurring as an alternate for beryl, *Norsk. Geol. Tidsskr.*, vol. 31.

Strelkin, M. F. (1935), Pegmatites of Kyrk-Bulak. In the book: The Tadzhik-Pamir expedition, 1934 (Pegmatity Kryk-Bulaka. V kn: Tadzhiko-Pamirskaya ékspeditsiya, 1934), *Akad. Nauk SSSR,* Moscow, Leningrad.

——— (1938), On stanniferrous pegmatites (K vopruso ob olovonosnykh pegmatitakh), *Izv. Akad. Nauk SSSR, Otd. mat. i est. Nauk*, ser. geol., No. 3.

——— (1941), Mineralogy of the Cherdoyak and Verkhne-Baimurzin stanniferrous deposits, Kalba-Nyrym pluton (K mineralogii Cherdoyakskogo i Verkhne-Baimurzinskogo olobyannykh mestorozhdenii, Kalba-Nyrymskii pluton), *Tr. Inst. geol. Nauk, Akad. Nauk SSSR*, issue 51, min. geokh. ser., No. 11.

Strunz, H. (1936), Datolith und Herderit. Ein Beitrag zur Kenntnis der Isomorphie zwischen Silikaten und Phosphaten, *Zs. f. Kristallogr.*, vol. 93, Nos. 1 and 2.

——— (1937), Sistematik and Struktur der Silikate, *Zs. f. Kristallogr.*, vol. 98, No. 1.

Sushchinskii, P. P. (1925), Description of the deposits of colored minerals in SE Transbaikalia (Ocherk mestorozhdeniya tsvetnykh kamnei yugo-vostochnogo Zabaikaliya), *Tr. Inst. prikl. Min.*, issue 16.

——— (1928), Aquamarine from Sherlovaya Mountain in Transbaikalian province (Akvarmarin s Sherlovoi gory v Zabaikal'skoi oblasti). *Izv. Donsk. politekhn, Inst.*, vol. 3.

Szelenyi, T. (1937), Spektralanaytische Bestimmung des Berylliumgehaltes der Bauxite, *Math. Natur. Auz. Ungar. Acad. Wiss.*, vol. 56.

Tetyaev, M. M. (1918), Tungsten and tin deposits of the Onen-Borzin district of Transbaikalian province (Vol'framovye i olovyanne mestorozhdeniya Onon-Borzinskogo raiona Zabaikal'skoi oblasti), *Mat. po obshch. i. prikl. Geol.*, issue 32.

Thurnwald, H. and A. A. Beneditti-Pichler (1932), Gravimetric microanalysis of beryllium silicate rocks. *Microchemie*, vol. 11.

Titov, V. L. (1855), Notes on deposits of colored minerals in salt lakes of the Nerchinst province (Zametki o mestorozhdeniyakh tsvetnykh kamnei v solyanykh ozerakh Nerchinskogo kraya), *Gorn. Zhurn.*, pt. 2, book 6.

Tolmachev, Yu. M. and A. N. Filippov (1934), Occurrence of lithium, rubidium, cesium, beryllium, and strontium in nephelines (O nakhozdenii litiya, rubidiya, tseziya, berilliya, i strontsiya v nefelinakh), *Dokl. Akad. Nauk SSSR*, nov. ser., vol. 3.

——— (1935), On finding rare alkali metals in amazonite (O nakhozdenii redikh shchelochnykh metallov v amazonitakh), *Dokl. Akad. Nauk SSSR*, vol. 1.

Toropov, N. A. and I. A. Bondar (1955), Fluoroberyllates and other crystal-chemical analogues of silicates and kindred substances (Ftorberillaty i drugie kristallo-khimicheskie analogi silikatov i im podobnykh veshchestv), *Usp. Khimmi*, vol. 24, issue 1.

Uspenskii, N. M. (1932), Beryl deposit in the emerald mines in the Urals. In the book: Proceedings of the 4th all-union Geological Conference on Non-ferrous Metals, issue 5. Minor and rare metals (Mestorozhdenie berilla iaumrudnykh kopei na Urale. V kn: Tr. IV vses. geol. konf. po tsvetnym metallam, vyp. 5. Malye i redkie metally), *Tsvetmetizdat*, Moscow, Leningrad.

——— (1938a), A discussion on the genesis of the Monetnaya Dacha emerald deposits in the Urals (Materialy dlya pozaniya genezisa mestorozhdeniya isumrudov Monetnoi dachi na Urale), *Zap. leningr. gorn. Inst.*, vol. 11, issue 1.

_______ (1938b), Mineralogy of emerald mines (K mineralogii izumrudnykh kopei), *Zap. ross. min. Obshch.*, vol. 67, issue 3.

_______ (1939), The Minetnaya dacha emerald deposit in the Urals (Mestorozdhenie izumrudov Monetnoi dachi na Urale), *Tr. tsentr. nauchn-issl. geol.-razy. Inst.*, issue 116.

Van Eeden, O. R., F. C. Partridge, L. Kent, and J. W. Brandt (1939), The mineral deposits of the Murchison range east of Leydsdorp, Union of South Africa, *Dept. of Min. Geol. Surv.*, Pretoria, No. 36.

Varlamoff, N. (1953–1954), Tendances actuelles dans l'etude des pegmatites a travers le Monde. Revue des travauz sur les pegmatites du Conge Belge et du Ruanda-Urandi; proposition d'une classification des pegmatites Congo Belge et du Ruanda-Urundi., *Bull. Soc. Geol. Belgique*, vol. 77, Nos. 7, 8, and 9.

Vernadskii, V. I. (1908), On vorobevite and the chemical composition of beryls (O vorob'ebite i khimicheskom sostave berillov), *Izv. Akad. Nauk SSSR*, ser. 6., 2 (abridged); the same in full, *Tr. geol. Muzeya*, vol. 2.

Vinogradov, A. P. (1950), Geochemistry of rare and disseminated chemical elements in soils (Geokhimya redikh i rasseyannykh khimicheskikh elementov v pochvakh), *Akad. Nauk SSSR*, Moscow.

Vlasov, K. A. (1936a), Genesis of emeralds (Genesis izumrudov), *Priroda*, No. 8.

_______ (1936b), Beryl deposit of emerald mines. In the book: Collection of Scientific paprs of komsoltes of the Academy of Sciences of the USSR (Mestorozhdenie berilla Izumrudnykh kopei. V kn: Sbornik nauchnykh rabot komosomltsev Akademii Nauk SSSR), *Akad. Nauk SSSR*, Moscow, Leningrad.

_______ (1938a), Catalytic role of fluorine in the desilication of pegmatites and in beryl genesis, Emerald mines, Middle Urals, (Kataliticheskaya rol'ftora v protsesse desilikatsii pegmatita i genezisa berilla, Izumrudn. kopi Sredn. Urala), *Tr. Lomonosovsk. Inst. Geochim., Kristallogr.* i *Min., Akad. Nauk SSSR*, issue 9.

_______ (1938b), Theory of desilication of granitic pegmatites (O teorii desilikatsii granitnykh pegmatitov), *Izv. Akad. Nauk SSSR*, ser. geol, No. 2.

_______ (1943), Significance of forms of granitic pegmatites (Znachenie form granitnykh pegmatitov), *Dokl. Akad. Nauk SSSR*, vol. 41, No. 9.

_______ (1946), Textural-paragenetic classification granitic pegmatites (Teksturno-paragenticheska klassifikatsiya graniitnykh pegmatitov), *Dokl. Akad. Nauk SSSR*, vol. 53, No. 9.

_______ (1951), Concerning the question of pegmatite genesis (K vopruso o genezise pegmatitov), *Dokl. Akad. Nauk SSSR*, No. 2.

_______ (1952), Textural-paragenetic classification of granitic pegmatites (Teksturno-parageneticheskaya klassifikatsiya granitnykh pegmatitov), *Izv. Akad. Nauk SSSR*, ser. geol., No. 2.

_______ (1956a), Factors of formation of various types of rare-metal granitic pegmatites (Faktory obrazonvaniya razlichnykh tipov redkometal'nykh granitnykh pegmatitov), *Izv. Akad. Nauk SSSR*, ser. geol., No. 1.

_______ (1956b), Emanation process and crystallization differentiation as leading factors in the formation of many rare-element deposits. In the book:

Problems of geochemistry and mineralogy (Emanatsionnyi protsess i kristallizatsionnaya differentsiatsiya kak vedushchie faktory obrazovaniya ryada mestorozhdenii redkikh elementov. V kn: Vorposy geokhimii i mineralogii), *Akad. Nauk SSSR*, Moscow.

——— and E. I. Kutukova (1960), Emerald mines (Izumrudnye kopi), *Akad. Nauk SSSR*, Moscow.

Volborth, A. (1954a), Väyrynenit $BeMn(PO_4)(OH)$, ein neues Mineral, *Anzeiger*, vol. 91, No. 1 bis.

——— (1954b), Väyrynenit $BeMn(PO_4)(OH,F)$, *Geologi*, Finland, vol. 6.

——— (1954c), Eine neue die Phosphatanalyse verkürzende Methods und ihre Anwendung in der Analyse der Berillium-Phosphate. *Zs. f. anorg. u. allgem. Chem.*, vol. 276, Nos. 3 and 4.

Vol'fson, F. I. (1953), Structures of endogenous ore deposits. In the book: Basic problems in the theory of magmatic ore deposits (Struktury endogennykh rudnykh mestorozhdenii. V kn: Osnovnye problemy v uchenni o magmatogennykh rudnykh mestorozhdeniyakh), *Akad. Nauk SSSR*, Moscow.

Washington, H. S. (1931), Beryllium in minerals and igneous rocks, *Am. Min.*, vol. 16, No. 1.

Warren, C. H. and R. T. Hill (1934), Structure of vitreous BeF_2, Zs. f. *Kristallogr.*, vol. 89.

Wehrenberg, J. P. (1954), A corrected unit cell for beryllonite, *Am. Min.*, vol. 39, Nos. 3 and 4.

Weissenborn, A. E. (1948), A new occurrence of helvite, *Am. Min.*, vol. 33, Nos. 9 and 10.

Winchell, A. N. and H. Winchell (1951), The elements of optical mineralogy, John Wiley and Sons, New York, 4th edition.

Yakzhin, A. A. (1937), The Kondakov muscovite deposit in eastern Siberia (Kondakovskoe mestorozhdenie muskovita v Vostochnoi Sibiri), *Tr. vost.-sib. geol. Tresta.*, issue 22.

Yggberg, E. R. (1941), Barylite in relation to other similar silicates, *Geol. För. Förth.* Stockholm, vol. 63, H. 4., No. 427.

Zachariasen, W. H. (1929), Die feinbauliche Relation zwischen Eudidimit und Epididimit, *Norsk. Geol. Tidssk*, Oslo, vol. 10.

——— (1930), On meliphanite and leucophanite, *Zs. f. Kristallogr.*, vol. 74.

——— (1931), Meliphanite, leucophanite, and their relation to melite, *Norsk. Geol. Tidssk.*, Oslo, vol. 12.

Zalashkova, N. E. (1957), Albitization stages in granitic pegmatites illustrated by one of the Altai pegmatite fields (Etapy al'bitizatsii v granitnykh pegmatitakh na primere odnogo iz pegmatitovykh polei Altaya), *Tr. Inst. Min. i. Geokhim. redk. Elem. Akad. Nauk SSSR*, issue 1.

Zambonini, M. F. (1919), Sur la veritable nature du titanolivine de la vallee d'Ala (Piemont), *Soc. Franc. Min. Bull*, vol. 42, No. 5.

Zil'bermints, V. A. and E. V. Rozhkova (1933), Occurrence of beryllium in vesuvianite (Raprostranenie berilliya v vezuvianakh), *Redkie Metally*, No. 5.

Zil'bermints, V. A. and A. K. Rusanov (1936), Occurrence of beryllium in fossil coals (O rasprostranenii berilliya v iskopaemykh uglyakh), *Dokl. Akad. Nauk SSSR*, vol. 2 (11), No. 1 (87).

Index